Environmental Quality and Safety
Vol. 3

Georg Thieme Publishers, Stuttgart
Academic Press, Inc., New York, N. Y.
A Subsidiary of Harcourt Brace Jovanovich, Publishers

Environmental Quality and Safety

Global Aspects of Chemistry, Toxicology and Technology as Applied to the Environment

Vol. 3

41 figures
39 tables

Contributors:

W. F. Almeida, Sao Paulo, Brazil
M. Blanc, Paris, France
P. Chovin, Paris, France
H. B. Corradini, Sao Paulo, Brazil
F. Coulston, Albany, USA
H. Frohberg, Darmstadt, Germany
R. Gaeta, Sao Paulo, Brazil
J. C. Gage, Lund, Sweden
B. W. Halstead, Colton, Cal., USA
P. B. Hutt, Rockville, Mo., USA
E. O. Kegan, Chicago, Ill., USA
G. Kimmerle, Wuppertal, Germany
J. H. Knelson, North Carolina, USA
F. Korte, München, Germany
E. Löser, Wuppertal, Germany

O. H. Lowry, St. Louis, Mo., USA
F. Moriarty, Abbots Ripton, Huntingdon, U.K.
E. M. Mrak, Davis, Cal., USA
T. V. N. Persaud, Winnipeg, Manitoba, Canada
S. Pigati, Sao Paulo, Brazil
S. Schvartsman, Sao Paulo, Brazil
J. S. Turner, New York. N.Y., USA
M. T. Ungaro, Sao Paulo, Brazil
F. A. C. Vaz, Sao Paulo, Brazil
C. H. Walker, Reading, U.K.
W. C. Wescoe, New York, N.Y., USA
J. H. Wills, New York, USA
F. P. W. Winteringham, Vienna, Austria

1974

Georg Thieme Publishers, Stuttgart
Academic Press, Inc., New York, N.Y.
A Subsidiary of Harcourt Brace Jovanovich, Publishers

© 1974 Georg Thieme Verlag, D-7000 Stuttgart 1, Herdweg 63, P.O.B. 732 – Printed in Germany by Maurersche Buchdruckerei, Geislingen an der Steige

For Georg Thieme Verlag ISBN 3 13 510801 5
For Academic Press ISBN 0-12-227003-7
Library of Congress Catalog Card Number: 70-145669

Contents

VI   Contents

How Safe is Safe? A Consumer's Viewpoint*

James S. Turner

Founder and Co-director
Consumer Action for Improved Food and Drugs

"How Safe is Safe?" is a misleading title for a conference on the Design of Policy on Drugs and Food Additives. It implies the quest for an objective, scientific if you will, standard of safety acceptable to all interested in the issue being considered. Unfortunately in the real world today's acceptable standard of safety may be more or less acceptable than yesterday's or tomorrow's.

In addressing the problem of nuclear reactor safety, Dr. Alvin Weinberg, Director of the Oak Ridge National Laboratories, put the question more precisely. He asked ... "How safe is safe enough?"[1] That is the question underlying the Design of Policy on Drugs and Food Additives. It is not primarily a question for scientists. Rather, as the subtitle of this conference suggests, it is a policy question. Dr. Weinberg has spelled out the distinction effectively.

"Many of the issues," he writes, that arise in the course of the interaction between science or technology and society – e. g., the deleterious side effects of technology, or the attempts to deal with social problems through procedures of science – hang on the answers to questions which can be asked of science and yet *which cannot be answered by science*. I (Weinberg) propose the term transscientific for these questions since, though they are, epistomologically speaking, questions of fact and can be stated in the language of science, they are unanswerable by science; they transcend science. Insofar as public policy depends on trans-scientific rather than scientific issues, the role of the scientist in contributing to the promulgation of such policy must be different than is his role when the issues can be unambiguously answered by science ...

"(W)hen what we (as scientists) do *transcends* science and when it impinges on the public, we have no choice but to welcome the public – even encourage the public – to participate in the debate. Scientists have no monopoly on wisdom where this kind of trans-science is involved: they shall have to accomodate to the will of the public and its representatives."[2]

"Safety" as it has come to be used within the context of the food and drug laws and the complex of regulations supporting them is a trans-scientific problem. The nature of the safety problem may be better understood if it is divided into three distinct components. Under current laws a substance can be found safe only if it has passed through three phases of consideration.

First is the objective, scientific, determination of the-discernible effects involved in the chemical's use. This determination is the responsibility of scientists.

Second is the judgment about which of the effects is a risk and which is a benefit. This judgment is ultimately made by the public, acting through its representatives, spokesman, or as individuals, but acting with a high degree of guidance from scientists, physicians or other trained professionals.

Third is the decision that the agreed-upon benefits of a given chemical exceed its agreed upon risks. This is a public, not a scientific, decision made in public forums in which scientists participate as

* Presented at the first Academy Forum, "How Safe is Safe? The Design of Policy on Drugs and Food Additives," May 15, 1973, in Washington, D. C.

equal, though in some cases better informed, participants with other segments of the public.

A safe chemical is one that has passed through all three phases satisfactorily. Its effects are known and agreed upon with some certainty by qualified scientists. The benefits and risks of the chemical have been sorted out accurately to the general satisfaction of the society. And the society has decided that the benefits of the use of the chemical in the way permitted outweigh its risks.

Unfortunately this is not the way the determinations of chemical safety always work. Three dramatic regulatory decisions during the past twenty years illustrate why the public increasingly doubts industrial, regulatory and scientific assertions that the food and drug supply are safe enough.

The approval and subsequent banning of cyclamates (including unnecessary references to the Delaney anticancer clause) illustrate the problems that occur when scientists cannot agree on the potential effects of a given chemical, but regulators act as if they do.

The approval of the Salk polio vaccine and the subsequent 260 cases of vaccine-associated polio, including ten deaths, demonstrates the tragedy that can result when risks and benefits are improperly identified or weighed.

The negligent release of certain lots of the Sabin Type III oral polio vaccine, and subsequent findings against the government for the action, suggest that science and scientists are going to be held to an increasing degree of responsibility for their decisions by the public.

Each of these events has a lesson which can be helpful in determining how safe is safe enough. In 1963 the Division of Biologics Standards (DBS) of the National Institute of Health, then the nation's vaccine regulators, approved certain lots of Sabin Type III polio vaccine for use in a Philadelphia mass immunization campaign.

A 41-year old Philadelphia housewife took a dose of one of the lots and contracted polio from the vaccine. She became a permanent quadriplegic. After reviewing the case, during seven years of legal proceedings, the Federal District Court in Philadelphia ruled that the vaccine lots had been released negligently by the DBS. It awarded damages of over $ 1 million to the injured party.

Evidence showed that government scientists responsible for protecting the public had kept shoddy, incomplete, or misleading records about vaccine safety. It showed that the statistical methods used to evaluate findings were at best shoddy – "a perfect example of the old ... chestnut 'garbage in garbage out'",[3] the judge said.

Evidence introduced into the record suggested that when the mass innoculation campaign was in the planning stages the polio advisory committee voted 6 to 4 to include a warning against the use of the Sabin Oral Vaccine in adults. The committee was informed by the manufacturer that " ... the company must give serious consideration to the possibility that the Type III Vaccine will have to be withdrawn from commercial sale ... if labeling precautions cannot be written with adequate safeguards that will not deter its sale ..."[4] Following this statement by the company, the committee reversed itself, removing the warning about adults.

A careful examination of the regulatory records on Sabin polio vaccine revealed a nightmare of improper, mistaken or negligent action – including a total lack of familiarity with laws and regulations governing vaccine regulation on the part of the responsible regulatory officials – all taken in the name of and on behalf of science.

The surprising reaction of officials faced with the responsibility for the $ 1 million judgment was to suggest that the regulations be changed so that their actions would become legal. When the safety problem is viewed in this kind of context the issues related to benefit and risk become less esoteric, abstract and philosophical.

The problem becomes a practical one. Mechanisms must be designed to insure that the individuals charged with applying the available scientific knowledge to regulatory decisions have a proper sense of responsibility and the clear knowledge that they will be held accountable for their mistakes as well as rewarded for their contributions.

Until these mechanisms are developed the public sense that the chemical environment is not safe enough will continue to grow. Unless the world of scientific decision making on behalf of the public is opened to public scrutiny and evaluation more and more policy restraints will be placed on the granting of responsibility to scientists. Alvin Weinberg puts the situation bluntly. "The republic of science can be destroyed more surely by withdrawal of public support for science than by intrusion of the public into its workings".[5]

The government's problem with certain lots of Sabin vaccine suggests how skeptical the public, through its transscientific institutions is becoming of socalled scientific discretion. The Salk vaccine incident suggests that the real safety problem is not necessarily a better *weighing* of benefits and risks. Rather, it may be necessary to develop a better way to *identify* the benefits and risks.

The 260 victims of polio contracted from the Salk vaccine have often been the center piece in a number of theoretical discussions about risk/benefit. The trade-off is always between the number injured by the vaccine versus the number who would have been injured if the vaccine had not been used. A January, 1973, article in *Nature* sums it up. „The situation, although regrettable, was certainly less severe than it might have been if the vaccine had not been used."[6]

This is a comforting thought. But it lets science and the regulatory officials responsible for applying it off the hook too easily. If they had done their job properly the full benefit of the vaccine could have been had without the 260 casualties. This certainly would have been better than what occurred.

No less an authority than Dr. James Shannon has said, in a 1966 speech, that the Salk vaccine represented a scientific error. "... the decision of the (polio) Foundation to throw its resources behind the development of an inactivated vaccine markedly increased the difficulties and greatly protracted the time required to develop the generally accepted polio vaccine we have today."[7] He suggests that the error in part might have resulted from the secrecy of Foundation proceedings.

Dr. Shannon's view is a retrospective one. It can be considered in future situations, but reasonable men could have disagreed about the choices when they were made in 1955. It is more difficult to accept the fact that in 1955 the bench scientists at the Divison of Biologics Standards responsible for evaluating the safety of Salk vaccine refused free doses for their children.

They did so because more than six months before the beginning of the Salk mass immunization program three monkeys came down with what appeared to be a paralysis caused by the vaccine. This warning did not cause those responsible for the program to search out a potential problem. Six months later when the first five vaccine-related cases of polio were detected, a massive crisis program was undertaken to find and correct the problem. Within thirty days the reason for live polio contamination of the vaccine had been discovered, corrected and the vaccine was back on the market.

In a program as important, sensitive and dramatic as the Salk mass immunization campaign, three sick monkeys should have been an effective early warning of the problems to come. That they were not suggests important weaknesses in the system for identifying risk and benefits which must be corrected before the weighing of benefit and risks can be seriously undertaken.

The manipulation of science to make risks appear more acceptable, illustrated by the Philadelphia Sabin case and the failure of science to detect warnings as in the Salk case, feed public skepticism about claims that all is well with food and drugs. This skepticism, shared by a good number of scientists, underlies the strong support for the Delaney anti-cancer clause of the Food and Drug Law which prohibits the use in human foods of any chemical which has caused cancer when ingested by man or animal.

In October of 1969, the Secretary of Health, Education, and Welfare removed cyclamate from the list of food chemicals Generally Recognized as Safe (GRAS) by qualified scientists. He removed the chemical not because scientists agreed that it was unsafe. But because it could no longer be said that scientists agreed it was safe. (A human metabolite of the chemical caused genetic damage in rats; it and the chemical caused teratogenic damage in chickens; the chemical bound itself to plasma thus inhibiting drug delivery to the body; it inhibited the effect of vitamin K; it had caused some unreported cancerous tumors in 1950 FDA tests and when combined with sacharrin it has caused cancer in rats.)

For apparently political reasons, the Secretary took the legally unnecessary step of invoking the Delaney anticancer clause to justify removal of the chemical from the GRAS list. It was unnecessary to invoke the clause because once safety became a question, the chemical could not be used unless it had been tested and shown to be safe.

This meant that its effects had to be demonstrated. Its beneficial and risky effects had to be sorted out. Then the risks and benefits had to be weighed. If qualified scientists had found during this period that the chemical did cause cancer when ingested by man or animal, then the Delaney clause could have been invoked. The previously made public determination that the potential risk of including a cancer-causing chemical in the food supply outweighs any benefits that that chemical might have would then have controlled the situation.

If this procedure − as outlined in the law − had been followed, the importance of the Delaney Clause could have been more accurately assessed and appreciated. Instead, the premature use of the clause led to a lot of misunderstanding about the purpose and principle underlying the clause.

The principle of the Delaney clause is that weighing of benefits and risk is not a purely scientific question. Rather it is a policy question that requires an informed pubilc decision. The principle of the Delaney clause is that the weighing of benefits and risks is not the sole province of a regulatory agency or its scientific advisors.

The Delaney clause applies this principle to those chemicals which cause cancer when ingested by man or animal. It does this on the advice of a large segment of the scientific community which argues that the effects of even traces of a cancer causing substance cannot be predicted. Relying on this advice the public had adopted the policy that no benefit is worth the possible hazard of adding a cancer-causing chemical to the food supply.

The Clause rests on scientific discretion. Scientists and scientists make the determination that an ingested chemical has caused cancer.

The Clause rests on the accepted operating principle that there is some relationship between effects of a chemical on animals and effects on men. This is the principle that allows drugs and food additives to be shown safe and marketed.

The Clause avoids the demand of absolute safety. Instead, it says that in relation to the cancer risk, the food supply will be safe enough if no additional cancer causing chemicals are added to it.

The Delaney Clause can certainly be improved. But the central principle upon which it rests must be kept intact. Safety is a policy question which demands the weighing of properly identified risks and benefits by the public. It is not an objective scientific determination. The weighing mechanism can be improved. But improvement will not be accomplished by giving regulatory authorities more bureaucratic discretion. The Delaney Clause, unlike any other section of the Food and Drug Law, recognizes and is premised upon the limitations of science.

The Food Safety Panel of the 1969 White House Conference on Food, Nutrition and Health stated the limitation on proving food chemical safety. The Panel said, „It is not possible to determine with absolute certainty the safety of the ever-increasing number of chemicals added to or present in our foods". As a member of the Panel I concurred with the statement.

To me, the statement appeared to be a warning. Since science could never be sure of a chemical's safety it seemed obvious that as a matter of policy we should be cautious in *allowing* the use of chemicals. Unfortunately many individuals both inside and outside of science took the statement to mean the opposite. Since, they argued, safety cannot ever be proven conclusively we ought to be cautious in *restricting* the use of chemicals.

It is this attitude against which public sentiment is reacting.

Increasingly scientific evidence relates various of these chemicals to serious problems of human health. Responsible scientists have suggested that certain chemicals may contribute to the development of certain kinds of mental retardation (95% of which is from unknown origins). A large portion of the cancer research community spends its time evaluating the capability of various chemicals to cause cancer (for which the cause is yet to be found). Some geneticists suggest that chemicals used in foods and drugs might play an important role in causing much of the society's genetic and mutagenic damage (for example 20 to 30 percent of American pregnancies and in spontaneous abortion, stillbirth or deformity).

Scientific research has identified a number of serious health problems for which the causes are at best elusive. It has also generated enough evidence to suggest a possible relationship between these disease conditions and the growing use of a number of chemicals in the drug and food supply. Diseases of unknown origin and chemicals with suspicious side effects combine to raise questions of drug and food additive safety and policy to a high level of public concern.

Increasingly pointed public questions are being raised about assumptions underlying chemical regulation.

Dr. Jacqueline Verrett and Jean Carper, who played such an important role in the cyclamate ban, ask: "When industry tosses around the term "benefit-risk" what do they mean? Do they mean *consumer health* benefits weighed against *consumer health* risks? Or consumer economic benefit against *consumer health risk?* Or some kind of *consumer social benefit* (such as time saving) against *consumer health risk?* Or on the other hand, do they mean *industry* economic benefit against *consumer health risk?*"[8] My experience is that they mean all of these. This fact too raises drug and food additive safety and policy to a high level of public concern.

The point of all this is that the safety of drugs and food additives as a function of the weighing of benefits and risks is not what the public concern is all about. The real problem is twofold. The effects of chemicals in food and drugs have not yet been determined satisfactorily. No generally accepted definition of benefits and risks has been agreed upon. It is on these two problems that, from the consumers point of view, the attention of science should be focused.

References

[1] Alvin M. Weinberg: Science and Trans-Science, prepared for presentation at the dedication of the Paul B. Johnson Science Tower, University of Southern Mississippi, Hattiesburg, January 28, 1972. This paper was based in part on lectures presented at the CIBA Symposium on Science and Civilization, London, June 30; at the Fourth International Conference on Science and Society: Science, Man and His environment, Herceg-Novi, July 6; at Argonne National Laboratory, November 8, 1971, and at National Institutes of Health, Bethesda, Maryland, March 15, 1972, p. 18

[3] Richard J. Griffin and Mary Jane Griffin, His wife, United States of America Civ A. No 39099, 351 Fed Sup 10. p. 29 fn 26. Here also see reference to "outrageous consumer risk."

[4] ibid. transcript of trail p. 485 During Cross examination of Dr. Alexander Langmuir

[5] Weinberg op cit p. 22

[6] H. V. Wyatt, Is Polio A Model for Consumer Research, Nature Vol 241 January 26, 1973

[7] James Shannon, NIH-Present and Potential Contribution to Application of Biomedical Knowledge, Remarks presented at the Conference on Research in the Service of Man Oklahoma City, October 25, 1966 p. 12 reported in New York Times October 26, 1966 p. 37

[8] Verrett, Caper personal communication

How Safe is Safe? A Scientist's Viewpoint*

Oliver H. Lowry. M. D.

Head of the Department of Pharmacology
Washington University School of Medicine, St. Louis

Summary   1. The human body and the interaction of drugs with the human body are so complicated, and so incompletely understood, that no one can yet predict ahead of time what dangers there may be from a new drug or a new application of a drug.
2. This complexity and lack of knowledge means that a semiempirical approach to drug safety is necessary.
3. Past experience with drugs plus progressive improvements in the ways to study interactions of drugs with the body, greatly improve and speed up this semiempirical drug testing process.
4. Until the human body is much better understood than at present, there will always be the possibility that a new drug in spite of apparently adequate testing may ultimately cause a small degree of harm to many people or a large degree of harm to a few people. Judgement as to potential benefit and possible risk from a new drug is often very difficult and should be made on the basis of the best scientific advice.
5. With these considerations in mind, in order to achieve for the public maximum drug safety on one hand and maximum benefits from drugs on the other, it is recommended first that basic research be strongly encouraged and in no way sacrificed for more obvious immediate health goals, and second that an advisory system to the FDA be set up to include a wide spectrum of basic biomedical scientists and clinical scientists from both inside and outside government.

The dangers associated with drugs are of two kinds; dangers inherent in the drug itself, and dangers from its misuse. I will restrict myself to inherent dangers from drugs used properly, even though the greatest dangers today may be from the improper use of drugs.

There can be no question about the central role of science in detecting dangers in drugs, and in discovering ways to increase drug safety. The value and the dangers of a drug can only be determined by objective testing, that is, by scientific evaluation. There is no other way. Attitudes about drugs are especially susceptible to myth and superstition. It is well known that what a doctor thinks and tells his patient about a drug can influence the effects. Doctors down through the ages usually did more harm

---

* Presented at the first Academy Forum, "How Safe is Safe? The Design of Policy on Drugs and Food Additives," May 15, 1973, in Washington, D. C.

than good because there were no hard therapeutic facts about their alleged remedies. Many a king was hastened to his grave by his well meaning physicians. Since those old days things have changed for the better as the result of scientific study. One of the first things that resulted from a really hard look was that most old time drugs were found to be junk and were discarded. There followed in the best medical circles almost a no drug period, a period of therapeutic nihilism, after which a new start was made, and over the past 40 years truly effective and relatively safe drugs have been developed. Science has brought this about, and we must seek ways from now on to bring science to bear in the most effective manner on drug safety problems, as well as on the development of better drugs – never forgetting we are a long way from effective treatment for some of our worst diseases.

There is one very large problem which every professional or layman concerned about drugs must take into account. This is that the human machine is almost unbelievably complicated and therefore the action of drugs to tamper with that machinery is likely to be very complicated. This machine already appeared exceedingly complex in 1938 when the Food, Drug, and Cosmetic Act was enacted. In the 35 years since then, science has accumulated a fantastic amount of information about the living machine, but in so doing we have learned that our machinery is actually far more complicated than anyone had realized, and today we are obviously still nowhere near a complete understanding of how the human machinery works. Drugs are simply chemical compounds which react with that machinery, hopefully to make it work better. Therefore, we are a long way from a full understanding of drug actions or drug dangers. Sometimes in

trying to repair our machinery with drugs we seem to be only a little better off than the man who succeeds in fixing his television set by giving it a kick.

One deceptive thing is that the body doesn't look all that complicated. I have a headache, I take a pill of a simple chemical compound, aspirin, and the headache goes away. What is so complicated about that? I assure you the process is very complicated, and until the last year or two not understood at all. Part of the action of aspirin now appears to be due to blocking the synthesis of a group of normal regulator substances that were only recently discovered by basic scientists and therefore are only now being thoroughly studied.

My view is that the complexity of the human body and its reactions with drugs, plus our incomplete knowledge, must to a large extent, determine what would be optimal policy on drugs and drug actions. Considering our ignorance, we have in fact been remarkably successful in using drugs to protect, repair, and alter human machinery, and although we are all aware of ill effects and dangers with many existing drugs, these side effects are minor compared to the great benefits from these drugs. I doubt that given the present state of knowledge about living things we could have expected a much better ratio of good to bad effects, no matter what laws had been passed or how they had been implemented.

Although we may be reasonably satisfied with past performance, we must not be satisfied to let it rest there. We must correct deficiencies of present drug classes, and we must find remedies for the many diseases for which no remedies exist.

Given our lack of full knowledge, one of the things we must clearly do is to encourage basic research on the living machine itself and how it interacts with drugs. There are those who say we have acquired enough knowledge and therefore let us now get on with the job of applying that knowledge to human problems. This is a recommendation that can only arise from a profound misunderstanding of the human organism. The very recent discouragement of support of basic science can only delay the development of safe drugs.

Except for this unfortunate trend, which I hope is temporary, I view the situation as very good for the future. As science has learned more about the living machine, it has acquired powerful tools for studying the reactions between drugs and that machine. Let me give one example. Most drugs are converted by the body into one or more products, which may be beneficial or harmful, or simply innocuous. One of the reasons why testing a drug on experimental animals is not sufficient, is that man may convert the drug into different products than is true for the particular experimental animals used. It is possible that a drug product produced by man alone, may be harmful. It is important therefore, to determine the fate of each drug in man. Thirty-five years ago the study of drug metabolism was slow and cumbersome and inadequate. Today there are laboratory tools and techniques which permit the metabolism of a drug to be determined rapidly and accurately even with small test doses in man himself. This increases the safety of the testing process itself, and permits rapid testing in experimental animals of the possible toxicity of such products as are produced in the human body from any given drug.

Altogether science now has increasingly better ways to study drugs. However, we are still a long way from knowing enough about the body to understand the mechanism of many drug actions and of many of the unpleasant or dangerous side effects. It is going to take a lot of imaginative basic research to dig these things out. Simple blind empirical testing of drugs is not enough.

A major qestion is how can we do better in regard to safety without stifling the development of new and better drugs. We have always been faced with two opposite dangers, under testing of drugs with too much risk of toxicity, and over testing with the certainty of greater suffering from disease because of undue delay in introduction of an important drug. There are those who believe the Salk polio vaccine was introduced prematurely. A delay of 2 or 3 years might have prevented the Cutter incident. On the other hand, it is practically a certainty that a 2 or 3 year delay in the introduction of the Salk vaccine would have resulted in 100,000 more cases of paralytic poliomyelitis. The benefit far exceeded the risk. As an opposite example, the benefit to be gained from having one more sedative drug did not justify the risk of Thalidomide introduction without far more exhaustive testing than it had recieved. To make decisions in regard to benefit versus risk is often very difficult. It would seem wise if the FDA had available the best advice in the country in some of these decisions. There is another consideration which also leads to the conclusion that there may be a need for better ways of providing advice from scientists both outside and inside government and industry. This arises as another important consequence of the exquisite complexity of the body and of its interactions with drugs. It is impossible for one person and difficult for a small group to assess adequately the procedures by which different types of drugs and food additives are tested and evaluated. Most of us have been impressed by the outstanding success of the peer review system of the NIH. Active investigators in different fields of biomedical research from all over the country provide a breadth of expert review that would be impossible by the NIH itself on an in house basis. This has proven an almost ideal way of getting the greatest public value out of federal support with a minimum of bureaucratic problems. I would strongly urge that, by some analogous system, greater advantage be taken of the scientific expertise of this country as a whole in the review of new drug applications, in the appraisal of existing drugs and in determining where basic research studies are most needed.

The NIH study section system would not be directly convertible for the purposes of drug evaluations. There are too many differences between the research grant situation and that of new drug evaluation. Without wanting to be too specific, and without claiming originality, let me suggest something like the following. There could be a roster of scientific advisers from the country over, chiefly from outside government, but also including many from the FDA, NIH, etc. This roster would include those knowledgeable about drugs and clinical applications plus a wide spectrum of other basic biomedical scientists. From this roster, advisory panels could be set up for each major new drug application. Or, what I believe would be preferable, standing advisory panels could be organized each with expertise in a particular field. It has been pointed out that there would be great value in having advice from such groups about the test program ahead of time, and during each phase, as well as appraisal of the results after completion. The panels could advise about whether short cuts are desirable, or further tests are needed. Such panels could also advise on the most important and difficult question of whether the potential value of a new drug justifies the risks involved in its

introduction. Advice from the panels would allow the FDA to make final decisions with greater assurance.

In addition to responsibilities for major new drug applications, the panels could also from time to time, be given assignments to review accepted drugs and drug uses, as has been done in the past, and is still being done by ad hoc panels, and would also be asked to suggest specific areas where more research is needed.

An important part of such an advisory system would be a National Food and Drug Advisory Council analogous to the National Advisory Councils of the NIH. To this council the panels would report at least some of their major decisions. The Council could enter into the more important problems and make recommendations for research support and for long range policy changes. I believe that such an advisory system could be of great value both to the drug companies and to the FDA.

Two difficulties with such a system have been pointed out to me. The first is that of the secrecy regarded as necessary during early stages of drug testing. I can't believe this is insurmountable. The panels might not be activated until after phase 1, at which time essential information about the drug would have to become rather widely disseminated anyhow. The second difficulty is that of conflict of interest. Many of those scientists who are knowledgable about drugs serve as consultants for one or another drug company. This also I believe can be handled. There are actually a great many younger investigators to draw upon, and conflict of interest would be no problem with many of the basic investigators who are not primarily working with drugs but who would be invaluable members of the advisory panels.

How Safe is Safe? A Producer's Viewpoint*

W. Clarke Wescoe

Vice Chairman of the Board and Director Sterling Drug, Inc., New York, New York 10016, USA

It is not a particularly prevailing attitude of the times that one designated a producer be invited to participate prominently in a program directed toward a discussion of public policy. To many it appears that the term producer has achieved a pejorative meaning in our society, that today it is considered almost improper to produce, that now to be socially respectable one only has to consume.

The very format of this forum may indicate to some that in the matter of safety relating to food additives and medicinal products there are, necessarily, divergent viewpoints among those who make, those who use, those who are concerned with biological science and those who are charged with the responsibility to administer the laws. I choose to think quite the opposite is true. In this, as in many other areas, it is not a matter of we and they, us and them, the good guys and the bad guys. It is not a matter of conflicting interests, of adversary relationships. Rather, it is a collective matter of trying to reach a common goal: the provision of calculable benefit to man with as little attendant risk as possible.

In a civilized society there is no more important goal. In pursuit of that goal we are all as one. There is no place for emotional catchwords, there are no reasons for artificial designations, there should be no acceptance of superficial stereotypes. Obviously, I am not only a producer; I am a consumer as well. In each of those stances I am caught up constantly in the assessment of benefits and risks. I choose to believe that as a producer, to use the vernacular of the day, I am the most deeply "concerned". I choose to believe that as a producer I am most likely to assess the circumstances most carefully for I must live with the assessments that are made in relation to the products with which I am associated. To be a producer is to conduct one's affairs all day, so that one can sleep easily all through the night.

We live in a "no-fault", "no-risk", "all-safe" society. The "no-fault" concept deals primarily with individuals; the "no-risk", "all-safe" concepts are associated primarily with products. We strive in our preoccupation with those concepts for a circumstance that man has never enjoyed and an utopian existence most probably beyond his reach. Man has always been at risk in his world and he always will be. As one risk has been removed, another, sometimes unpredicted risk, inevitably has been added. Our very concern today is an example of that historic repetition. Disease has been suppressed, contagion has been conquered, nutrition has been improved, but the very agents that produced advances once hailed as miracles, are now called into question. Society must continue to live with risks, as it always has. The risks must be calculated and assessed and then hopefully controlled as a result of balanced, unemotional discussion, in the absence of fanaticism,

---

* Presented at the first Academy Forum, "How Safe is Safe? The Design of Policy on Drugs and Food Additives," May 15, 1973, in Washington, D. C.

hysteria and hyperbole. Public policy should derive from reason, objectivity, and scientific evaluation of pertinent data. But balanced, unemotional discussion has always been difficult to obtain. I know of no particular groups who have achieved this goal in terms of the absolute. Obviously, objectivity is at risk in any controversy.

Consequently, in striving for objectivity it is necessary to scrutinize carefully the circumstances that may compromise it. It is just this necessity that brings us together today to discuss the safety of food additives and medicines. No discussion of that nature can be held without mentioning the forty-nine words that have come to be known as the "Delaney amendment": *Provided, That no additive shall be deemed to be safe if it is found to induce cancer when ingested by man or animal, or, if it is found, after tests which are appropriate for the evaluation of the safety of food additives, to induce cancer in man or animal.* Herein, special legislation deals in singular, unique fashion with the manifestation of a single chemical toxicity. I discuss it with considerable trepidation for as Professor Arthur Bestor has written: "Tolerance of opposing views is conceded to be a fine thing, generally speaking, where routine matters only are involved. But on certain issues one position (seems) so incontrovertibly right and the other so infernally wrong that to be tolerant is to become the accomplice of wickedness."

I am one of those trained in the biological sciences who believes that biology is never a matter of absolutes, that all biologic phenomena must be expressed as possibilities rather than absolutes. In that belief, I am confirmed by numbers of prominent scientists. Beyond that, trained as a pharmacologist, I consider the matter of dose/response to be fundamental. In that consideration, I am even joined by eminent scientists who are not pharmacologists. For instance, Dr. John Higginson, Director of the International Agency for Research on Cancer has said that knowledge of concentrations at which a substance becomes carcinogenic may allow it to be used in lower concentrations. Here is a leading pathologist who invokes the principle of dose/response.

The words of the "Delaney amendment" allow no consideration of dose/response as I read them. I am aware that there are others who believe that the principle of zero tolerance must be accepted for any substance shown in any concentration to be carcinogenic in animals. In their thinking a safe level for man cannot be established for agents shown in any species to be carcinogenic; they do, however, recognize as a realistic notion the concept of "socially acceptable risk." That notion is foreclosed by the amendment. The experimental feeding of high concentrations of a particular substance, as a caricature of what man conceivably could ingest, in addition to being toxicologically naive also ignores basic pharmacologic principles. It is possible with high concentrations to overload the system of elimination by which a substance normally would be handled; under those circumstances alternative pathways of elimination can be called into play or the substance can accumulate in an abnormal way. The alternate (unreal) pathway or the accumulation itself could be the factor implicated in the end-result observed. An experiment of this nature bears little relationship to reality.

Those who do not believe in a "no-effect" level essentially discard the all-embracing ground rules of statistical biology scientifically established by Sir Ronald Fisher which have been validated repeatedly in every other sphere of science. Beyond that, they tend to ignore the difficulties involved in extrapolating animal data in a meaningful way to man.

Most recently, the Delaney amendment was called into play when a prohibition was placed necessarily on the use of diethylstilbestrol as a feed additive for cattle. That particular decision was a triumph of superior, sophisticated analytical technique that permitted the measurement of 120 parts per trillion of DES in cattle liver (not, as I read it, the musculature of the cattle). Inevitably, as we develop highly sophisticated techniques we shall begin to discover the presence in tissues of more and more substances in lesser and lesser amounts. This possibility has now become apparent to perceptive laymen, as witness the editorial from The New York Times of Monday, April 30 entitled "Policy on Infinitesimals". A portion of that editorial reads: „Such sensitivity in measuring infinitesimal quantities is a respectable scientific feat, but how meaningful is it as a guide to the public? Is there a significant – even an appreciable – risk of anyone getting cancer from eating meat containing so tiny a quantity of DES? How does the "risk" the FDA has moved against compare with the risks of breathing normal polluted air in Manhattan or downtown Washington. D. C. – or with the risk of having a chest X-ray or smoking a single cigarette. The point is that the Delaney amendment is an all or nothing affair, and presumably would have applied if the analytical equipment had found only one thousandth of a trillionth part of DES. This sounds more like fanaticism than intelligent public policy. Would not Congress be well advised to consult the scientists on what meaning, if any, the law should give to infinitesimal quantities?"

That editorial expresses the difficulties inherent in the legislative prescription of absolutes relative to biological systems.

All that we discuss of safety must, of course, be examined from the standpoint of evaluating the magnitude of the possible risk involved in comparison with the extent of the benefit desired. In respect of food additives of certain sorts (flavors, colors) the benefit derived from a societal standpoint may be so small as to obviate the consideration of exposure to any risk, no matter how small. I must remark, however, that I could not conceive that any human has ever been exposed to a risk of cancer because he ate meat stamped by governmental inspectors with F. D. and C. Violet 1. In respect of other food additives (those used for purposes of preservation, those used for special dietary purposes) the benefit derived may be significant enough to allow the consideration of a certain degree of assessable risk at a low level.

I presume there is no time available to deal at length with the matter about which present legislation is silent: the tumorigenic or carcinogenic properties of natural foods. Just for the sake of completeness we should not fail to mention the long years and the many generations that have witnessed the consumption of cabbage, spinach and brussels sprouts all of which are goitrogenic if fed to animals in high enough quantities, and the more recent detection of the known carcinogens, aflatoxins and safrole, in natural products that are widely ingested.

At least in respect of these natural foods we have epidemiologic and geographic studies available to us. In respect of food additives, the case is more complex. Food additives become widely distributed in random fashion: their presence is often unknown or unsuspected in many foods and beverages. The very ubiquitous nature of their use requires a close assessment of their possible risks. It requires, as well, careful analysis of their toxicologic properties. The enactment of legislation in 1958 relative to food additives was a necessary and important step despite the fact that the fortynine words could have, in the opinion of some of us, been better written in a different way.

In respect of drugs (I prefer to call them medicines), we are faced with considerations of a different order for here we talk about products designed to produce great benefit. We talk necessarily, however, of products that carry an inherent risk for a drug by its very nature cannot be totally safe for everyone – the basic tenet of pharmacology is that any drug action is a toxicity, even the desired action, simply because in that action some cellular process is modified. Although, in respect of these desirable toxic actions we can tell with reasonable certainty the parameters of the risk, we cannot provide a certificate of safety.

Most of science, but few of the general public, understand this principle relating to medicines. Rene Dubos perhaps put it most clearly when he spoke generally of technological innovation: "Willingness to take risks is a condition of biological success... Excessive concern with safety is often incompatible with economic growth... To demand a certified verdict of safety before accepting a new technological innovation would clearly result in paralysis of progress." The public has learned to live willingly with risk in many spheres of activity and, it should be noted, without recognizing that in doing so they have calculated an acceptable benefit/risk ratio. People drive motor cars despite the appalling death toll on our highways; they smoke, although they have been warned of the dangers to health involved with it; they engage in dangerous recreation without a second thought; they submit to surgery oblivious to its morbidity and mortality rate. Regrettably, the public is not attuned to the same evaluation of benefit/risk as it

relates to medicines and science. The public requires education in this area, the sort of education that a forum like this may provide and the sort that could be provided by the talented efforts of the journalists who are present.

There is perhaps no other group of products so well regulated and so carefully controlled as are medicines in this country. Once more, in this field the producer has no conflict of interest with the consumer; neither does he have conflict with true science or with equitable regulation.

Medicines differ from food additives and environmental chemicals in significant ways: they are designed from the beginning of chemical synthesis to achieve a benefit for man (the improvement of health, the alleviation of symptoms, the cure of disease); exposure to them is limited in terms of population and duration of use; they are administered in a controlled manner and in a dosage form that is recommended after exhaustive investigation; they are taken under the direction of a professional person who by reason of education and experience can decide whether obvious advantages justify an assessable risk.

Because of background information available from years of intensive and expensive efforts in pharmaceutical research carried out in industrial, academic and governmental laboratories there are well-defined tests for activity, efficacy and safety available to us. Over the years, animal models have been developed, sophisticated analytical techniques have been devised. Yet, despite all the collected information, all the facts we can learn from laboratory studies, and the undoubted intellectual attractiveness of studying reactions to medicines in animals, laboratory investigation in animals remains today still an attractive hypothesis. No animal, including the subhuman primate, is entirely and predictably like man. Differences in metabolic fate, differences in sensitivities, differences in immune mechanisms separate man from laboratory animals. For many differences there are no known short-term predictive tests. The truth is that absolute safety cannot be guaranteed despite years of intensive laboratory experimentation. The final truth is that for medicines the ultimate test is careful evaluation and experience in man.

As man differs from other animals, so humankind differs among itself. An infant is not a small adult, a pregnant woman is different from a non-pregnant one, enzymatic systems differ in the various races of man (a fact that leads to differing tolerances to medicines), we are, each of us, genetically different from hundreds of millions of others. Man is not a homogeneous species.

Because man is heterogeneous, unanticipated and unpredictable side-reactions occasionally occur from medicines. Fortunately, many of these are subjective only, most are limited in extent and reversible in action if the medicine is withdrawn or the dose lowered; rarely, an unpredicted side-reaction, usually an idiosyncrasy, can be life-threatening.

Although laboratory and clinical investigations are carefully controlled, the data from them subjected to intense scrutiny and statistical evaluation, the same is not true for adverse-reaction reporting. Most adverse reaction reports are anecdotal in nature, poorly evaluated, and often the result of *post hoc ergo propter hoc* reasoning, neglectful of other variables. I have known examples, for instance, of adverse reaction reporting where careful analysis of body fluids failed to reveal the presence of the medicine presumably implicated but did reveal the presence of another medicine. Our mechanisms of surveillance of so-called adverse reactions are neither scientific nor modernized;

they hark back to the days of Hahnemann, who kept diaries of experiences.

The nature of biology, characterized by individual variation, has encouraged the biological scientist to develop means for describing quantitatively the behavior of a larger system by study of small samples. He relies upon these well established statistical methods of evaluation to insure reproducibility, to insure against the factor of chance. In many circumstances, a negative result is just as important as a positive one, yet there are those who will believe *only* if a positive result occurs; they are those who are only concerned with "heads" on the coin.

The decision to release a medicine for use in man has always been an agonizing one for the producer and for the regulatory agency. The tendency exists always to ask for more tests, to delay the decision, for a non-decision is easier to make than a positive one. Different tests are required for different classes of medicine. Careful guidelines are constantly evaluated, for unnecessary tests put handcuffs on investigation and delay the introduction of medicines. The final decision is always weighted with the ultimate consumer in mind. Public policy is well established through the new drug application procedure.

Recently, the question of carcinogenicity and mutagenicity of medicines has been raised, in part related to an extension of the philosophy surrounding the testing of food additives and environmental chemicals. Pharmaceutical manufacturers, regulatory personnel and academic scientists have worked intensively and cooperatively on this problem of high priority about which all have a sense of urgency. There is general agreement that the normal mutation rate in man is unknown, that there is absence of concrete data to link mutagenesis with carcinogenesis, that the relevance of mutagenic testing in bacteria or yeasts is remote as a definitive test, that testing must be performed in mammalian species even though the relevance of such testing is not yet known. There is no suggestion at the present time of the need for rigid recommendations and hopefully there will never be rigid ones legislated. There is, however, a determination that the principles of pharmacology and toxicology will not be ignored in such testing. Testing in animals is fraught with variables — purity of material administered, diet consumed, air pollutants, water purity among others. Agreement is general that differences in testing must apply for medicines that are taken only occasionally, medicines taken only for short terms, and medicines taken for prolonged periods. By heeding the principles of pharmacology, caricature experiments can be avoided. Appropriate attention must be paid to dose/response, to route of administration (similar to clinical use), elimination pathways, and duration of exposure. Here is an example of progress voluntarily achieved, progress that removes the necessity for special legislation. There is nothing, and logically so, of more concern to man than his health and those factors that affect it. That concern dictates the necessity for him to be educated — fairly, with all sides of the question presented, and the concept of benefit/risk consistently explained. There is

no reason for "scare" headlines of inflammatory statements created out of flimsy bases. When scientific meetings are held today and nothing real or evidential is found to be said, the reports should give those facts. No service is performed by reporting the likelihood of delayed, insidious effects about which nothing is known and which could not be measured, or the possibility of subtle damage, so subtle that it cannot be found. All of us are concerned with safety, and, I believe, the producer most of all. All of us are vigilant in searching out those factors affecting safety. To the reasonable man, vigilance means, as Arthur Bestor put it: "The precise indentification of real dangers, not the hysterical shouting of 'Wolf', 'Wolf', when a mouse creeps out of the woodwork."

Complex issues demand careful and critical analysis. Reason, not emotion, should rule the day. The quiet voice is not easily heard in the din of chaotic clamor. All of us might well remember the words of Emerson in 1834 when he spoke to Phi Beta Kappa at Harvard on the responsibilities of the American Scholar. We may not all be scholars, but we do search for truth. This is what Emerson said: "Let him not quit his belief that a popgun is a popgun, though the ancient and honourable of the earth affirm it to be the crack of doom."

Pesticide Residues and Radioactive Substances in Food: a Comparative Study of the Problems *

Report of a Panel of Experts Organized by the Joint FAO/IAEA Division of Atomic Energy in Food and Agriculture Held in Vienna, 12–16 October 1970

Industrial growth and agricultural intensification dictated by the needs and demands of the increasing world population have led to major advances in terms of human health, comfort, convenience and welfare. These developments have also led to measurable chemical contamination of the human environment, especially within recent decades.

Certain problems, such as those of residual pesticides or radioactive substances and their significance in food and environment are very complex and not easily understood by the layman. Therefore, the scientist has a special responsibility to study their nature, magnitude and possible biological significance, and to present his conclusions impartially. This is an essential basis to the development of any necessary controls which, if realistic, must take into account established benefits as well as possible risks.

The Joint FAO/IAEA Panel held in Vienna, 12–16 October, 1970 was convened to bring together scientists concerned on the one hand with pesticide residues, on the other hand with contamination by radioactive substances in order to exploit common information sources and resources and to identify priorities. Therefore, the report which follows should represent a step towards better coordination and cooperation on the problems of environmental protection as a whole.

* The publishers and editors of EQS are indebted to the International Atomic Energy Agency in Vienna for permission to publish in full the report which follows and to the Joint FAO/IAEA Secretariat for the necessary arrangements. The editors feel that the report is timely and will be of particular interest to readers of EQS.

1. Introduction

While it may be important to establish controls to limit contamination of food and environment, it is equally important not to impair the associated benefits to human health, comfort and welfare, for example those deriving from the increasing use of pesticides for the protection of growing and stored food as well as human and animal health, and the use of nuclear power and nuclear techniques in industry, agriculture and medicine.

For controls to be realistic in this context it is necessary to study the nature, magnitude and possible significance to human health of contaminating chemical residues, whether radioactive or not, in food and environment. The resources and skill of the available scientific manpower trained to study these complex problems are limited. Therefore, it is important to pool information sources and the resources needed for the study of both types of problems and to identify priorities. This panel represents a multidisciplinary and somewhat novel approach to the problems of pesticide residues and radioactive substances in food.

At an early stage the discussions illustrated the timely need for bringing together experts concerned with the two different kinds of food and environmental contamination. The participants were able to define areas of mutual ignorance, misunderstandings in matters of terminology and the need for clarification.

Public sensitivity was clearly influenced adversely through lack of effectice and balanced communication. There was evidence that the hazards of nuclear warfare were associated in the public mind with the belief that even minimal levels of radioactive contamination or radiation exposure were a sinister threat to human health. This, despite the fact that man has always been and forever must be, exposed to measurable levels of radioactivity from purely natural sources.

Similarly all pesticides tended to be regarded as persistent poisons ultimately contaminating the entire biosphere. However, research and development are resulting in an increasing number of available pesticides that are rapidly degraded in the environment and by normal food processing to levels where they can no longer be detected or to chemical derivatives of negligible or of no toxicological significance.

The panel stressed that although they were concerned with two important aspects of food contamination, man was concerned with the sum-total of what should not, or need not, be in his plate of food and drink, and in his environment. Food might contain, in addition to residual traces of pesticides or radioactive material, food additives such as colouring matter, artificial flavours, sweeteners, preservatives, antibiotics, and unintentional contaminants such as traces of detergents, lead, arsenic and mercury from

various sources, including natural ones. Any possible hazard from ingested radionuclides was due to their ionizing radiations emitted in the process of radioactive decay. But man was continuously exposed to natural ionizing radiation due to cosmic rays and to the ever present natural radioelements of all living tissues, e.g. carbon-14 and potassium-40. He was also exposed through inhalation to a range of atmospheric pollutants, e.g. those arising from the combustion of fossil fuels for power, heat and transport. Thus, while there is indeed a need for constant study and specialized research into these problems there is also a need for balanced authoritative reporting and communication to the public in the context of food and environmental contamination as a whole.

2. Background Information

As background material for their comparative study the panel studied certain published documents and prepared working papers related to courrent programmes of the United Nations Agencies and Non-Governmental Organizations concerned with problems of pesticide residues in food and environment and human exposure to radiation listed in appendix 7.2. In the particular context of exposure limits (maximum permissible concentrations of pesticide residues in or on food, maximum permissible radiation doses, dose limits, etc.) the following programmes were discussed:

2.1. International activities on the measurement and control of pesticide residues in food

No studies have been completed reflecting the total human exposure to pesticides from all potential sources such as air, water, food, household applications and disease control. Occupational exposure (e.g. of spray operators) has been studied and represents a potential hazard for limited population groups. The dietary intake from foods containing traces of residual pesticides or their decomposition and reaction products resulting from agricultural application or chemical protection during storage has been the subject of many investigations, possibly because of the direct application of pesticides to crops and the large populations involved. Although other means of population exposure to pesticides are recognized and may be important in certain cases, these have been comparatively little studied. Such means also include food exposed to pesticides under other conditions than those of agricultural crop protection (see document 7.2.21.).

Taking into account the needs and benefits of pest control in modern agriculture, the Joint FAO/WHO programme on pesticide residues seeks to protect the population from potentially undesirable exposure through the ingestion of possible residues in food by recommending or establishing internationally acceptable limits. The meetings of experts convened under this programme study the nature and magnitude of pesticide residues which actually occur, or are indicated by research to occur, following agricultural practice. When the evidence indicates that these residues at stages suitable for sampling in food or its intermediates are unlikely to lead to an intake greater than the "acceptable daily intake" by man, they can be recommended as tolerances, i.e. maximum permissible concentrations. The FAO/WHO meetings of experts have considered up to the time of writing (March 1971) approx. 100 compounds (insecticides, stored products fumigants, fungicides, herbicides and some insecticide synergists). Maximum acceptable daily intake (ADI) figures have been es-

tablished for approx. 55 compounds and "tolerances" or temporary tolerances for a range of food products or intermediates for each of about 40 compounds. These tolerances are considered by the Codex Committee on Pesticide Residues with a view to their ultimate acceptance by member states as international food standards through the machinery of the Joint FAO/WHO Codex Alimentarius Commission. Specific problems of analytical methodology and the nature of terminal residues arising from the Joint FAO/WHO programme are referred to the Pesticides Section of the International Union of Pure and Applied Chemistry (IUPAC). In addition, because of the extensive use of isotopic tracer techniques in basic studies of pesticide residues the Joint FAO/IAEA Division of Atomic Energy in Food and Agriculture has initiated a training and research programme designed to facilitate the use of isotopically labelled pesticides with particular reference to the problems indicated by the Joint FAO/WHO programme (e.g. see 7.2.13.). The derivation of ADI's invariably involves a critical review of what is known about the metabolism, toxicology, and pharmacology of the parent compound or the derivatives likely to occur in the terminal residue. Particular attention is given to the data of extended feeding trials at graded intake levels with experimental animals, and, when available, with man and a "no offect level" estimated. No effect levels indicated by adequate numbers of suitable observations have usually been divided by an appropriate safety factor before translating them into an ADI for man.

2.2. International activities related to the measurement and control of radioactive substances in food

Man may be exposed to ionizing radiation from external sources (cosmic radiation, natural radioelements of the earth's crust, external artificial radioactive sources, X-ray apparatus, etc.) or from internal sources (natural radioelements such as potassium-40 and carbon-14 present in all living tissues, and artifical radionuclides absorbed or ingested by the body). The panel was mainly concerned with traces of artificial radioactive substances contaminating food. The panel stressed that the significance of human exposure to artificial radioactivity as a result of food contamination could only be meaningfully considered in the context of man's total exposure to ionizing radiation. Moreover, natural radiation appeared at present to be by far the larger component in this total exposure of members of the public. However, the panel also recognized that in the present state of knowledge exposure to atomic radiation from natural sources was not necessarily a justification for additional exposure to artificial sources. Such additional exposure must involve a study of risk/benefit ratios.

The International Commission on Radiological Protection (ICRP) makes recommendations on "maximum permissible doses" for radiation workers and "Dose Limits" for individual members of the public and these have been widely adopted internationally e.g. by the International Atomic Energy Agency (IAEA). The ICRP has estimated "maximum permissible body burdens" for radiation workers and corresponding "maximum permissible concentrations" of radionuclides in air and water. For members of the public no such concentrations have been established but for planning purposes guidance is provided by the principle that dose limits for members of the public be set at a factor of ten below the corresponding limits for radiation workers.

The IAEA has published (document 7.2.23) "maximum permissible annual intakes" for "workers" and corresponding limits form ;members of the public". These figures, expressed in microcuries of a particular radionuclide were "obtained by multiplying the relevant maximum permissible concentration given by the ICRP by the following standard intakes of air and water. Air breathed by workers during the work is taken as 2500 m³/yr. Air breathed by adult individuals of the general public is taken to be 7300 m³/yr. Water in the form of food or fluids taken in by adult members of the general public is taken to be 0.8 m³/yr." The panel was advised that ICRP was planning to change the format of its recommendations so that maximum permissible concentrations would be replaced by annual intake limits for inhalation or ingestion. The panel noted that the dose limits given by ICRP and the IAEA-derived limits for annual intakes refer to the total dose from all sources but exclude that due to natural radioactivity or that received as a result of the medical examination or treatment of patients.

The United Nations Scientific Committee on the Effects of Atomic Radiation (UNSCEAR) was established by the General Assembly of the United Nations in 1955 with the following principal term of reference: – "To receive and assemble in an appropriate and useful form the following radiological information furnished by States Members of the United Nations or members of the specialized agencies: (i) Reports on observed levels of ionizing radiation and radioactivity in the environment; (ii) Reports on scientific observations and experiments relevant to the effects of ionizing radiation upon man and his environment already under way or later undertaken by national scientific bodies or by authorities of national Governments." In its yearly progress reports (e.g. see 7.2.17) UNSCEAR summarizes the assembled information and data and "transmits from time to time . . . the documents and evaluations . . . to the Secretary General (of the UN) for publication and dissemination to States Members . . . .".

Of particular relevance to the problem of food contamination are the Committee's periodical global collections and reviews of radioactivity data in samples of food and environment and their relation to the peaceful or other uses of atomic energy.

3. Comparative Aspects of Pesticide and Radioactivity Problems

The panel compared the principles and information sources employed by pesticide toxicologists and radiological protection specialists in the development of maximum permissible or acceptable limits of exposure to pesticide and radioactive substances respectively. Some common problems were identified and differences in the principles employed were also noted. These are briefly tabulated in Appendix 7.1.

Both types of contaminant find their way into the human body through food webs, both undergo enormous dilution and/or dispersion in the biosphere following their use or release. However, while possible population exposure to pesticides is likely to be associated mainly with the ingestion of food carrying pesticide residues, irradiation due to the ingestion of radioactive substances in food is likely to represent only a fraction of the total radiation exposure which must include natural radiation from the environment. The toxic forms of pesticides tend to disappear through the natural processes of chemical decomposition and enzymic attack which vary greatly according to temperature, tissues affected, etc. Contaminating radionuclides tend to disappear through the

natural but invariable and uncontrollable processes of radioactive decay. Both pesticides and radioactive substances may be concentrated by living organisms, especially in aquatic or marine environments which in some cases suggest special hazards which require study and control.

While both pesticide residues and radioactive substances are subject to legislative control in many countries and while, in both cases, there are internationally recommended exposure limits, there are apparent differences in the basic philosophies adopted. For example, in the Joint FAO/WHO programme the socalled "Acceptable Daily Intake" (ADI) for man is based on the concept of the experimentally determined "no-effect level". That is, a level of dietary residue intake below which no effect on the ingesting organism could be detected and this, after division by an appropriate safety factor, leads to the ADI, defined as "The daily intake (mg of the chemical per kg body weight) which, during an entire lifetime, appears to be without appreciable risk on the basis of all known facts at the time." The ICRP recommendations for "maximum permissible doses" on the other hand are based on the concept of "acceptable risk" and involve the "cautious assumption that any exposure to radiation may carry some risk" of deleterious effects which, even below the set limits may be finite, but acceptable. Moreover, these maximum permissible doses relate to the total radiation exposure of which that contributed by artificial radioactive substances in food would only be a very small fraction. Superficially, this appears to be a fundamental difference of approach in establishing limits of exposure – the no effect level or "threshold concept" of the pesticide toxicologist and the "extrapolation concept" of the radiological protection specialist based on the cautious assumption that there is a linear dose effect relationship extrapolated to zero dose. On the other hand it is important to consider the comparison further: Without further qualification the "no effect level" is inevitably a function of the sensitivity of the techniques available to the pesticide toxicologist. As more sensitive biochemical and physiological techniques become available so will the levels of diatary intake of a pesticide residue, at which absolutely no effect on the biochemistry or physiology of the ingesting animal can be detected, tend to become lower and lower and must approach zero. The problem will then be to decide at which level will the "effect" or, therefore, the associated "risk", however small, be acceptable in the context of human health. In developing its recommendations, on the other hand, the ICRP simply recognizes that in the scientific sense there is no dose level, however small, that does not have some biological effect and this in turn virtually dictates an acceptable "risk" concept – " ... unless man wishes to dispense with activities involving exposures to ionizing radiations, he must recognize that there is a degree of risk and must limit the radiation dose to a level at which the assumed risk is deemed to be acceptable to the individual and to society in view of the benefits derived from such activities" (document 7.2.16). The discussion of this subject clearly emphasized the need for clarification and better mutual understanding of the terms and their definitions used by those concerned with limiting exposure to pesticide residues and radioactive substances respectively (see section 5.2.).

At present there are no internationally recommended limits for radioactive substances in food. However, the Maximum Permissible Concentration values for water $(MPC)_w$, for the 168-h week, recommended by the ICRP may, with certain limitations, be applied to food. However, it was noted that MPC_w values

have been established primarily for occupational exposure and for adults only, assuming a 50-year exposure at constant level. Modifications of these limits for other purposes would require careful account being taken of the likely and important differences between the conditions of occupational exposure and those of normal food and drink consumption by different members of the public.

Many factors may profoundly affect the significance of a radioactive substance in the diet, e.g. the relative abundance in the diet of other non-radioactive isotopes of the same element or related elements of similar biochemical behaviour; habit, age, sex of the exposed person, and the chemical and particulate form of the radionuclide. Moreover, the acceptability of any limit for ingested radioactive material will depend upon the radiation dose known to be, or likely to be, received from all other sources both internal or external.

4. Terminal Pesticide Residues and Radioactive Substances in Food as a Function of Habitat and Dietary Habit

A common problem to the study of the possible significance of terminal chemical residues in food, whether derived from pesticides or from artificial environmental radionuclides, was the need for information on the nature, sources, and history of the ingested food. This problem was discussed and some priorities suggested. Particular account was taken of the FAO dietary studies (document 7.2.4.).

4.1. Food consumption and dietary patterns

Diet varies considerably from country to country. In North America and Europe wheat is the principal dietary cereal. In the Far East and India rice is the principal cereal. Some coastal populations may eat far more fish than inland communities. These and other variations influence the level of dietary intake of radioactive substances and the quantity and nature of ingested "terminal pesticide residues". The range and quantity of pesticides (insecticides, fungicides, herbicides, etc.) used in the production and storage of food often vary according to country, crop and climate. Dietary variations also occur within countries and between different ethnic, social, and income groups.

Comparatively little information is available relating to population groups which might be subject to unusual exposure as a result of their special location or dietary habit. Information for that purpose would have to be sought specially and is not the kind usually collected in the preparation of food balance sheets, since these are based upon the rate of disappearance of food commodities at national level. Food balance data are of course dependent upon the accuracy of reporting and can only be an approximation in certain instances, e.g. in the case of highly perishable items. It was believed, however, that improvements in data reporting were unlikely to occur in the near future.

A narrower picture could be obtained by requesting the housewife to maintain a record of food purchases which then allows estimation of the food intake on the basis of the family unit. Only in those cases where a special problem is believed to exist (relating to specific dietary problems) are surveys of food intake of individuals attempted. Differences in socio-economic status, between countries and between individuals within a country markedly affect the dietary pattern, the high income groups usually having a greater proportion of animal protein in the diet. This not only alters the pesticide exposure pattern but in addition may alter the susceptibility to the level of pesticide which may be considered safe. It was also drawn to the attention of the meeting that fluid intake studies (including alcoholic beverages), were rarely reported despite the importance of such studies, especially when considering fall-out problems.

4.2. Terminal pesticide residues

Attention was drawn to the WHO pilot computer study which was a theoretical estimate of daily intakes of pesticide residues on the basis of certain national diets assuming that the terminal residue would be at the same level as the maximum permissible residue (tolerance) at the point of recommended enforcement (for examples of FAO/WHO recommended tolerances see document 7.2.22). This suggested that some pesticides might lead to terminal residues in excess of the ADI unless losses or degradation to less toxic derivatives after the point of tolerance application were sufficiently great. This study therefore usefully drew attention to pesticides for which there was a special need for studying their degradation from the time of tolerance enforcement to the point of human ingestion, taking especially into account the effects of storage, commercial processing and cooking.

Food derived from chemically-protected crops and livestock is not the only factor in population exposure to pesticides. Such factors as inhalation exposure and the increasing household use of pesticides should also be considered. This wide and regular use of pesticides also results in further problems, e.g. the formation of environmental pools of relatively persistent pesticides and contamination such as encountered with DDT in salmon in Lake Michigan, and indirect contamination due to the distribution of pesticides in food webs (e.g. by the use of waste proteins for animal foods).

4.3. Radioactive substances in food

Despite the wide spectrum of radioactive fission products arising in nuclear reactors or from explosive nuclear reactions only a few "critical" radionuclides have merited study in the context of food contamination.

This conclusion is based on experience and study since the beginning of the atomic energy era. This experience also includes the many observations made following the very rare nuclear accident – rare because of the rigorous precautions invariably taken to ensure safety and the containment of possible leakages of radioactive material. The needs for reactor safety and for the control of radioactive waste, unlike other pollution problems, had been envisaged and provided for since the construction of the first reactor. In no sense did present precautions and study represent any kind of „firebrigade action".

Iodine-131, caesium-137, strontium-89 and strontium-90 represent the critical radionuclides in the context of food contamination. Iodine-131 accumulates in the thyroid, caesium-137 circulating throughout the body irradiates all tissues and the strontium isotopes whose biochemical behaviour resembles that of calcium tend to accumulate in calciferous tissues. This in turn leads to the concept of "critical organs" as the best indicators of possible tissue irradiation following the ingestion of contaminated food. The relative importance of a critical radionuclide in a particular case depends on several factors which include the mechanism of release, the time elapsed between release and ingestion, the nature of the contaminated food commodity, the dietary habits of the consumers involved, etc.

Just as "cristical nuclides" or "critical organs" have been identified as the more sensitive and useful indicators of possible risk associated with radioactive contamination it has also been possible to identify certain critical food items as those which represent the major sources of intake of a particular radionuclide. The relative importance of these items will also depend on the dietary habits of the exposed group. For example, when milk is an important part of the diet, it will be the critical food with respect to radiostrontium or radioiodine. For the purpose of comparing possible risks to the public from dietary radioactivity, it has also been useful to identify "critical groups" of exposed persons, who, for reasons of habit and location, would be the most exposed. The panel noted some examples of this overall "critical pathway" approach which had proved useful in the study and development of controls of radioactive waste discharge from nuclear reactors. Thus, "laverbread" made from the seaweed *Porphyra umbiliculis* had been identified as a critical food because it tended to concentrate ruthenium-106 present in discharge from the Windscale reactor site in the UK. It was a dietary constituent of local importance to a small critical group of about 100 laverbread consumers. Phosphorus-32 in fresh water fish in the Columbia river of the USA and zinc-65 in oysters near the Bradwell site in the UK were other examples.

A major advantage of the critical pathway approach is that it obviates the need for the elaborate and comprehensive routine monitoring of samples representing all the possible complex pathways (see section 5.1.) by which accidental or controlled releases of radionuclides could ultimately reach all membres of the population.

The study of radiotoxicity is simplified by the fact that, at the extremely low chemical concentrations at which radionuclides appear in living tissues, any toxic effects are a function of the tissue radioactivity alone. This can be readily measured and characterized by well established methods. The toxicity of pesticide residues, on the other hand, depends on the chemical nature and magnitude of the residue and these are often very complex and difficult to quantify.

In the discussion of the possible effects of population exposure to radiation from the specific ingestion by man of artificial radioactive substances in food it was noted that such exposure was small compared with that due to natural background radiation. Moreover, genetic or somatic effects in populations exposed to relatively high external natural background radiation, such as in Kerala, India and some areas in Brazil, had not apparently been dected. As an example of higher-than-average exposure to ingested radioactivity it was mentioned that populations living on a diet of reindeer and caribou meat relatively rich in the natural radionuclide polonium-210, presumably from prehistoric times to the present, receive a 10–15 times higher dose of radiation than the average world population, apparently without effect.

The panel noted that, as in the case of pesticide residues, the processing of peeling, washing, etc., often result in substantial decontamination. In the case of short-lived radionuclides, adequate decontamination can be achieved by storage of the contaminated commodity for sufficient time before ingestion, e.g., of dairy products made from milk contaminated by iodine-131.

The panel briefly discussed the problem of the use or disposal of edible tissues carrying radioactive substances as a result of using radioactive isotopes under controlled laboratory or field conditions for routine tests, diagnosis, research, etc. While the panel recognized that the concentration of a particular radionuclide present in derived foodstuffs might be at a level that would give rise to radiation doses well below the dose limits recommended by the ICRP for members of the general population, the use or disposal of such contaminated tissues must always be a matter for the national controls or legislation in force at that time. Under no circumstances could the panel formulate general recommendations on this subject. This discussion, however, led to the question of the molecular form of such radioactive contaminants. The biological effect of radiation from such residues is the result of the radiation dose absorbed by the tissue. The radioactivity of the radionuclide present is not determined by its molecular form. However, the molecular form or chemistry of the radioactive residue did dictate its deposition, fate or excretion by the organism and in this indirect manner could affect the radiotoxicity of the ingested radionuclide. For example, tritiated thymidine is not appreciably degraded and excreted but is incorporated into chromosomes. Toxicity of an ingested pesticide is invariably due to its molecular properties alone.

5. Priorities, Research and Information Needs

The panel noted that exposure to radiation through the ingestion of artificial radionuclides at the present levels found in food and drink were very much less than those corresponding to the ICRP dose limits for members of the public. Moreover, this exposure of the population was a very small addition to the doses from natural sources to which the entire population has been and must continue to be exposed.

The ever increasing range of available pesticidal formulations, the fact that the terminal residue in food was likely to be a mixture of several pesticides, impurities, and their derivatives, the lack of information on the overall fate of the pesticide residue in many cases suggested a higher priority for research on pesticide residues than on radioactive substances in food. In particular, there was a need for integrated studies, from the point of application of the pesticide to the terminal residue, taking into account the fate of all the derivatives including metabolites whose chronic toxicity and fate in the environment were comparatively little studied.

The panel also noted the need to study the fate and significance of industrial and domestic chemical waste which entered the agricultural environment and possibly food. Many such chemicals were not designed for use in connexion with food and were, therefore, not subject to the rigid screening for possible toxicological effects as were pesticides. There was a growing need to study the nature, magnitude and significance of these residues in the agricultural environment and its water sources. This need was illustrated by recent findings that mercury which is accumulated by edible fresh water fish such as pike, perch and barbut and in certain food items may reach unacceptable dietary levels.

The great and often unique value of isotope tracer techniques in basic studies of these problems was noted. The use of radioactive or unstable isotopes for larger scale pollution studies was often handicapped, however, by fear of radioactive contamination. In this context the Joint FAO/IAEA Division was urged to explore the possibility of using stable isotopically labelled materials where the scale of the pollution study might preclude the use of radioactive material on the grounds of cost or potential radiation hazard.

The desirability of encouraging radioisotope studies on a large scale to investigate the rate of degradation and removal of pesticide or chemical residues was not favoured by the meeting. Despite the fact that such experiments could be designed (e.g. with short-lived radioisotopes) which would be devoid of any possible hazard to the public it was felt that the encouragement of such experiments could result in undesirable publicity or unnecessary alarm.

Recent years have witnessed a remarkable increase in the sensitivity of the research tools for studying the effects of chemicals on living organisms. There were now many examples where histological, enzymic and other biochemical changes could be detected *in vitro* and *in vivo* at levels of exposure well below those inducing signs of poisoning in the exposed organism.

The interpretation of these detailed biochemical effects was another problem, but there was no doubt about the value of their detection when evaluating acceptable or safe levels of exposure. They represented a tremendous advance over the use of classical dose mortality curves as the sole index of toxicity to experimental animals.

The panel noted the value of isotope techniques in developing methods for detecting significant biochemical changes in exposed tissues and the Joint Division's role in the context of pesticides and pollutants, for example in the encouragement and development of labelled substrate techniques for sensitive measures of enzyme inhibition.

In discussing the effects on pesticide residues of commercial and domestic food processing, meal preparation etc., the panel noted that a growing number of data were becoming available. However, many of these were buried in the literature or national administration files and even if these could be extracted and collected, a large number of important questions would remain unanswered, for example many such data referred to "disappearance" of the parent pesticide. There was often a lack of data on the presence of derivatives and reaction products which might have significance in the context of chronic toxicity. Isotopic tracer techniques were especially valuable in this respect since they often indicated the presence of unextracted or chemically undetected moieties of the terminal residue. There was a particular need for more information on food processing and preparation habits in developing countries and their effects on pesticide residues under the local conditions. The panel noted that in studying a particular pesticide residue and in developing limits for acceptable human exposure it was usually implicitly assumed that such exposure meant exposure to that potentially toxic agent in isolation. In fact individuals of a population were invariably exposed to various agents simultaneously; usually to two or more pesticide residues in addition to other chemical residues (e.g. lead, mercury), atmospheric pollutants, food and feed additives, drugs, cosmetics, radiation, etc. Therefore, the question arose as to whether such multiple exposure *in toto* would also be acceptable on the basis of the limits developed independently. The possibility that the effects of multiple exposure might be more than "additive" as a result of "potentiation" or "synergism" was discussed at the 1967 Joint Meeting of FAO and WHO experts on pesticide residues (document 7.2.20). The panel felt that the concentrations reached in the tissues of exposed human beings were usually so low as to render significant potentiation unlikely in practice. However, in the case of possible genetic effects academic study of simultaneous exposure to certain chemical residues and to radiation in this context should be encouraged.

5.1. Monitoring programmes and epidemiological studies

Monitoring programmes usually involve the systematic analysis of samples of food, environment, animal or plant tissues for biological, chemical or radioactive contamination. In the context of pesticides (see 7.2.22.), sampling may be "objective", i.e. on a random basis, or "subjective" when samples are taken to demonstrate a known or suspected contamination. In the context of radioactivity, sampling on the basis of the critical pathway approach (see 4.3.) might be described as "subjective". Monitoring programmes are used to check that limits are not being exceeded or to indicate trends for the purpose of developing or imposing control measures on a rational basis.

One of the most important exercises undertaken by certain countries in recent years has been the "total diet" study designed to determine actual pesticide residues (determined usually as the parent pesticide) in ready-to-eat foods as consumed by individuals of the population. Sampling on the basis of "high consumption" patterns (ninth decile figures) as practised, for example, in the US, results in pesticide intake figures in excess of what is representative of the average population. While this approach – which is analogous to the idea of the "critical group" in radiological protection – provides for safety margins as far as protective measures for total population may be concerned, it has been argued that the usual dietary variation has already been incorporated into the safety factors used in establishing the ADI values and, for the purpose of comparing the actual and the acceptable pesticide intake on a national basis, *average* consumption figures would therefore be a more realistic basis. Whatever basis is chosen for "total diet" studies the need for appropriate statistical guidance, especially in relation to sampling, cannot be overstressed.

The monitoring programme of the United States was reviewed in detail. The majority of the samples are taken in relation to surveillance. These procedures include objective sampling at the wholesale-level, and subjective sampling.

In the case of imported food, spot sampling of various commodities at the point of entry identifies problem areas. The subsequent repeated sampling of products which are likely to contain high pesticide residues results in biased data. In the case of the "market-basket" or "total diet" surveys, the samples are obtained from retail stores using a basic shopping list conceived as a two-week-supply of food for an adolescent male between the ages of 16 and 19 years. The food is then prepared as for consumption in a diet kitchen and analyzed for pesticide residues.

The difference between the maximum theoretical intakes from prepared foods, calculated on the basis of recommended tolerances or ADI's, and the much lower levels usually recorded as being ingested in fact on the basis of the market-basket-surveys were discussed. These were probably due to the effects of processing, storage, etc. and to the unlikelihood that a particular pesticide would have been used on the maximum scales anticipated as a precautionary measure in the development of "tolerances". It was noted that with the exception of aldrin and dieldrin the residues found in market-basket-surveys indicated that the actual ingestion of pesticides rarely exceeded one tenth of the acceptable daily intake. (See Duggan, document 7.2.6., Harries, J.M., Jones, C.M., and Tatton, J.O.G., J.Sci.Fd.Agric., 20, (1969), 242, Abbott, D.C., Homes, D.C., and Tatton, J.O.G., ibid. 245).

While the surveys currently undertaken by certain countries could be regarded with satisfaction, it was emphasized that such programmes are still required in developing areas. With the change in emphasis from food quantity to food quality in these areas the need for such surveys becomes increasingly important.

The panel was informed that radionuclide monitoring has been considerably reduced in relation to food, since the problem is felt to be of relatively minor importance at present. In air and water the levels being found are less than 1% of the "permissible" levels. While the panel considered it unlikely that a dangerous build-up of radioactivity in food could occur in the context of the currently recognized dose limit of 0.5 rem/year to members of the public, it was felt that the possibility of concentration effects in certain living orginisms of food webs from low levels of environmental radionuclides should, as in the case of pesticide and other chemical residues, continue to be studied carefully.

The panel noted that in terms of monitoring activities certain contaminants had received comparatively little systematic attention. For example, certain persistent metabolites of organochlorine insecticides, polychlorinated biphenyls, lead, cadmium, and mercury which are a cause for concern as environmental pollutants. The panel felt strongly that a survey of these problems, coupled with an attempt to identify compounds likely to cause problems in the future, should be undertaken by a UN agency.

The world-wide usage, often involving enormous areas of agricultural land, the tendency of sprays to drift, etc., all emphasize the importance of worldwide monitoring programmes for pesticide residues. Significant contamination by radioactive substances on the other hand would almost invariably be linked to a known centre or discharge point and significant contamination would be of a relatively local nature. Monitoring therefore would be most effective on a subjective basis – i.e. the sampling and radiochemical analysis of samples deliberately taken in or near the affected locality.

For these reasons the panel felt that there would be no advantage in creating special monitoring networks for both pesticide and radioactive substances in food and environment. However, because of the common problems of representative sampling (see above) and the value of milk as an indication of both pesticide and radiochemical contamination (see below) in many regions of the world, this was one useful medium for simultaneous monitoring at existing centres. In this context the panel's attention was drawn to the working party on monitoring of the Scientific Committee On the Problems of Environment (SCOPE) formed under the International Council of Scientific Unions (ICSU) in 1970. The cost of following the pattern of pesticide contamination in human food and its intermediates is high. It was considered useful if a "marker-food" could be used as for radionuclides. In the United Kingdom, animal fats including mutton and cattle kidney-fat, butter, etc., had been used as "marker-foods" in attempts to monitor for exposure of the population to organo-chlorine insecticides.

Finally, the panel stressed the importance of linking chemical monitoring programmes, where practicable, with parallel epidemiological studies and ecological observations. The health and behaviour of human, domestic animal, and wild life populations (including their sensitive individuals) were the ultimate index of the significance of food and environmental contaminants.

5.2. Coordinated multidisciplinary studies

The panel felt that its own discussions had illustrated how experts in the area of food and environmental contamination work in relative isolation. The contamination of food and environment by pesticides and radionuclides, though important, were but two aspects of the many faceted problem of food and environmental contamination. The panel wished strongly to recommend the Directors General of both IAEA and FAO to examine the possibility of convening further meetings in which experts could be brought together from different disciplines. The panel noted for example that a number of specialists concerned with different aspects of food contaminants required information on dietary intake. Since the interpretation of the data is frequently difficult, a nutritionist should be consulted prior to commencement of dietary intake studies and appropriate statistical guidance followed.

There was a need for clarification and unification of the terms used in connexion with food and environmental contamination by chemicals, whether pesticidal, radioactive or of some other category. In the panel's own deliberations some terms were introduced which were well enough understood by the specialists directly concerned but were regarded as confusing by specialists in other areas. The meanings of similar or identical terms varied according to the area of application. The meaning of "acceptable daily intake" for a terminal pesticide residue in food differed very significantly from the daily intake limits derived for certain radionuclides in food or water (as in document 7.2.23.), the latter corresponding more to the term "permissible level" originally used in the Joint FAO/WHO meeting on pesticide residues (e.g. see Evaluation of the toxicity of pesticide residues in food, FAO Meeting Report, No. PL/1963/13, Rome, 1964) but later discarded (see 7.2.20.). Similarly, differently derived terms were sometimes assumed to have the same meaning or were so used, e.g. "environmental tolerance" and "practical residue limit".

Such considerations illustrated the need for coordinated study and resolution at international level.

5.3. Communication with the public

The panel considered that a major problem exists in relation to the need for improved communication in the field of environmental pollution in order to ensure a balanced presentation to the public. Whilst the panel recognized that it was not within its province to recommend methods of public communication, it did feel able to identify some serious problems. Unnecessary alarm often arises through a combination of factors:

(a) The need for freedom of the press and other news media in relation to public information and the commercial nature of „news".

(b) The complex technical nature of many of the problems involved.

(c) The occasional but regrettable tendency for some scientists to make public announcements or communications outside their area of competence.

(d) The tendency to report effects or possible hazards associated with contaminants out of context, for example without regard to the fact that an artificially high and non-typical concentration of pesticide was used in a toxicological or pathological study, without interpretation of results in relation to dosage, without critical allowance for inadequately planned experimentation, without regard to the many everyday hazards and ex-

posures associated with normal human behaviour and environment, without regard to the need for priorities dictated by limitations of the resources available for dealing with all contamination problems, and sometimes without regard for risk/benefit ratios.

The panel stressed the importance of informing and guiding the student population in these matters as an essential basis to their social and professional responsibilities as scientists.

6. Panel Recommendations

As a result of its deliberations, the panel addressed the following general recommendations to the Directors General of FAO and IAEA: –

1. Recognizing the urgent and important need to inform the public in simple unambiguous language about the *relative* hazards and exposures to different contaminants of food and environment, the panel recommends the Directors General, in cooperation with other UN Agencies, to improve joint public communication in this area.

2. Recognizing the need and value of interdisciplinary meetings on the problems of food and environmental contamination by all classes of chemicals including radioactive substances to examine the possibility of convening further meetings in which experts could be brought together from different disciplines in order better to establish priorities, to ensure the use of more uniform and less ambiguous terminology, and better to exploit common information sources and resources.

Taking especially into account the role and facilities available to the Joint FAO/ IAEA Division, the panel wished to draw the attention of the Directors General to the following research needs:

3. The need for continuing study of the overall fate of pesticide residues with particular reference to the effects of industrial and domestic processing as practised in developing countries. Priority should be given to compounds for which tolerances have been recommended but where calculations suggest, that acceptable terminal residues would be conditional upon post tolerance-point degradation or disappearance.

4. The need for continuing study of the nature, magnitude and significance of terminal pesticide residues in food, drinks and beverages.

5. The potential value of model pollution studies in selected critical areas. e.g. a large scale study of the fate and persistence of a pesticide or pollutant labelled with a stable (non-radioactive) isotope in an agricultural area where aquatic or marine contamination might be expected to result.

7. Appendices

7.1. Tabulated comparison of pesticide residue and dietary radioactivity problems

[Occupational exposure to either pesticides or radiation NOT considered]

Item	Pesticides	Radionuclides and their radiation
1. Significant natural background	None (some substances with pesticidal properties occur naturally in a few plant species).	All life forms are exposed to cosmic rays and to radiation due to ^{40}K, ^{14}C, radioelements within the range of atomic Nos. 81–92.
2. Global environmental contamination above background levels	Many crops and animal species appear to contain detectable traces of certain persistent organochlorine compounds, especially DDT. Levels declining with increasing restrictions on use of these compounds in agriculture. This has led to the concept of "practical residue limits", i.e. maximum concentrations of persistent pesticides likely to be found in certain foods, e.g. milk, meat fat.	Entire biosphere and all living tissues contain detectable traces of radioactive fallout, e.g. ^{90}Sr. Levels declining with reduction of atmospheric nuclear weapons testing and as a result of radioactive decay.
3. Nature of population exposure	Mainly internal from ingestion of terminal residues in food and drink.	Externally and internally, the latter usually small fraction of total exposure.
4. Basic mechanism of toxic action	Diversity of mechanisms, e.g. inhibition of different enzyme systems, interference with vital metabolic processes, etc. All are determined by the molecular form of the absorbed pesticide residue.	One basic mechanism, i.e. the interaction of radiation with living tissue which is independent of the chemical form of the ingested radioactive substance. Chemical form can only influence deposition and retention of the radionuclide in the exposed organism but not its radioactivity.
5. Basic public health principles	Exposure below set limits assumed to be without appreciable risk, even after a lifetime of such exposure (threshold concept – see section 3 of the report).	Exposure even at lowest levels assumed to carry some risk (linear extrapolation concept) which below recommended limits is deemed acceptable (see section 3 of report).

Item	Pesticides	Radionuclides and their radiation
	Concept of "critical pathways" little studied, but may be important (e.g. rural populations living in areas of intensive chemical protection or public health pesticide application may be critical groups).	Concept of "critical pathways" widely used (critical nuclides – critical foods – critical population groups – critical organs) leading to working limits derived from the ICRP recommended dose limits for members of the public (equivalent to $1/10$ of the corresponding limits for radiation workers).
	Practical working limits (tolerances) designed to cover entire range of agricultural sources of food contamination.	Working limits usually designed for specific event or potential source of contamination.
6. Influence of habitat on potential exposure	Critical population groups possibly associated with areas of intensive agricultural or public health pesticide usage. Relatively little studied in the case of pesticides (see sections 4.1. and 4.2. of report).	Critical population groups widely scattered (in case of radioactive fallout exposure) or near nuclear installations in relation to accidental or controlled releases of radioactive materials (see section 4.3. of report).
7. Influence of dietary habit (of item 9)	Food processing, cooking etc. have marked effect on the nature, magnitude and, therefore, on the toxicity of the terminal residue.	Food processing, cooking, etc. may reduce chemical concentration of radionuclides but will not directly affect their radioactivity.
8. Influence of food chain biology and biochemistry	Is important for specific compounds. E.g. fish can concentrate DDT from aquatic environments. Feeding habits of wildlife may results in relatively high residues, e.g. birds eating seeds carrying fungicidal seed dressings.	Is important for specific radionuclides. E.g., ruthenium-106 may be concentrated by sea-weed, zinc-65 by oysters, phosphorus-32 by fish.
9. Influence of "age" of residue or time of food storage before ingestion (cf item 7)	Pesticide residues tend to become modified chemically through spontaneous decomposition, reaction with food constituents, enzymic attack, etc. This usually, but not invariably, leads to compounds of lower acute toxicity. Decomposition is a function of time, temperature, food and pesticide.	Radionuclides decay spontaneously according to the "half-life" of the radionuclide which is known precisely. Unaffected by temperature, chemistry of the food, or by chemical form of the radionuclide.
10. Concentration limits in food	"Residue tolerances" or maximum concentrations of a specific pesticide residue allowed on specified food or its intermediates (raw fruit, vegetables, cereals, milk, fat, etc.) e.g. those recommended by Joint FAO/WHO meetings. Some countries have taken unilateral action in this context. Tolerances are *not* derived from ADI's but reflect the needs of "good agricultural practice". A tolerance is only recommended provided it is believed not to lead to a daily intake in excess to the ADI allowing for further degradation or loss of the pesticide from the point at which the tolerance is applicable to the instant of human ingestion, i.e. the terminal residue.	Limits corresponding to pesticide residue "tolerances" in food have not and cannot be recommended for various reasons (see text of report). Concentrations which give rise to radiation exposure not exceeding the dose limits recommended by ICRP for members of the public have been derived for guidance. ICRP Maximum Permissible Concentrations of radionuclides in water for 168 h week of occupational exposure can with certain limitations and modifications be applied to food consumed by members of the public (but see section 3 of the report).

Item	Pesticides	Radionuclides and their radiation
11. Limits for body intake or body burdens.	Maximum Acceptable Daily Intake for pesticide residues and intentional "food additives" developed by WHO, on the basis of long term experiments to establish the "no effect level" i.e. the level of dietary residue intake below which no effect on the ingesting organism can be detected – see section 3 of report.	Subject to defined assumptions and restrictions "maximum permissible burdens" for specific radionuclides have been estimated which give rise to radiation doses not exceeding the ICRP limits for occupational exposure, but see section 3 of report.

7.2. Documents and working papers studied by the panel

7.2.1. Terminal pesticide and radiochemical residues in food as a function of habitat and dietary habit. Background statement prepared by Joint FAO/IAEA Secretariat.

7.2.2. Terminal pesticide and radiochemical residues in food as a function of habitat and dietary habit. Background statement prepared by the WHO Secretariat.

7.2.3. FAO Pesticide Programme. FAO Information Sheet AGP: PP/INF/70/1.

7.2.4. Variations in dietary pattern as a means to determine probable intake of pesticide or radiochemical residues. Working paper prepared by J. R. Lupien (FAO).

7.2.5. Influence of diet on nature & magnitude of terminal pesticide residues. Working paper prepared by D. J. Clegg.

7.2.6. Influence of diet on nature and magnitude of terminal pesticide residues in the United States. Working paper prepared by R. E. Duggan.

7.2.7. Influence of the nature and origin of foodstuffs on the quantity of radioactive materials in human diet. Notes for discussion prepared by R. Scott Russell.

7.2.8. Questions of disposition of milk or meat from farm animals that have received radioisotopes. Notes for discussion prepared by G. Ward.

7.2.9. The influence of food processing on the fate of pesticide residues. Working paper prepared by H. Stobwasser and J. Kirchhoff.

7.2.10. On the aquatic radioisotope studies of the Department of Radiochemistry, University of Helsinki, note prepared by J. K. Miettinen.

7.2.11. Biological and chemical factors in the modification of radiochemical residues. Working paper prepared by J. K. Miettinen.

7.2.12. Multidisciplinary approach to the problems of undesirable residues in food. Working paper prepared by F. Coulston.

7.2.13.*) Nuclear techniques for studying pesticide residue problems. Proceedings of a panel organized by the Joint FAO/IAEA Division of Atomic Energy in Food and Agriculture, Vienna, 16–20 December 1968. IAEA/STI/PUB/252, Vienna, 1970.

7.2.14.*) Recommendations of the International Commission on Radiological Protection. Report of Committee II on Permissible Dose for Internal Radiation. ICRP Publication 2. Pergamon Press, London, New York and Paris, 1960.

7.2.15.*) Principles of Environmental Monitoring Related to the Handling of Radioactive Materials. A report by Committee 4 of the International Commission on Radiological Protection, ICRP Publication 7, Pergamon Press, London, New York, Paris, 1966.

7.2.16.*) Recommendations of the International Commission on Radiological Protection, ICRP Publication 9. Pergamon Press, London, New York, Paris, 1966.

7.2.17.*) Report of the United Nations Scientific Committee on the Effects of Atomic Radiation, United Nations, New York, 1969.

7.2.18. Working papers and draft report prepared for the 20th Session of the United Nations Scientific Committee on the Effects of Atomic Radiation held in Geneva, September, 1970.

7.2.19.   "Definition of Terms Used" and tabulated estimates of "Acceptable Levels of Radionuclides in Human Diet" extracted from an unpublished 'Manual on the Assessment of Acceptable Levels of Radionuclide in the Human Diet' prepared by a Joint FAO/IAEA Expert Panel which met in Lisbon, 1967.

7.2.20.*)   Report of the 1967 Joint Meeting of the FAO Working Party of Experts on Pesticide Residues and the WHO Expert Committee on Pesticide Residues, WHO Technical Report Series, No. 391, Geneva 1968.

7.2.21.*)   Pesticide Residues in Food. Report of the 1968 Joint Meeting of the FAO Working Party of Experts on Pesticide Residues and the WHO Expert Committee on Pesticide Residues, WHO Technical Report Series, No. 417, Geneva, 1969.

7.2.22.*)   Pesticide Residues in Food. Report of the 1969 Joint Meeting of the FAO Working Party of Experts on Pesticide Residues and the WHO Expert Group on Pesticide Residues. WHO Technical Report Series No. 458, Geneva, 1970.

7.2.23.*)   Basic Safety Standards for Radiation Protection. IAEA Safety Series No. 9. STI/PUB/147, Vienna, 1967.

*) Published documents. Information on the availability or content of the other documents listed may be obtained by writing to the Secretariat or to the authors concerned.

Opening Address at the International Symposium on the Establishment of Air Quality Standards

Paris, Oct. 1972, organized by the International Academy of Environmental Safety

Monsieur Blanc

Directeur général de la protection de la nature et de l'environnement, Paris

Madame, Monsieur le Président,
Messieurs les Professeurs

Comme tout à l'heure Monsieur le Professeur Truhaut vous l'a dit, Monsieur Robert Poujade aurait été particulièrement heureux et honoré d'être parmi vous aujourd'hui, si le Conseil des Ministres ne se réunissait pas chaque Mercredi matin en France.

C'est pour moi un grand honneur et un grand plaisir de m'entretenir avec des savants, car entre l'action du Gouvernement et la recherche, doit s'établir des liaisons confiantes et continues: n'oublions pas qu'en France, ce sont des scientifiques, et je saluerai dans votre assemblée certains des pionniers, qui, dans les années 1950, ont fait prendre conscience de l'importance de la Protection de la Nature et de l'Environnement notamment au sein du Conseil National de la Protection de la Nature. C'est dans les années 1960 que l'opinion publique ainsi éclairée par des chercheurs ou des professeurs, a accordé à ces problèmes toute l'importance qu'ils méritaient. Enfin, c'est dans les années 1970 que le Président de la République et le Premier Ministre ont modifié d'abord les structures de l'Administration, d'autre part le 2 Février 1971, les structures du Gouvernement Français lui-même, pour que soit prise en considération la Protection de la Nature et de l'Environnement.

Et c'est pourquoi je suis très heureux aujourd'hui de saluer des professeurs éminents, des experts universellement reconnus qui, représentant l'Allemagne, l'Argentine, la Grande-Bretagne, le Canada, les Etats Unis d'Amérique, l'Italie, le Japon, les Pays-Bas, la Tchécoslovaquie, l'Union de Républiques Socialistes Sovietiques et la Yougoslavie, sont venus mettre en commun les résultats de leurs recherches; et, c'est un hommage à rendre aux savants, les questions qu'ils se posent.

Comme il est habituel lors d'un symposium, je dois me présenter et confesser que je ne suis pas un scientifique. C'est pourquoi j'aborde avec beaucoup d'humilité vos travaux. Par contre, si tant est qu'on puisse un jour se prétendre économiste, c'est surtout en cette qualité que j'évoquerai l'intérêt d'une telle réunion et également les réalisations françaises.

* * *

D'abord, pourquoi attachons-nous une très grande importance aux normes?

Eh bien, je rappellerais que le père de la méthode expérimentale nous a enseigné que « rien n'est poison, tout est poison et que tout est un problème de dose ».

L'Administration ne peut pas se satisfaire d'une absence de normes: en effet, en France comme à l'étranger, une règlementation qui se borne à dire « on ne dépassera pas un niveau tel qu'il constitue une gène pour le voisinage » n'a aucune valeur, ni juridique, ni bien entendu scientifique. La gène est une notion subjective qui s'apprécie selon les tempéraments, d'autre part la gène est une notion variable qui doit se mesurer au regard de l'environnement industriel, c'est-à-dire de l'addition des pollutions. Aujourd'hui à cette notion de simple addition des pollutions, nous ajoutons celle de combinaison des pollutions, car vous savez que deux corps, même s'ils ne sont pas nocifs, peuvent en se combinant spontanément constituer un danger. Et puis une notion purement subjective de gêne, ignore les données sociales, par exemple la densité des populations, donc le risque humain que courent ceux qui sont l'objet de ces agressions. En outre, car au titre de la production c'est une réflexion que nous nous devons d'avoir à l'esprit, la notion de gêne en milieu rural est encore plus difficile à approcher, puisqu'il s'agit là de dégats causés au cheptel, aux végétaux et notamment à la forêt.

Enfin, une réglementation qui n'aurait aucune base scientifique serait totalement incontrôlable, car ceux qui seraient chargés de l'appliquer n'auraient aucune référence.

* * *

Mais à l'inverse, nous pensons que des normes excessives ou des normes qui ne seraient pas scientifiquement prouvées, présenteraient elles-mêmes de graves dangers. Par exemple nous nous devons de distinguer clairement les atteintes à la santé, qu'il s'agisse d'atteintes immédiates ou d'atteintes à long terme, des simples incommodités qui ne présentent aucun danger pour l'homme. En effet, certaines poussières, la vapeur d'eau également, sont bien souvent et de plus en plus critiquées par une opinion mal informée, alors que des atteintes infiniment plus graves, invisibles et inodores, n'apparaissent pas immédiatement.

Si les savants ne nous indiquent pas les priorités réelles à accorder à chacun des dangers, nous serons tentés de leur attribuer à chacun la même importance, et dans cette hypothèse, deux risques sont à redouter.

Le premier risque serait de faire supporter aux contribuables ou aux consommateurs une charge excessive. Un chiffre constituera une approche de ce problème. Il me suffira de vous dire que le contribuable de l'Etat en France a participé dans l'année 1972 à environ 3000 Millions de travaux. Le contribuable des collectivités locales, mais c'est le même homme qui est contribuable de l'Etat et contribuable des collectivités locales, a financé de l'ordre de 2000 Millions de travaux.

C'est pourquoi entre ces deux excés, l'absence de normes, ou des normes trop générales et non scientifiquement prouvées, je pense qu'il y a la nécessité de trouver un juste milieu, et c'est un problème que Monsieur le Professeur Dorst a évoqué tout à l'heure.

* * *

L'Administration, le Gouvernement, le Législateur, se doivent d'agir pour deux raisons: d'abord, poussés qu'ils sont par l'opinion, ensuite et surtout, pour éviter que la situation ne s'aggrave. C'est pourquoi il me semble qu'il faut d'abord accélérer les travaux fondamentaux afin d'atteindre cette exactitude scientifique dont nous avons autant besoin que les hommes de science que vous êtes. Pour ce faire, je pense que votre symposium, s'il se prolonge par des échanges de recherches constitue une inappréciable contribution à cette œuvre commune pour éviter que des équipes dans des pays différents, ne poursuivent des recherches identiques. Cette coopération entre les universités des différents pays à mon sens, doit s'accompagner d'un reserrement des liens entre les laboratoirs publics et les laboratoirs privés, entre la recherche fondamentale et l'application industrielle afin que les résultats de vos recherches passent le plus vite possible de la théorie à la pratique.

Mais en de nombreux cas, nous ne pouvons patienter trop longtemps sur les résultats ultimes de ces recherches et nous devons nous fonder simplement sur des résultats partiels, des résultats provisoires dès qu'ils ont atteint un gegré suffisant de probabilité. C'est pourquoi je souhaiterai que les savants n'attendent pas la certitude pour nous faire part de leurs premières conclusions, afin que nous puissions, mois après mois, adapter une règlementation que nous considérons comme évolutive. La collaboration entre les scientifiques présente à mes yeux un autre avantage.

En effet, il est nécessaire, que dans un monde où les communications se diversifient et s'amplifient, les règlementations de chacun des pays soient aussi proches que possible les unes des autres afin que la protection de la Nature et de l'Environnement atteigne un double objectif, celui-là même que les distingués représentants de l'Argentine et de l'Italie tout à l'heure ont souligné: améliorer le cadre de vie, mais en même temps développer la production, puisque ce développement de la production participe lui-même à l'amélioration du cadre de vie.

* * *

Après vous avoir très brièvement exquissé la nécessité profonde à mes yeux d'une collaboration entre les hommes de science que vous êtes et l'Etat, je voudrais maintenant vous dire, simplement dans le domaine de la pollution atmosphérique, les décisions et les réalisations du Gouvernement français.

Deux dates sont à retenir: les décisions prises par le Président de la République en Conseil Restreint le 2 Novembre 1971, et l'exécution de ces mesures lors d'un comité interministériel le 27 Janvier 1972.

La coordination dans le domaine de la pollution atmosphérique a été confiée à Monsieur Robert Poujade. Cette coordination s'exerce à un triple plan? d'abord entre les Ministères eux-mêmes, afin que dans le domaine de l'air les lois, les décrets,

les arrêtés et les circulaires pris à l'initiative des Ministères tel que l'Industrie, l'Agriculture, l'Equipement, concourent tous à cet objectif qui est double: en priorité ne pas aggraver la situation présente, ensuite réparer les dégats subis.

* * *

Deuxième axe de coordination, c'est de rapprocher par un effort commun les travaux de l'université et les travaux de l'industrie afin que se développe en France, en liaison bien entendu avec les expériences étrangères, une industrie de la détection, de la prévention et de la réparation des nuisances.

* * *

Le troisième degré de coordination consiste à accélérer les efforts de l'Etat et des collectivités locales. A cet égard, je suis heureux de rendre hommage aux laboratoires municipaux, aux laboratoires de l'Université qui, jusqu'à présent, constituent le plus clair de notre connaissance des dangers de la pollution atmosphérique.

En effet, à ces deux dates que je rappelais tout à l'heure, le Président de la République et le Gouvernement ont estimé qu'il fallait d'abord connaître la situation et c'est pourquoi il a été décidé que dans toutes les usines nouvelles et dans toutes les zones industrielles, des appareils de mesure, en commençant par le dioxyde de soufre, seraient mis en place. Ces appareils de mesure seront groupés en réseaux soient manuels, soient automatiques. Et c'est au niveau du recoupement et de l'exploitation de ces mesures que nous établierons une liaison étroite avec la météorologie nationale. L'office National de Météorologie' à la demande de M. Poujade, développe ses prévisions à court terme mais des prévisions intéressant des zones restreintes, car les prévisions à court terme et ponctuelles nous intéressent plus que les prévisions à long terme sur de vastes zones, je vais vous dire pourquoi tout à l'heure. En effet, nous voudrions prévoir les sauts de vent et les inversions de températures qui à nos yeux ont une importance considérable sur les dangers de la pollution.

* * *

Nous venons de voir comment nous nous efforçons de connaître la situation, ensuite le deuxième effort est de prévenir la pollution. Vous savez que le Gouvernement français vient de réduire les teneurs toxiques, résidus de combustion de gaz des automobiles. Dans ce domaine comme dans celui du bruit, nous avons entamé une réflexion avec le Ministère des Finances pour tenter de bâtir une imposition qui favorise les voitures moins nocives sur le plan des échappements ou quant à leur niveau sonore. Un décrêt qui paraîtra avant la fin de l'année permettra au Gouvernement de soumettre à homologation ou à octroi de label, les matériels et équipements de fabrication d'énergie, et d'imposer la publicité des composants, notamment toxiques, des combustibles. Au plan des contrôles, des brigades mobiles ont été mises sur pieds par la Police Nationale, avec notre appui financier, pour mesurer le bruit et les toxiques émis par les véhicules. Connaître, prévenir, j'aborderai maintenant le troisième aspect de la politique du Gouvernement, c'est guérir.

* * *

Deux résultats sont d'ores et déjà acquis: d'une part une accélération très considérable avec l'aide des professions dans le domaine de la désulfuration, qu'il s'agisse de désulfuration des fuels, ou de désulfuration des fumées. Au titre de la désulfuration des fumées, nous avons distingué des méthodes les plus adaptées aux très grandes unités, telles que les centrales d'électricité de France, ou aux chaudières de moyenne importance, car il semble, ce sont des scientifiques, Monsieur le Professeur,

qui nous l'ont indiqué, que en coût et avantage des procédés, il faille choisir deux axes de recherche différents.

Le deuxième résultat consiste dans le pouvoir qu'aura désormais l'administration, lorsque les prévisions météorologiques laisseront apparaître un danger particulier de pollution, d'ordonner une substitution de combustible et notamment l'utilisation de fuels à basse teneur en soufre. Sur ce plan là, les pouvoirs de l'administration iront plus loin même puisqu'elle sera autorisée à demander que les fabrications se réduisent, et à la limite, que les usines s'arrêtent. Ce pouvoir est limité à 48 heures, néanmoins vous mesurez les conséquences sur l'emploi et sur la production que de telles mesures peuvent avoir; et c'est pourquoi il nous apparaît indispensable que les scientifiques ici présents, comme leurs collègues d'autres disciplines, puissent éclairer l'administration afin, justement, de concilier la protection de la population et le niveau de production.

* * *

Dans quel cadre une telle politique se développe? Celui d'une concertation avec les branches industrielles elles-mêmes. L'administration propose un niveau qui lui semble raisonnable d'atteindre, compte tenu des techniques connues en France ou à l'étranger, compte tenu aussi du coût d'investissement et de fonctionnement des équipements anti-pollution, compte tenu enfin de la charge financière qui en résultera. Jusqu'à présent, les règlementations ont été prises avec l'accord des professions. Qu'il s'agisse des cimenteries, de la sidérurgie ou des papeteries. Mais je voudrais souligner qu'au stade de la réglementation, le Gouvernement conserve l'initiative et la décision.

Les niveaux étant ainsi fixés, l'administration ne choisit pas les moyens pour les atteindre. Nous pensons en effet, que le choix des moyens orientera l'industrie vers les équipements les mieux aptes à atteindre les niveaux imposés pour un coût équitable. Et là encore, nous retrouvons toute l'importance d'une étroite coopération entre la recherche fondamentale que vous représentez et les applications industrielles. En effet, le choix des moyens peut aller jusqu'au choix d'une nouvelle technologie, nous pensons en effet que désormais, la recherche ne peut plus se préoccuper seulement de l'augmentation de la production ou de l'amélioration de la productivité, mais doit se préoccuper des conséquences sur la nature et l'environnement de telle ou telle technologie nouvelle.

D'ailleurs je pense que sur ce plan la connaissance économique n'est pas encore suffisante car, si la dépense directe est immédiatement perceptible la dépense indirecte l'est beaucoup moins, et que l'on néglige pas trop les coûts indirects de la pollution et des nuisances bien souvent parce que c'est la collectivité qui les supporte. C'est pourquoi nous espérons que le groupe que Monsieur Poujade vient de mettre en place avec l'Institut National de la Statistique et la Direction de la Prévision du Ministère des Finances, permettra une approche globale en coût d'investissement et en frais de fonctionnement, soit de la protection, soit de la production sans protection. Nous pensons, nous en avons déjà quelques preuves au plan notamment des papeteries, qu'une usine propre dont le coût incorpore la prévention des nuisances a une rentabilité plus grande qu'une usine sale. En effet, pour assumer le coût de la prévention, on est obligé d'étudier beaucoup plus soigneusement tous les autres postes des frais de fabrication.

Ces règles s'appliquent immédiatement aux usines nouvelles, aux usines qui s'agrandissent ou aux usines qui se modernisent. Mais restent les usines anciennes et c'est pourquoi nous avons bâti des accords de branche qui laissent habituellement 5 années aux usines anciennes pour se conformer aux règlementations nouvelles. Un examen est opéré par le Ministère de l'Economie et des Finances, le Ministère de l'Industrie et nous-mêmes sur la situation de la branche considérée, en termes de croissance du chiffre d'affaire, en termes de capacité d'autofinancement et également ment en termes d'emplois dans la région considérée.

Si une aide particulière est nécessaire, c'est ce groupe qui le décide.

En effet, comme la plupart des pays industriels, nous appliquons en France le principe « les pollueurs seront les payeurs ».

Sur le plan de la compétition internationale, comme sur le plan de l'emploi régional des adaptations peuvent s'avérer nécessaires. C'est pourquoi par le jeu des prix, lorsque les prix sont fixés par l'Etat, par le jeu de prêts au titre de la modernisation, de la reconversion ou de l'expansion régionale, des aides temporaires et limitées et au coup par coup peuvent être octroyées. L'aide peut revêtir également la forme de redevances professionnelles ou de taxes parafiscales pendant la durée de la mise des usines anciennes au niveau des usines nouvelles.

Il est trop tard pour aller plus loin et je m'excuse d'avoir été aussi long, mais je pense que les savants doivent connaître les préoccupations et les actions du gouvernement afin d'adapter les exigences' c'est à dire la règlementation aux risques réels; et je reviens à cette nécessité de connaître les risques réels puisque je vous ai mesuré le coût de la prévention.

* * *

Mais les professeurs que vous êtes ont un autre rôle à jouer, celui d'informer le public et, tout à l'heure lorsque vous indiquiez les risques d'utiliser certains termes sans les expliquer, je crois que vous aviez bien raison. Et puis surtout, vous avez à former. Je ne vise pas seulement des disciplines spécifiques; certes, il est nécessaire de disposer de spécialistes, mais, compte tenu de la multiplicité des problèmes que recouvre la protection de la nature et de l'environnement, je crois qu'il est encore plus important de sensibiliser – notamment tous les techniciens et tous les administrateurs – dans chacune de vos disciplines, à ces problèmes.

Ainsi – ensemble – nous pourrons répondre au souhait que le Président de la République formulait en Janvier 1972 lorsqu'il indiquait que la morale de l'environnement impliquait que l'expansion économique s'opère au profit de l'Homme.

Les Principales méthodes automatiques de dosage des polluants atmosphériques

P. Chovin

Laboratoire Central de la Préfecture de Police, Paris, France

Summary A survey is given on automatic, physico-chemical methods for the determination of air pollutants. The detection of sulphur dioxide, total hydrocarbons, single hydrocarbons, nitrogen-oxides, and oxidants, is discussed in detail. Advantages and disadvantages of the different methods are compared.

Zusammenfassung Es wird eine Übersicht über automatische, physikalisch-chemische Methoden zur Bestimmung von Luftverunreinigungsstoffen gegeben. Besonders werden diskutiert Schwefeldioxyd, Gesamtkohlenwasserstoffe, einzelne Kohlenwasserstoffe, Stickoxyde und Oxidantien. Vor- und Nachteile der einzelnen Methoden werden einander gegenübergestellt.

* This paper was presented in part at the International Symposium on the Establishment of Air Quality Standards, Paris, Oct. 1972, organized by the International Academy of Environmental Safety.

L'importance de plus en plus grande qui s'attache de nos jours à la lutte engagée contre la pollution atmosphérique suppose un postulat: pour combattre efficacement l'ennemi, il faut le connaître, connaître la pollution, c'est en mesurer les niveaux. Il importe donc de disposer de méthodes sûres, sensibles, précises, de bonne répétabilité, et de surcroît automatiques. Si cette dernière condition est remplie, l'échantillonnage peut alors résulter de la facile circulation dans l'appareil de l'atmosphère à doser, auquel cas l'enregistreur trace une courbe continue qui représente – avec un éventuel décalage dans le temps dû à la lenteur des réactions – la variation de la concentration du polluant dans l'atmosphère au point de prélèvement considéré. Il peut se faire que cette courbe soit inexploitable comme telle si sa sinuosité est trop accentuée. On préfère alors déterminer la teneur moyenne du polluant dans l'air pendant une durée d'échantillonnage déterminée, celle-ci pouvant s'étendre de 5 mn à 24 h et même davantage. Pour passer des valeurs instantanées aux valeurs moyennes, il faut intégrer, ce qui peut se faire soit avant, soit après l'analyseur.

Avant l'analyseur, l'intégration est physico-chimique. Elle consiste soit stocker à débit constant l'atmosphère à doser dans un sac, soit à piéger le polluant par dissolution, absorption, adsorption, réaction sur un milieu approprié, etc.; dans tous les cas, la mesure sera conduite postérieurement à l'échantillonnage, sur l'échantillon moyen recueilli.

Après l'analyseur, l'intégration est électronique et peut donner la valeur moyenne au moyen d'un dispositif imprimant. En général, cette solution est plus onéreuse que la précédente et ne fournit pas de résultats de meilleure qualité.

Ces problèmes d'échantillonnage instantané ou moyen étant supposés résolus, on trouvera dans ce qui suit quelques indications concernant les méthodes modernes de dosage des principaux polluants. Toutefois, en ce qui concerne le monoxyde de carbone, le lecteur est prié de se reporter à l'article du même auteur paru dans ce recueil.[1]

1° Dosage du dioxyde de soufre, SO_2

De nombreuses réactions plus ou moins spécifiques du SO_2 ont été utilisées pour son dosage et la plupart d'entre elles permettent l'automatisation, c'est-à-dire la mise en œuvre dans un appareil qui fonctionne indépendamment de l'opérateur et qui délivre soit la valeur instantanée de la teneur du polluant dans l'atmosphère, soit la valeur moyenne après un temps d'intégration correspondant au temps d'échantillonnage choisi. Nous passerons dans ce qui suit en revue les principales de ces méthodes.

a) Méthode à l'eau oxygéné: détermination de « l'acidité forte »

La réaction du SO_2 sur l'eau oxygénée peut se formuler comme suit:

$$SO_2 + H_2O_2 \longrightarrow SO_4H_2$$

La méthode revient à doser l'acidité sulfurique formée après que l'on ait fait barboter un volume déterminé d'air dans une solution d'eau oxygénée amenée au pH 4,5. Le dosage se fait au moyen d'une solution 0,004 N de borate de sodium.[2]

Un appareil dû à Debrun (Electricité de France), destiné, comme la loi française y oblige, à mesurer la teneur du SO_2 sur les sites présents et futurs des centrales thermiques, réalise automatiquement le dosage.[3]

Il consiste en une cellule dans laquelle d'une part l'air barbote après passage dans un filtre pour arrêter les poussières, et d'autre part une pompe introduit le réactif titrant. La pompe est elle-même asservie à la mesure du pH, ce qui est réalisé par le moyen d'une électrode appropriée et d'une électrode de référence.

La mesure du volume de réactif délivré par la pompe est une mesure directe de la quantité de SO_2 qui a été arrêtée par la solution pendant la durée d'échantillonnage choisie. La pompe est agencée de telle sorte que des tops peuvent être envoyés dans une ligne téléphonique à un poste central en nombres proportionnels au volume du réactif délivré. Cet appareil a l'intérêt pour la France de mettre en œuvre la méthode qui a été normalisée et qui est considérée comme méthode officielle française du dosage du SO_2, malgré son manque de spécificité.

b) Dosage par conductimétrie

La dissolution du SO_2 dans l'eau produit des ions SO_3^{--} et SO_3H^-, dont la présence modifie la conductibilité électrique de la solution. On peut aussi utiliser la formation des ions SO_4^{--} et SO_4H^- qui se forment dans une solution d'eau oxygénée selon la réaction précédente. Sur ce principe, plusieurs appareils ont été commercialisés qui réalisent d'une part la mise au contact d'un volume déterminé d'air et d'un volume déterminé de réactif, par le moyen d'une pompe proportionnante et d'autre part la mesure de la conductibilité électrique avant capture du SO_2 et après celle-ci.

Dans la plupart de ces appareils la variation de la conductibilité électrique, mesurée à l'aide de deux paires d'électrodes, se traduit, par l'intermédiaire d'un amplificateur électronique, par un tracé sur un enregistreur. Cette méthode n'est pas plus spécifique que la précédente.

c) Méthode de West et Gaeke

La méthode de West et Gaeke consiste à faire réagir le SO₂, piégé dans une solution de tétrachloromercurate de sodium, sur un réactif constitué par une solution aqueuse renfermant du formaldéhyde et de la pararosaniline en solution acide[4]. Si l'acidité est suffisante la pararosaniline est décolorée par l'acide chlorhydrique de telle sorte que le réactif est pratiquement incolore. Après passage du SO₂, il se forme un produit qui est coloré et dont la teinte peut servir de mesure à la quantité de SO₂ qui a traversé la solution. Cette méthode est considérée comme spécifique du SO_2.

L'automatisation de cette méthode se réalise, comme pour beaucoup d'autres, à l'aide d'un appareillage genre Technicon qui réalise, par le moyen d'une pompe péristaltique, le cheminement et le mixage des solutions devant former le réactif ainsi que leur contact avec l'air à doser. Finalement un photocolorimètre a cellules photoélectriques mesure la teinte prise par la solution.

d) Coulométrie

Le SO_2 réagit sur le brome en donnant de l'acide sulfurique selon l'équation de réaction:

$$SO_2 + Br_2 + 2H_2O \longrightarrow SO_4H_2 + 2BrH$$

Cette méthode a pu être automatisée de la manière suivante:

Dans une cellule renfermant une solution de bromure de potassium on produit du brome par électrolyse, en s'arrangeant pour que la quantité de brome reste constante dans la solution, par exemple en déterminant par le moyen d'un jeu d'électrodes appropriées le potentiel d'oxydo-réduction de celle-ci et en asservissant l'électrolyse aux résultats de la mesure précédente. Si l'on fait arriver dans la solution un air chargé de SO₂, du brome sera consommé,

ce qui entraînera une variation du potentiel d'oxydo-réduction, et déclenchera une électrolyse de sorte que la concentration du brome dans la solution retrouve sa valeur initiale. On voit dans ces conditions que la mesure du SO₂ peut se ramener à celle de la quantité d'électricité qui a traversé la cellule pour l'électrolyse du bromure de potassium et la formation du brome[5]. Cette méthode est douée d'une spécificité relative, les réducteurs pouvant consommer du brome, tout comme le SO₂.

Divers appareils ont été construits sur ce principe, par exemple le Titrilog américain et le dispositif de la Société Philips. Ce dernier a reçu des perfectionnements permettant de l'installer sur les sites où l'on désire mesurer le SO₂. L'appareil peut à volonté, interrogé par un opérateur du poste central, faire la mesure demandée, vérifier son zéro ou encore faire son propre étalonnage grâce à une source de SO₂ incorporée. Finalement les données de l'appareil sont transmises par ligne téléphonique.

e) Dosage par spectrophotométrie de flammes

Une méthode récente a permis la mise sur le marché d'appareils extrêmement sensibles pouvant mesurer de petites quantités de SO₂ et, plus généralement, de dérivés soufrés présents dans l'atmosphère. Le principe en est le suivant: si l'on s'arrange pour brûler les composés à doser en milieu réducteur, par exemple en entourant la flamme d'une atmosphère d'hydrogène, les composés soufrés se réduisent en soufre élément, lequel en brûlant émet des radiations qui sont spécifiques et que l'on peut recueillir sur un photomultiplicateur, plus particulièrement en filtrant les radiations autour de 530 nm avec une bande passante très étroite de 5 nm. Ce type de détecteur donne des résultats semblables avec les dérivés du phosphore, mais les radiations émises correspondent à d'autres longueurs d'ondes de telle sorte que, avec un filtre approprié, la méthode est tout-à-fait spécifique des dérivés soufrés[6]. Si l'on veut éliminer l'hydrogène sulfuré et les mercaptans, il faut faire précéder l'appareil d'un tybe absorbeur renfermant du chlorure mercurique déposé sur un support approprié, qui retient ces composés gênants et laisse passer le SO_2.

2° Dosage des hydrocarbures imbrûlés

Sous ce vocable, on entend les constituants de l'essence qui ont pu passer dans l'atmosphère par le jeu des évaporations au niveau du carburateur ou du réservoir, de même que ceux qui se retrouvent dans les gaz d'échappement pour avoir échappé partiellement à la combustion. Dans le cas présent, on distingue deux type de méthodes selon que l'on s'intéresse aux hydrocarbures totaux ou bien aux hydrocarbures individuellement présents dans l'atmosphère.

a) Dosage des hydrocarbures totaux

On met en œuvre pour ce dosage un « détecteur à ionisation de flamme» dont l'utilisation a été proposée il y a déjà plusieurs années pour la chromatographie en phase gazeuse. Le fonctionnement de ce détecteur est basé sur le fait que lorsqu'un hydrocarbure brûle en présence d'air ou d'oxygène, l'attaque progressive de la molécule qui aboutit finalement à la formation d'eau et de gaz carbonique se traduit par la formation intermédiaire d'ions gazeux, c'est-à-dire de débris chargés électriquement que l'on peut recueillir en entourant la flamme de deux électrodes portées à une différence de potentiel suffisante. Dans ces conditions, le courant d'ionisation peut servir de mesure à la quantité d'hydrocarbures présente.

On doit remarquer tout d'abord que la réponse d'un tel détecteur n'est pas la même pour tous les hydrocarbures: elle est à peu près proportionnelle au nombre d'atomes de carbone présents dans la molécule. Il s'ensuit que l'on ne pourra pas donner un résultat valable dès que l'on aura plusieurs hydrocarbures différents dans un même échantillon. Pour pouvoir tourner la difficulté, on étalonne l'appareil au moyen d'un hydrocarbure choisi conventionnellement et en général au moyen de n.-hexane.

On a proposé des méthodes pour corriger le renseignement fourni par l'appareil de la teneur de l'atmosphère en méthane, hydrocarbure le plus abondant et totalement dénué de réactivité dans la formation du smog photochimique de Los Angeles.

b) Dosage des hydrocarbures individuels

Pour pouvoir parvenir à distinguer les différents hydrocarbures présents dans l'atmosphère et qui peuvent être extrêmement nombreux (on en a dénombré une ccrtaine) il convient de les séparer préalablement et nulle méthode n'est mieux adaptée que la chromatographie en phase gazeuse. On peut automatiser celle-ci par un jeu de vannes et de minuteries qui permettent le prélèvement de l'échantillon pendant un certain temps et l'envoi d'une portion aliquote moyenne dans le chromatographe. (Pour une revue des différentes techniques utilisables, voir [7]).

Cependant si la somme des hydrocarbures totaux est déjà très faible dans l'atmosphère, la concentration de chacun des hydrocarbures pris isoléments l'est davantage et l'appareillage risque de manquer de sensibilité.

3° Dosage des oxydes d'azote NO_x

Sous le nom général d'oxydes d'azote on considère, en pollution atmosphérique le monoxyde NO et le dioxyde NO_2. On sait que ces oxydes d'azote prennent part au déroulement des réactions photochimiques qui aboutissent à la formation du smog oxydant dans les atmosphères très polluées renfermant en particulier des hydrocarbures. C'est à Los Angeles que ce genre de phénomène a été observé pour la première fois, lequel s'accompagne comme son nom l'indique de la formation de substances à caractère oxydant telles l'ozone et des nitrates de péracyle.

Le dosage des oxydes d'azote peut se faire automatiquement de deux manières différentes:

a) Par automatisation de la réaction de Griess-Salzmann [8]

Lorsque le dioxyde est mis en présence d'eau, il réagit pour donner lieu à la formation d'un mélange d'acide nitrique et d'acide nitreux selon l'équation de réaction:

$$2NO_2 + H_2O \longrightarrow NO_2^- + NO_3^- + 2H^+$$

Pour doser NO_2, on tire parti de la formation de l'ion nitrite que l'on fait réagir sur une amine pour faire un sel de diazonium, par exemple sur l'acide sulfamique:

$$SO_3H - C_6H_4 - NH_2 + NO_2^- + 2H^+ \longrightarrow SO_3H - C_6H_4 - \overset{+}{N} \equiv N + 2H_2O$$

Ce sel de diazonium est ensuite amené à réagir sur une autre amine, non diazotable celle-là, pour former un dérivé azoïque, c'est-à-dire un colorant. C'est ainsi qu'on a la réaction suivante en utilisant la N (α-naphtyl) éthylènediamine:

$$SO_3H - C_6H_4 - \overset{+}{N} \equiv N + C_8H_7 - NH - CH_2 - CH_2 - NH_2 \longrightarrow$$
$$SO_3H - C_6H_4 - N = N - C_8H_6 - NH - CH_2 - CH_2 - NH_2$$

Le colorant formé est rouge violacé et la teinte prise par la solution peut servir de mesure à la quantité de NO_2 présent dans l'échantillon d'atmosphère mis en œuvre. Il est nécessaire de prendre un certain nombre de précautions pour que cette réaction puisse être menée à bien et en particulier de suivre scrupuleusement la formule indiquée par Buck et Stratman [9] si l'on veut que l'étalonnage puisse se faire sans complication au moyen d'une solution dosée de nitrite de sodium. Dans ces conditions, la stœchiométrie de la réaction, qui, théoriquement devrait être égale à 0,5 est en réalité égale à l'unité.

On voit que cette réaction permet de doser NO_2 seul.

Pour doser NO_x, c'est-à-dire la somme $NO + NO_2$, il faut oxyder préalablement le monoxyde NO en dioxyde NO_2 ce qui se fait au mieux par le moyen d'acide chromique réparti sur ponce, à une température de 60° C environ. L'automatisation de ces réactions est réalisée au moyen de l'appareil Technicon du genre de celui qui a été mentionné à propos du dosage du SO_2 par la réaction de West et Gaeke.

b) Méthode par chimiluminescence

Lorsqu'on amène le monoxyde d'azote NO à réagir avec de l'ozone (qui peut être formé dans un ozoniseur adjoint à l'appareil) il se forme du dioxyde NO_2 mais sous une forme excitée c'est-à-dire ayant un excès d'énergie. Cet excès est perdu par émission de photons $h\nu$ qui peuvent être mesurés par un photomultiplicateur [10].

$$NO + O_3 \longrightarrow NO_2^* + O_2$$
$$NO_2^* \longrightarrow NO_2 + h\nu$$

Sur ce principe ont été construits des appareils qui permettent donc le dosage du monoxyde. De manière analogue, mais à l'inverse de ce qui a été dit précédemment, si l'on veut doser le dioxyde, il faut d'abord doser la somme $NO + NO_2$ et soustraire le NO dosé indépendamment. Pour ce faire il faut donc réduire le dioxyde NO_2 en monoxyde NO ce qui peut être obtenu en portant le gaz à doser à une température élevée, environ 800 à 900° C, ce qui provoque la dissociation selon:

$$NO_2 \longrightarrow NO + O$$

C'est le NO résultant de cette dissociation, auquel vient s'ajouter le NO préexistant qui sont alors dosés pour obtenir la somme NO_x.

4° Dosage des oxydants

Un dosage automatique de l'ozone a été proposé récemment qui se rapproche de celui qui vient d'être indiqué à propos du dosage du NO par chimiluminescence: si l'on fait réagir l'ozone (qu'il s'agit cette fois de doser et non plus de considérer comme réactif ajouté) sur de l'éthylène, il se forme un adduct qui lui aussi a un contenu énergétique trop élevé de sorte que pour revenir à l'état fondamental, cet adduct émet des photons mesurables par le moyen d'un photomultiplicateur[11].

$$O_3 + CH_2 = CH_2 \longrightarrow (adduct)^*$$
$$(Adduct)^* \longrightarrow adduct + h\nu$$

Cette méthode est sensible et spécifique de l'ozone.

Conclusion

Cette brève revue donne un aperçu des méthodes dont les physico-chimistes disposent à l'heure actuelle pour mesurer les polluants atmosphériques dans les sites qui auront été choisis comme représentatifs de ce que la population peut respirer en moyenne pendant 24 heures. On ne doit pas se dissimuler que la plupart de ces appareils sont chers et que leur stabilité n'est pas encore absolue tout au moins pour bon nombre d'entre eux. Il en résulte que installer un réseau d'appareils automatiques pour recueillir des données éventuellement transmises par ligne téléphonique ou par radio, est une chose, mais assurer la maintenance du réseau est une autre chose, probablement plus compliquée que la première.

Bibliographie

[1] P. Chovin, ce recueil, 1974, 31
[2] Dans « Méthodes de mesure de la pollution atmosphérique », Organisation de Coopération et de Développement Economique, Paris 1964
[3] Debrun, dans « Proceedings of the 2d. International Congress for Clean Air, Washington, D.C., Décembre 1970
[4] P. W. West et G. C. Gaeke, Anal. Chem., 1956, 28, 1816
[5] J. E. Dickinson, J. Air Poll. Control. Assoc., 1957, 6, 224. H. Landsberg et E. E. Escher, Ind. Engng Chem., 1954, 46, 1422
[6] M. Bowman et M. Berosa, Anal. Chem. 1968, 40, 1448
[7] P. Chovin, Bull. Soc. Chim. France, 1968, 2191
[8] B. E. Salzman, Anal. Chem., 1954, 26, 1949
[9] Buck et Stratmann, Int. J. Air Water Poll., 1966, 10, 313
[10] A. Fontijn, A. J. Sabadell et R. J. Ronco, Anal. Chem.; 1970, 42, 575.
[11] G. W. Nederbragt, Avan der Horst et J. van Duijn, Nature, 1965, 206, 87. G. J. Warren et G. Babcock, Rev. Sci. Instr., 1970, 41, 280.

Le monoxyde de carbone*

P. Chovin

Laboratoire Central de la Préfecture de Police, Paris, France

Summary   The effects of carbon monoxide in man are indicated. Especially proposals are given for the calculation of the carboxy-hemoglobin-formation as related to carbon monoxide concentration. General biologic effects due to the change of the equilibrium of the oxygen concentration in blood by carbon monoxide and the inhibition of biological catalysts are discussed. Furthermore, a survey is given on the methods of analyzing carbon monoxide in the gaseous phase and in blood, respectively.

Zusammenfassung   Es werden die Effekte von Kohlenmonoxyd auf den Menschen, besonders Vorschläge zur Berechnung der Carboxyhämoglobin-Bildung in Abhängigkeit von der Kohlenmonoxyd-Konzentration angegeben. Allgemeine biologische Effekte durch die Verschiebung des Gleichgewichts der Sauerstoffkonzentration im Blut durch Kohlenmonoxyd und die Inhibierung biologischer Katalysatoren werden diskutiert. Darüberhinaus wird eine Übersicht gegeben zu den Methoden der Analyse von Kohlenmonoxyd sowohl in der Gasphase als auch im Blut.

* This paper was presented in part at the International Symposium on the Establishment of Air Quality Standards, Paris, Oct. 1972, organized by the International Academy of Environmental Safety.

Le monoxyde de carbone est le résultat de la plupart des combustions de matières organiques, effectuées en présence d'une quantité insuffisante d'oxygène. On en rencontrera donc non seulement dans les effluents gazeux des foyers de combustion utilisant du charbon ou du fuel mais également comme résultat du fonctionnement des véhicules automobiles, de feux d'immeubles ou de forêts, etc... En fait, dans l'atmosphère des villes, le monoxyde de carbone a principalement pour origine les véhicules automobiles: une statistique, dressée aux Etats-Unis, permet d'estimer que, sur 214 millions de tonnes de polluants émises pendant l'année 1968, le monoxyde de carbone intervient à lui seul au total pour 100 millions de tonnes, ce qui représente à peu près 46,7 % des émissions. Sur ce total, les transports interviennent pour 63,8 millions de tonnes et les véhicules à moteurs, à eux seuls, pour 50,2 millions de tonnes, soit 27,6 % des émissions de toutes natures. A la différence des autres polluants, c'est surtout dans les villes qu'on le rencontre, où il est le plus abondant de tous les polluants que l'on peut déceler: les mesures qui ont été faites, tant à Paris par nous-mêmes que dans d'autres villes de France ou d'autres pays, ont montré que des concentrations moyennes horaires de 50 parties par million pouvaient être facilement atteintes en certains carrefours particulièrement encombrés. C'est ainsi qu'à Lyon, par exemple, pendant les journées des 2 et 3 novembre 1970 qui ont connu des circonstances météorologiques favorables à l'installation d'une haute pollution, des teneurs moyennes horaires de 60, 65, 70 et même 75 ppm ont été enregistrées entre 17 et 19 heures. Les valeurs instantanées de pointe peuvent être beaucoup plus importantes et dans Paris, par exemple, on a observé que sur 15 216 prélèvements instantanés annuels, 0,21 % étaient supérieurs à 100 ppm et 0,01 % étaient supérieurs à 200 ppm. Ces valeurs constituent, bien évidemment, des maximums. Pour situer le niveau de pollution de notre capitale, on peut donner le résultat suivant: la moyenne géométrique de l'ensemble des déterminations horaires qui ont été effectuées à l'aide de 11 appareils automatiques pendant l'année 1971 s'est établie au niveau de 16 ppm environ.

Effets sur les êtres humains

On s'est, bien sûr, de longue date, préoccupé de l'action du monoxyde de carbone sur les individus. Mais, au début de ces études, seules les intoxications aiguës, voire mortelles, étaient prises en considération et ce n'est que depuis peu qu'une attention particulière a été portée sur les effets des concentrations faibles du genre de celles que l'on rencontre dans l'atmosphère des villes. Parmi tous les polluants, le monoxyde de carbone est celui dont le premier stade du mécanisme de fixation est le mieux connu, ce qui a favorisé de nombreuses études sur ce sujet. On sait que l'oxygène et le monoxyde de carbone se disputent la possession de l'hémoglobine,

pour former, le premier de l'oxyhémoglobine, le second de la carboxyhémoglobine, selon le schéma de réaction suivant:

$$CO + HbO_2 \rightleftharpoons HbCO + O_2$$

$$\frac{[HbCO] \cdot pO_2}{[HbO_2] \cdot pCO} = M$$

La constante M est très élevée et l'on admet pour l'homme M = 210[1].

Grâce à cette formule, on peut calculer la quantité de carboxyhémoglobine formée dans le sang lorsqu'un individu respire indéfiniment dans une atmosphère renfermant une concentration donnée, C, en monoxyde de carbone. Moyennant certaines hypothèses, justifiées par ailleurs, on est arrivé au résultat suivant[2]:

$$(HbCO) \% = 0,16 \, C$$

dans laquelle C est exprimé en parties par million en volume.

En fait, ce qui précède correspond à l'aspect statique de la fixation du monoxyde de carbone sur l'hémoglobine, mais il faut prendre en consiration l'aspect dynamique c'est-à-dire la vitesse avec laquelle le monoxyde de carbone se fixe. De nombreux chercheurs se sont penchés sur cette question et l'on n'a que l'embarras du choix entre les diverses formules qui ont été proposées.

La plus précise est incontestablement celle de Coburn et Coll. qui traduit un modèle théorique où tous les facteurs susceptibles d'intervenir ont été pris en considération[3].

$$\frac{A \, [COHb]_t - \dot{V}_{CO} \, B - P_{I_{CO}}}{A \, [COHb]_o - \dot{V}_{CO} \, B - P_{I_{CO}}} = e^{-tA/V_bB}$$

dans laquelle:

$$A = P_{C_{O_2}} / M \, [O_2Hb]$$

avec $P_{C_{O_2}}$ = pression de O_2 dans les capillaires pulmonaires au niveau de la mer (environ 100 mm Hg).

et M   = affinité relative de Hb pour CO et O_2 = 218.

$[COHb]_t$ et $[COHb]_0$ = concentrations de la carboxyhémoglobine aux temps t et zéro (en ml de CO par ml de sang).

$\dot{V}_{CO}$ = vitesse de production du CO endogène.

Pour un être sain, $\dot{V}_{CO}$ = 0,007 ml/mn.

$P_{I_{CO}}$ = pression partielle du CO dans l'air inspiré.

$P_{I_{CO}}$ = CO (ppm) × pression barométrique × 10^{-6}.

$$B = \frac{1}{D_L} + \frac{P_L}{V_A}$$

avec D_L =   pouvoir de diffusion pulmonaire pour CO, environ 30 ml/mn. mm Hg

P_L =   somme des pressions partielles des gaz alvéolaires à l'exclusion de la vapeur d'eau (47 mm Hg à 37° C) soit: P_L = 760 – 47 = 713 mm Hg

V_A = ventilation alvéolaire.

V_b =   Ventilation sanguin, environ 5500 ml pour un homme de 70 kilogrammes.

La formule de Coburn n'est pas d'un maniement aisé. On peut lui préférer la formule de Hanks et Farquhar, résultat d'expériences d'expositions soigneusement contrôlées et qui cadre très bien avec la réalité et avec le modèle théorique de Coburn et Coll.[4]

$$(HbCO \%) = 0,1465 \, C \, (1 - e^{-0,1735 \, t})$$

On peut voir, d'après cette formule, qu'au bout d'un temps infini, la teneur du sang en carboxyhémoglobine serait donnée par la relation:

$$(HbCO \%)_\infty = 0,1465 \, C$$

ce qui cadre, à 10 % près, avec la formule précédente, établie sur la base de travaux plus anciens.

Par ailleurs, la pente à l'origine est 0,0252 C et j'ai montré que le coefficient 0,0252 dépend en fait de l'activité du sujet[5]. Dans les expériences de Hans et Farquhar, ce coefficient correspond au repos. Or, pour des activités plus élevées pouvant aller jusqu'à un travail intense, sa valeur pourrait monter jusqu'à 0,065 et même davantage.

En fait, la carboxyhémoglobine n'est pas la seule ferroprotéine susceptible de fixer le monoxyde de carbone. La myoglobine du muscle peut former, de son côté, de la carboxyhémoglobine mais la constante d'équilibre de cette réaction est beaucoup plus faible que celle relative à la carboxyhémoglobine, de sorte que ce processus ne semble jouer qu'un rôle négligeable dans l'action du monoxyde de carbone sur le corps humain.

Il peut ne pas en être de même pour certains ferments ou catalyseurs biologiques qui peuvent être inactivés par le monoxyde de carbone du fait de leur combinaison avec ce composé. Nous en verrons quelques exemples dans la suite.

On peut se poser la question de savoir quel est le bilan de la fixation du monoxyde de carbone dans l'organisme. Sa présence résulte, d'une part de ce qui peut être fixé sur l'hémoglobine par la respiration, d'autre part de ce que l'expiration peut éliminer. On s'est aperçu rapidement qu'il fallait tenir compte également de ce que le corps humain est susceptible de former, par le processus dit endogène, résultant de la destruction de l'hémoglobine avec formation corrélative de bilirubine et de biliverdine, par ouverture du cycle complexe formé des quatre cycles pyrroliques bien connus. Au total, si l'on tient compte de cette formation endogène, qui est normalement de 0,4 cm³/h mais qui peut atteindre 1,4 cm³/h chez la femme au lendemain de l'accouchement, on arrive au schéma suivant donné par Coburn, qui résume la représentation que l'on se fait actuellement des facteurs qui influencent le stockage du CO dans l'organisme[6].

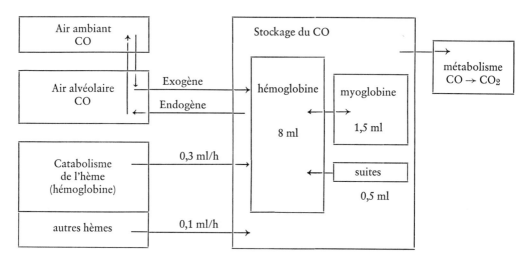

Schéma du mécanisme du stockage de CO dans l'organisme. D'après Coburn.

Les effets biologiques du monoxyde de carbone

Il semble que ces effets soient à ramener à deux causes essentielles.

La première résulte du déplacement de la courbe d'équilibre de l'oxygène lorsque simultanément du monoxyde de carbone est présent dans le sang. Il s'ensuit une diminution de la pression d'oxygène disponible dans les capillaires qui, si elle est pratiquement négligeable dans le sang artériel pour des teneurs même relativement importantes en monoxyde de carbone, peut prendre des valeurs significatives dans le sang veineux à la sortie des organes irrigués, particulièrement de ceux qui sont gros consommateurs d'oxygène, tels le myocarde, le muscle du cœur. On a pu montrer que si un sujet est exposé à une pollution correspondant à un niveau de 70 parties par million de monoxyde de carbone, la pression d'oxygène veineuse peut subir un abaissement pouvant aller de 4,6 à 6,2 mm de mercure selon l'avidité de l'organe irrigué pour l'oxygène[7]. On peut se demander si une telle différence de 4 à 6 mm de mercure peut être importante. On n'a pas encore de réponse correcte à cette question. Mais on peut chercher des causes qui provoqueraient un abaissement équivalent. Il faudrait, par exemple, qu'une personne qui ne serait pas exposée au monoxyde de carbone voie son débit sanguin s'abaisser de 13 à 37 % pour que l'on observe une diminution équivalente de la pression veineuse d'oxygène. Cet effet n'est évidemment pas négligeable et l'on a tendance à penser maintenant que c'est le cerveau, organe le plus sensible à une dette d'oxygène, qui est amené à souffrir le plus intensément d'une exposition au monoxyde de carbone. Des tests destinés à essayer de mettre en évidence cette action ont été réalisés[8 à 15] et c'est ainsi que l'on a pu montrer, par exemple, que pour des expositions à des niveaux qui sont de l'ordre de grandeur de ceux que l'on rencontre dans l'atmosphère des villes, on peut observer une détérioration de l'aptitude à exécuter un calcul mental, ou bien encore une élévation du seuil de perception lumineuse. On a également noté une certaine perturbation de la vision périphérique ou une diminution de la faculté d'estimation de l'égalité ou de la différence de temps pour des phénomènes dont la durée pouvait être égale ou variable. Enfin, on a observé une diminution de la faculté d'estimer à sa vraie valeur la vitesse d'un véhicule.

En fait, ces résultats sont controversés par d'autres auteurs qui n'ont pas réussi à mettre en évidence des faits du même genre mais il est juste de dire que lorsqu'on s'adresse, pour ces tests, à des êtres humains qui savent par conséquent à quel genre d'expérimentation on va les soumettre, ils peuvent, même inconsciemment, subir une réaction de défense vis-à-vis de l'agression dont ils savent qu'ils vont être victimes, réaction qui peut perturber les réponses fournies aux tests.

La conclusion que l'on doit tirer de ces essais est qu'il serait hasardeux de prétendre que, même aux basses concentrations, le monoxyde de carbone est sans effet sur l'être humain. Dans cette voie, on ne peut pas ne pas être frappé par les statistiques fort précises qui ont montré que le poids des enfants mis au monde par des mères qui fument est significativement inférieur à celui des enfants issus de mères qui s'abstiennent de l'usage de la cigarette. Le second mécanisme d'action du monoxyde de carbone est à rapporter à l'effet d'inhibition exercé sur certains catalyseurs biologiques. C'est ainsi que la fixation du cholestérol sur la tunique interne des ar-

tères semble gouvernée par un processus de biocatalyse et lorsque ce processus est perturbé par la présence de monoxyde de carbone, on constate un enrichissement de la paroi aortique en cholestérol, c'est-à-dire que l'on franchit le premier pas vers l'artériosclérose. Il est juste de dire que des phénomènes du même genre sont observés lorsque l'on maintient des individus dans une atmosphère raréfiée en oxygène, comme c'est le cas pour ceux qui vivent en haute altitude, de sorte que l'on ne sait pas encore très bien si cette action ne serait pas plutôt à ramener à un défaut d'oxygène. De même, sans que l'on sache bien encore s'il s'agit d'un effet catalytique ou d'un défaut d'oxygène, la perméabilité des parois des artères est affectée par le monoxyde de carbone: cette perméabilité augmente et le système lymphatique peut entrer plus ou moins en communication avec le système cardiovasculaire. Il en résulte une augmentation du volume du plasma, pouvant entrainer une élévation de la tension artérielle et une élévation de la teneur du plasma en protéines[17]. En revanche, il semble bien que la fixation des graisses sur les tuniques des artères soit gouvernée uniquement par un processus biocatalytique. Ce phénomène est particulièrement important pour les artères coronaires et constitue une seconde raison de penser que le monoxyde de carbone peut avoir une influence sur l'infarctus du myocarde, la première raison étant, comme on l'a vu précédemment, la diminution de la pression d'oxygène disponible dans celui des muscles qui effectue sans discontinuer le travail le plus intense. Il n'est donc pas hasardeux d'avancer aujourd'hui l'hypothèse selon laquelle l'augmentation réelle et observée du nombre des infarctus du myocarde peut être regardée bien plus comme une conséquence de l'utilisation de la cigarette que comme une conséquence de la pollution atmosphérique.

Methodes de dosage du monoxyde de carbone

Si l'on parcourt la littérature relative au dosage du monoxyde de carbone, on est frappé par le nombre très important de méthodes qui ont été préconisées. Cela tient à ce que, jusqu'à l'avènement de méthodes modernes et d'appareillages sophistiqués, aucune de celles qui étaient mises en œuvre n'était réellement, ou précise, ou pratique. Nous limiterons donc volontairement cet expose aux procédés les plus couramment utilisés, en mentionnant seulement ici pour mémoire l'usage des tubes détecteurs qui permettent d'avoir une simple indication sur le niveau de pollution observé.

La plupart des méthodes que je retiendrai sont automatiques et peuvent conduire à des réalisations d'appareillage susceptibles de se prêter à la détermination de la teneur en monoxyde de carbone d'échantillons d'air prélevés, soit dans des sacs en matière plastique, instantanément, soit pendant un certain temps appelé « temps d'échantillonnage» et ramenés au laboratoire pour examen. On conçoit donc que l'on puisse effectuer une surveillance des niveaux de pollution par cette méthode, mais aussi en faisant circuler l'atmosphère à doser dans l'appareil en ayant implanté celui-ci à proximité du carrefour à surveiller.

1° Appareils basés sur l'oxydation catalytique du CO et la mesure de la chaleur dégagée

Lorsqu'on fait passer une atmosphère renfermant du monoxyde de carbone sur un catalyseur tel l'hopcalite, l'oxydation qui le transforme en CO_2 dégage une certaine quantité de chaleur. Il s'ensuit que la température de la masse d'oxydant s'élève et par suite, s'élève aussi celle du gaz qui sort de la chambre de réaction. Pour un débit donné de gaz, l'élévation de température se stabilise lorsque l'équilibre est atteint entre la chaleur fournie par la réaction et celle qui est perdue par rayonnement, convection ou conduction. Sur ce principe, on a construit des appareils où la teneur en monoxyde de carbone se déduit de l'élévation de température d'un élément sensible plongé dans la masse du catalyseur et que l'on compare à celle d'un élément analogue mis au sein d'un remplissage inerte. Comme éléments sensibles, on a utilisé les couples thermo-électriques et l'on a proposé des cellules constituées par 55 couples différentiels dont les soudures chaudes sont plongées dans l'oxydant et les soudures froides dans de la ponce de même granulométrie. L'appareil peut fonctionner en marche continue et se prête à l'enregistrement[16].

2° Analyseurs infra-rouge non dispersifs

Le monoxyde de carbone possède un spectre d'absorption dans la partie infra-rouge du spectre. De nombreux appareils ont été basés sur le principe suivant[18 à 21]:

Si l'on dispose d'une source de radiation infra-rouge, d'un tube-laboratoire dans lequel on fait circuler l'atmosphère à doser et d'un détecteur connecté à un appareil de mesure approprié, on disposera d'une réponse pour tout gaz présent dans le tube-laboratoire absorbant dans la région du spectre qui parvient au détecteur. Si l'on veut que l'appareil soit sélectif, c'est-à-dire qu'il ne réponde que pour un polluant déterminé, il faut, ou bien utiliser une source sélective, par exemple par l'emploi de filtres, en particulier de filtres interférentiels, ou bien utiliser des détecteurs sélectifs qui seraient calés sur la longueur d'onde caractéristique d'absorption du gaz à doser. Un détecteur spécifique peut être constitué par une cellule opto-acoustique renfermant le gaz à doser, ici le monoxyde de carbone, sous une pression appropriée. Dans le rayonnement issu du tube d'analyse, le CO présent dans le détecteur n'absorbe que les radiations caractéristiques de son propre spectre. Si l'atmosphère à doser renferme ce même gaz, une partie des radiations actives qui parvenaient en son absence au détecteur se trouve soustraite et la réponse de celui-ci se trouve abaissée. Le fonctionnement d'un tel détecteur est donc basé sur l'échauffement du gaz qu'il renferme sous l'influence de la radiation infra-rouge qui lui parvient. Au lieu de mesurer cet échauffement, on préfère mesurer la variation de pression qui en résulte et un bon moyen consiste à hacher le flux lumineux à faible fréquence pour que les « bouffées de chaleur » qui prennent naissance dans le détecteur impriment un mouvement alternatif à un diaphragme flexible constituant l'une des parois de la cellule. En réalité, ce diaphragme est avantageusement commun à deux cellules, la seconde étant une cellule de comparaison renfermant aussi du CO, mais irradié au travers d'un tube dit de comparaison contenant un gaz exempt de ce composé. Si le diaphragme est l'une des armatures d'un condensateur, celui-ci peut faire partie d'un montage électronique et la réponse est, en définitive, pratiquement proportionelle à la teneur du gaz à examiner en monoxyde de carbone. D'excellents appareils utilisant ce principe sont désormais disponibles sur le marché, qui permettent des mesures précises dans les domaines 0–100 ppm, 0–500 ppm, 0–10 % ou davantage, et qui, couplés à un enregistreur, autorisent des relevés continus.

Cette technique est très utilisée par les constructeurs de véhicules automobiles qui veulent suivre la composition des gaz d'échappement de leurs moteurs.

Le Laboratoire Central de la Préfecture de Police a mis au point un dispositif contenant un analyseur infra-rouge mais tel que le résultat fourni correspond, non pas à la valeur instantanée de la teneur de l'atmosphère en monoxyde de carbone, mais à sa valeur moyenne horaire. Pour parvenir à un tel résultat, il est nécessaire d'intégrer. Ceci peut se faire au moyen d'un intégrateur électronique mais cette solution est chère et nous lui avons préféré celle qui consiste en une intégration « pneumatique », l'appareil comportant, grâce à un jeu de vannes électromagnétiques et une minuterie, deux sacs en matière plastique de 10 à 12 litres de capacité, dont l'un se remplit en une heure de l'atmosphère à examiner tandis que l'autre, qui a été rempli pendant l'heure précédente, se vide dans l'analyseur. Six appareils de ce type ont été installés dans Paris ainsi que 5 autres pour lesquels l'intégratien est réalisée électroniquement. Les résultats sont équivalents et ont permis au Laboratoire Central de faire une étude extrêmement soignée de la pollution régnant dans 11 des 25 carrefours les plus pollués de la capitale[22].

3° Méthode par réduction de l'oxyde de mercure

La méthode met en oeuvre la réaction du monoxyde de carbone sur l'oxyde de mercure suivant la réaction[23]:

$$CO + HgO \longrightarrow CO_2 + Hg$$

et profite des propriétés de la vapeur libérée pour en effectuer le dosage au moyen de la raie de résonance du métal. Le montage est du type différentiel et comporte deux chaînes d'oxydation aboutissant chacune à une cuve en quartz à faces parallèles, disposées de part et d'autre d'une lampe à vapeur de mercure dont la lumière est filtrée pour ne laisser passer que les radiations voisines de 253,7 nm. Cette chaîne comporte un tube renfermant de l'oxyde rouge de mercure (200 ± 0,02° C). L'une es parcourue par l'atmosphère à examiner, l'autre par un gaz de comparaison exempt de monoxyde de carbone. Deux cellules photo-électriques montées en pont sont reliées à un amplificateur et à un enregistreur. La sensibilité maximale correspond à une déviation de l'échelle pour une partie de monoxyde de carbone dans 5 millions de parties d'air (0,02 ppm) et la précision est encore de 2 % du domaine de mesure choisi. Les appareils de ce type sont utilisés pour mesurer la pollution de fond par le monoxyde de carbone, loin de toute zone urbaine.

4° Dosage par chromatographie en phase gazeuse

De nombreuses publications ont été consacrées au problème du dosage du monoxyde de carbone par la technique de la chromatographie en phase gazeuse [24, 25]. Cependant, les détecteurs utilisés doivent être pourvus d'une sensibilité suffisante pour permettre l'estimation de très faibles traces de monoxyde de carbone. A cet égard, les détecteurs dits à fils chauds, ou catharomètres, encore appelès cellules de conductibilité thermique, ne sont pas suffisamment sensibles. En revanche, on a proposé l'emploi de détecteurs à hélium ou ultrasoniques et surtout de détecteurs à ionisation de flamme dont la sensibilité est plus de 1000 fois plus élevée que celle des catharomètres. Le cas de ces détecteurs est à examiner spécialement, car ils ne manifestent vis-à-vis du monoxyde de carbone qu'une réponse insignifiante. Mais on tourne la difficulté en transformant le monoxyde de carbone, à sa sortie d'une colonne classique de tamis moléculaire 5 A, en méthane par hydrogénation dans un four à catalyse, et c'est le méthane formé que l'on dirige dans le détecteur à ionisation de flamme. Les difficultés qui ont marqué la naissance de ce procédé, et qui concernaient le taux de conversion du monoxyde de carbone en méthane, sont aujourd'hui aplanies, de sorte que ces appareils, qui sont doués d'une très grande sensibilité, sont également employés pour mesurer la pollution de fond. Ils présentent cependant un inconvénient, celui de ne pas donner de mesure continue. L'automatisation de tels appareils est possible par le moyen de vannes électro-magnétiques et de minuteries, de sorte que l'on peut obtenir, soit des valeurs successives de prélèvements instantanés, soit, en intégrant pneumatiquement dans un sac comme il a été dit précédemment, des valeurs moyennes successives pendant la durée d'échantillonnage choisie.

5° Méthodes de dosage du monoxyde de carbone dans le sang

On ne saurait passer sous silence à propos du monoxyde de carbone le dosage de ce composé dans le sang. Nous nous contenterons, pour ne pas alourdir l'exposé, de citer les principales méthodes utilisées, renvoyant aux ouvrages spécialisés pour les détails. Nous classerons ces méthodes en méthodes non destructives et méthodes destructives.

Les premières sont basées sur les propriétes spectroscopiques de l'oxyhémoglobine et de la carboxyhémoglobine et une méthode particulièrement attrayante a été mise au point, par Lawther et Commins, qui permet de n'utiliser qu'une simple goutte de sang prélevée à l'extrémité du doigt [26].

Les méthodes destructives reviennent à libérer le monoxyde de carbone de sa combinaison avec la carboxyhémoglobine et à doser le monoxyde de carbone ainsi dégagé par diverses méthodes. Parmi celles-ci, on citera l'utilisation des tubes détecteurs [27 à 29] ou des sels palladeux [30 à 40], la spectrophotométrie infra-rouge non dispersive [41 à 50], enfin la chromatographie en phase gazeuse. On n'aurait garde d'oublier qu'il existe une relation entre la teneur en monoxyde de carbone du sang et celle de l'air alvéolaire. Cette relation ets linéaire [51 à 57] et les plus récentes expériences auxquelles s'est livré le Laboratoire Central de la Préfecture de Police montrent qu'on peut écrire:

$$(HbCO) \% = k \ (CO \ alvéolaire \ ppm)$$
avec: k = 0,125 à 0,150 selon les auteurs.

La détermination de la teneur de l'air alvéolaire en monoxyde de carbone est très aisément réalisée par la méthode dite « de la respiration retenue » (braethholding) qui consiste à remplir les poumons d'air, attendre 20 secondes que les échanges respiratoires se fassent au niveau des alvéoles, expirer les ²/₃ de l'air ainsi emmagasiné pour balayer l'arbre bronchique et recueillir finalement le dernier tiers dans un sac en plastique grâce auquel on effectuera la mesure par un analyseur infra-rouge non dispersif.

Conclusion

Le monoxyde de carbone n'est probablement pas le polluant le plus nocif, bien qu'il se rencontre dans l'atmosphère dans des proportions qui sont très largement supérieures à celles des autres polluants, ce qui a incité certains auteurs à définir les « indices de pollution », formules mathématiques composites dans lesquelles les concentrations de divers polluants sont ajoutées les unes aux autres après pondération par des coefficients numériques. Il est dommage que chaque auteur ait proposé sa formule et qu'on ne se soit pas encore mis d'accord d'un point de vue international sur une formule générale et unique. Quoi qu'il en soit, on ne saurait oublier qu'une large portion de la population des villes et même des campagnes s'expose volontairement au monoxyde de carbone en fumant la cigarette ou le cigare. Des études récentes ont même montré que les fumeurs exposaient les non fumeurs vivant dans les mêmes

locaux, par exemple dans des bureaux, à une pollution qui est loin d'être négligeable. Ce n'est pas une raison suffisante pour renoncer à supprimer les autres causes de pollution et c'est la raison pour laquelle la règlementation prévoyant l'abaissement des émissions de polluants par les véhicules automobiles, en particulier l'abaissement du monoxyde de carbone, a été promulguée, avec date d'effet au 1ᵉʳ octobre dernier. Cette règlementation doit abaisser de 40 % les émissions en monoxyde de carbone et de 35 % celles des hydrocarbures par rapport aux émissions des véhicules non anti-pollués. Il a même été prévu, à l'occasion des travaux d'une commission qui a été réunie par le Premier Ministre et qui a établi un rapport intitulé: « Automobiles et Nuisances: pour un programme d'action », que la France proposerait aux Instances Européennes siégeant à Genève, un nouvel abaissement d'environ 20 % pour le monoxyde de cabrone et 10 % pour les hydrocarbures, pour les années qui viennent. Moyennant quoi, il est à peu près certain que les abaissements des émissions contrebalanceront, et même surpasseront, l'effet que l'on est en droit d'attendre d'une augmentation du parc automobile et du trafic automobile dans les villes. C'est à cette condition que l'on sauvegardera ce patrimoine commun qu'est la pureté de l'air que l'on respire, pureté à laquelle tout être humain a un droit imprescriptible.

Bibliographie

[1] J. Sendroy, S. H. Liu et D. Van Slike, Am. J. Physiol., 1929, *90*, 511
[2] J. R. Goldsmith et S. A. Landaw, Science, 1968, *162*, 1352
[3] R. F. Coburn, R. E. Forster et P. B. Kane, J. Klin. Invest., 1965, *41*, 1899
[4] T. G. Hanks et R. D. Farquhar, Rapport final de contrat PH-22-68-31, juin 1969, National Air Pollution Control Administration, Durham, N.C.

[5] P. Chovin et J. Richalet Ann. Falsif- et Expert. Chim., 1973, 177

[6] R. F. Coburn, Acta Med. Scand. Suppl., 1967, 472, 269

[7] S. Permutt et L. Fahri, National Academy of Sciences (Washington, D. C.), 1969, p. 18

[8] R. A. McFarland et Coll., J. Aviation Med., 1944, 15, (6), 381

[9] H. H. Halperin, J. Physiol., 1959, 146, (3), 583

[10] L. Parmeggiani, Med. Lavoro it., 1956, 47, 377

[11] M. Pilman, Sovet vestnik. oftal. 1934, 4, 433

[12] M. Pilman, Sovet. vestnik. oftal., 1935, 6, 361

[13] M. Pilman et Taradina, Sovet. vestnik. oftal., 1935, 7, 203

[14] R. R. Beard et G. A. Wertheim, Amer. J. Public Health, 1967, 57, 2012.

[15] P. Mikulka, Communication présentée devant la 5ème Conférence annuelle sur la Pollution atmosphérique dans les espaces confinés, 1969

[16] M. Katz et J. Katzman, Canadian J. Research, 1948, 26, 318

[17] J. Siggaard-Andersen, F. Bonde Petersen, T. I. Hansen et K. Mellemgaard, Scand. J. Clin. Lab. Invest., 1968, 22, Suppl. 103, 39.

[18] W. G. Fastie et A. H. Pfund, J. Opt. Soc. Amer., 1947, 37, 762

[19] K. F. Luft, Z. Physik, 1943, 24, 97

[20] A. H. Pfund, Science, 1939, 90, 326

[21] A. H. Pfund et C. L. Gemmill, Bull. Johns Hopkins Hosp., 1940, 67, 61

[22] P. Chovin et Coll. dans « Etudes de pollution atmosphérique à Paris et dans les départements périphériques en 1970 », Rapport n° 65 794/D-PA, avril 1971; Etudes de pollution atmosphérique à Paris et dans les départements périphériques en 1971, Rapport n° 68 632/D-PA, juin 1972, Laboratoire Central de la Préfecture de Police Edr.

[23] V. Tomberg, Experentia, 1954, 10, 388

[24] G. J. Cvejanovich, Anal. Chem., 1962, 34, 654

[25] J. J. Madison, Anal. Chem., 1958, 30, 1859

[26] B. T. Commins et J. P. J. Lawther, British J. of Ind. Medicine, 1965, 22, 139

[27] L. Vignoli, B. Cristau, J. P. Defretin et R. Vignoli, Arch. Mal. Prof., 1960, 21, 201

[28] J. N. Waggoner et M. L. Pernell, U.S. Armed Forces Med. J., 1955, 6, 121

[29] H. I. Chinn, N. E. R. Pawel et R. F. Redmond, J. Lab. Clin. Med., 1955, 46, 905

[30] M. T. Ryan, I. Nolan et E. I. Conway, Biochem. J., 1948, 42, LXIV

[31] M. Feldstein, M. A. Niels et M. D. Klendshoj, Canad. J. Med. Technol., 1954, 16, 81.

[32] G. Le Moan, Ann. pharm. françaises, 1952, 10, 269.

[33] L. Vignoli, B. Cristau, J. P. Defretin et R. Vignoli, Arch. Mal. Prof., 1960, 21, 432

[34] R. Fabre, R. Truhaut et F. Berrod, Ann. pharm. franç., 1951, 9, 625

[35] R. Wennesland, Acta physiol. scandin., 1940, 1, 49

[36] T. H. Allen et W. S. Root, J. Biol. Chem., 1955, 216, 319

[37] R. Truhaut et C. Boudene, C. R. Acad. Sci., 1963, 256, 5433

[38] R. Fabre, R. Truhaut et F. Berrod, Ann. pharm. franç., 1951, 9, 625

[39] G. Le Moan, Ann. pharm. françaises, 1952, 10, 269.

[40] A. Badinand, A. Boucherle et F. Serusclat, J. Med. Bordeaux, 1957, 5, 621

[41] P. J. Lawther et G. H. Apthorp, Brit. J. Ind. Med., 1955, 12, 326

[42] R. F. Coburn, G. K. Danielson, W. S. Blakemore et R. E. Forster, II, J. Appl. Physiol., 1964, 19, 510

[43] M. Dakak, « Recherches expérimentales sur l'oxycarbonisme chronique – Etude analytique et biologique » Thèse de Doctorat, Faculté de Pharmacie, Paris 1954

[44] H. Moureu, P. Chovin, L. Truffert et J. Lebbe, C. R. Acad. Sci., 1956, 242, 2417.

[45] H. Moureau, P. Chovin, L. Truffert et J. Lebbe, C. R. du XIXème Congrès du G.A.M.S., Paris 1956, Septembre, p. 235

[46] H. Moureu, P. Chovin, L. Truffert et J. Lebbe, Chimie Analytique, 1957, 39, n° 1, 3

[47] H. Moureu, P. Chovin, L. Truffert et J. Lebbe, Lavoro Umano, 1957, IX, n° 2, 49

[48] H. Moureu, P. Chovin, L. Truffert et J. Lebbe, Arch. Mal. Prof., 1957, 18, n° 2, 116

[49] H. Moureu, P. Chovin, L. Truffert et J. Lebbe, Bull. Soc. Chim., 1957, 24, 1155

[50] V. Tomberg, Experentia, 1954, 10 (9), 388

[51] T. Sjöstrand, Acta Physiol. Scand., 1948, 16, 201

[52] Siösten et T. Sjöstrand, Acta Physiol. Scand., 1951, 22, 129

[53] P. J. Lawther et G. H. Apthorp, Brit. J. Ind. Med., 1955, 12, 326

[54] L. Parmeggiani, S. Cambruzzi et G. Colombo, Med. Lav., 1958, 49, 428

[55] P. E. Sturrock et G. Kitzes, Wright-Air, Development Center Technical Report 57–291. ASTIA Document AG 118274, 1958, mars

[56] R. H. Jones, M. P. Ellicott, J. B. Cadigan et E. Gaensler, J. Lab. Clin. Med., 1958, 51, 553

[57] J. D. Hackney, G. A. Kaufman et H. Lashier, Proceedings of the Fourth, Air Pollution Medical Research Conference, San Francisco, Décembre 1960

Problems Encountered in the Toxicological Testing of Environmental Chemicals

H. Frohberg

Institut für Toxikologie, E. Merck, Darmstadt, West Germany*

Summary There are two ways for assessing the hazards presented by potential environmental noxae, namely, the epidemiological statistical evaluation and the animal experiment.

As far as these substances are concerned that are exclusively used in industry epidemiological statistical analysis is facilitated by the limited number of persons that are occupationally exposed and especially by the fact that the extent of exposure to the special substance can be quantified.

Thus one can understand that with the exception of 4-aminodiphenyl and nitrogen mustard gas the cancerogenic effect of certain industrial chemicals was recognized *at first* by exact medical observations in man and not in animal experiments.

As far as those environmental substances are concerned, that have no importance in the working process epidemiological investigations only gave little relevant information about the type and degree of the actual risk for human health till now.

Exceptions in this respect are epidemiological investigations on the induction of lung cancer in cigarette smokers and on the induction of cancer of the liver by aflatoxin contaminated food. Therefore animal experiments are necessary. Since toxic environmental substances often act on the human organism for longer periods of time chronic animal experiments are necessary for the evaluation of the risk.

The assessment should be based on the results of relevant animal experiments yielding quantitative dose-response relationships and thus allowing a calculation of the risk.

In such investigations the mode of application should correspond to the human exposure; otherwise "false positive reactions" could result due to inadequate mode of application.

Misleading results as far as the assessment of the risk for man is concerned may be due to the use of inadequate animal species also. The same applies to the use of inappropriate test models.

Here for instance the in vitro mutagenicity tests should be mentioned, whose results most often cannot be extended to mammals and even less to man, as demonstrated most impressively by the example of caffeine.

* This paper was presented in part at the working party on "Problems Evaluating Cytotoxic Effects of Environmental Chemicals" of the Forum for Science, Economics, and Politics, Bonn, Febr. 1973

Like all other toxic reactions all cytotoxic effects are dose-dependent and thus calculable.

Besides there exist threshold-levels below that such damage is not be expected.

Zusammenfassung   Es gibt zwei Möglichkeiten zur Ermittlung der Gefahren durch potentielle Umweltnoxen, die epidemiologische, statistische Untersuchung und die Tierversuche.

Bei Substanzen, die ausschließlich in der Industrie verwendet werden, sind epidemiologische, statistische Untersuchungen durch die begrenzte Anzahl der am Arbeitsplatz exponierten Personen und durch die Meßbarkeit des Ausmaßes der Exposition erleichtert. So ist es erklärlich, daß mit Ausnahme von 4-Aminodiphenyl und Stickstofflostgas die krebserzeugende Wirkung von Arbeitsstoffen primär durch exakte ärztliche Beobachtungen am Menschen und nicht im Tierversuch erkannt wurde.

Für reine Umweltgifte, also Stoffe, die im Arbeitsprozeß keine Bedeutung haben, förderten mit Ausnahme des Lungenkrebses bei Zigarettenrauchern und des Leberkrebses durch Aflatoxin-kontaminierte Nahrung die epidemiologischen Untersuchungen nur wenig Gültiges über Art und Ausmaß der tatsächlichen Gesundheitsgefährdung zutage. Deshalb sind Tierversuche erforderlich. Da Umweltgifte langfristig auf den menschlichen Organismus einwirken, sind chronische Tierversuche notwendig.

Zur Risikobeurteilung dürfen nur die Ergebnisse relevanter Tierversuche herangezogen werden, aus denen aufgrund quantitativer Dosis-Wirkungs-Beziehungen Risikokalkulationen möglich sind.

Die Applikationsarten sollten hierbei denen der menschlichen Expositionen entsprechen, da durch Einsatz inadequater Applikationsarten „false positive reactions" erhalten werden können.

Auch die Verwendung ungeeigneter Tierarten kann im Hinblick auf den Menschen irreführende Ergebnisse zur Folge haben. Das gleiche gilt für den Einsatz falscher Versuchsmodelle. Hierzu wären z. B. alle in-vitro Mutagenitätsteste zu rechnen, deren Ergebnisse, wie es das Coffein-Beispiel so eindringlich zeigt, nicht auf Säugetiere und erst recht nicht auf den Menschen zu übertragen sind.

Alle cytotoxischen Effekte sind ebenso wie alle anderen toxischen Reaktionen dosisabhängig und damit kalkulierbar. Auch existieren Schwellenwerte, unterhalb derer derartige Schädigungen nicht mehr zu erwarten sind.

Introduction

In the past, toxicology was concerned almost exclusively with the study of acute poisonings and of the possibilities of rational treatment of poisonings. At present, emphasis has shifted to the detection of possible chronic intoxications. The paramount task in this field is to detect and to quantify possible hazards to health which might be presented by natural or by synthetic substances, in order to establish basic guidelines for their selective prevention. Toxicology thus acquires a key role in environment research and environment protection. The main working tool of this environmental toxicology is the animal experiment, supplemented by techniques and methods pertaining to the domains of pharmacology, haematology, clinical and analytic chemistry, biochemistry, pathology, teratology, cancerology and genetics. Very great importance also attaches to findings on healthy and on ill human subjects, which may confirm or, on the contrary, cast doubts upon, the results of animal experiments.

Amongst the large number of environment pollutants with largely known toxic potentialities, we shall single out for special consideration the group of cytotoxic compounds which are either known to cause cytotoxic health damage in man or may be presumed on the basis of animal experiment findings to present health hazards of this kind (Table 1).

Epidemiological studies aimed at the detection of potential cytotoxic noxae in the environment differ from those relating to other toxic agents in that the effects of cytotoxic agents, owing to the long latency times involved, may only appear many years, or even decades, after the relevant exposure; this applies to carcinogenic effects, and even more so to mutagenic effects whose manifestations can only be detected in subsequent generations, if at all. Moreover, epidemiological studies in the general population, involving the effects of a large number of diverse factors which it is difficult or impossible to control, are far more difficult than studies of groups of occupationally exposed persons whose numbers are limited.

Table 1 Cytotoxic compounds in the environment

Compound	Animals			Man		
	carcino-genic	terato-genic	muta-genic	carcino-genic	terato-genic	muta-genic
aromatic amines	+++	—	+++	+++	—	—
aflatoxin	+++	+++	+++	?	—	—
arsenic	—	+++	—	+++	—	—
asbestos	+++	—	—	+++	—	—
benzene	—	+++	—	+++	—	+++*
lead	+++	+++	+++	—	—	+++*
cadmium	+++	—	—	—	—	—
cycasine	+++	+++	+++	?	—	—
epoxides	+++	?	+++	—	—	—
N-nitroso-compounds	+++	+++	+++	?	—	—
polycyclic hydrocarbons	+++	—	+++	?	—	—

+++ = positive, ? = probable, — = no definite positive data
    * = An increase of the chromosomal aberration rate was observed in persons exposed to higher concentrations of the product

Table 2 First observations of carcinogenic action

Industrial substance	Man		Animals	
	Year	Authors	Year	Authors
Tar	1775	Pott	1918	Yamagiva and Ichikawa
Asbestos	1930	Merewether and Price	1941	Nordmann and Sorge
Arsenic	1815	Richerand	ϕ	
Beryllium	ϕ		1946	Gardner and Heslington
Nickel	1932	Bridge	1952	Hueper
Chromates	1912	Pfeil	1958	Hueper
Benzene	1897	Le Noir and Claude	ϕ	
2-naphthylamine	1895	Rehn	1938	Hueper et al.
4-aminodiphenyl	1952 ?	Walpole et al.	1952	Walpole et al.
	1955	Melick et al.		
Benzidine	1940	Gross	1946	Rhoads et al.

ϕ = carcinogenic action not proven

This explains why, with the exception of 4-aminodiphenyl and nitrogen mustard gas, the carcinogenic action of various industrial compounds was detected primarily by exact medical observations on man, and not in animal experiments. Confirmation by animal experiments has often lagged several decades behind the medical observations, e.g., by nearly 50 years in the case of chromates, over 40 years in the case of 2-naphthylamine, and even 150 years in the case of tar products (Table 2).

Asbestos

A good illustration of the importance of epidemiological studies is provided by the example of asbestos.

The worldwide consumption of asbestos is steadily increasing, and amounts at present to nearly 5 million tons per year (*Woitowitz,* 1972). In the German Federal Republic at present about 15 000 people are employed in raw asbestos processing and asbestos-cement production, and a much larger number still are employed in the manufacture and processing of asbestos-containing products.

Consequences of a prolonged exposure to asbestos are asbestos-induced pulmonary fibrosis, the so-called asbestosis, lung cancer and, in the case of exposure predominantly to a certain type of asbestos, also the otherwise very rare mesothelioma of the pleura and peritoneum (*Jacob* and *Bohlig,* 1955; *Selikoff* et al. 1968).

Asbestos is now considered a hazard not only in the context of industrial medicine but also from the ecological point of view, because cases of bronchial carcinoma and of mesothelioma have been reported not only in occupationally exposed persons but also in people living in the vicinity of asbestos mines, namely of crocidolite mines, in South Africa and of docks and asbestos factories in England, Scotland, Dresden and Hamburg. Other potential ecological hazards due to asbestos, under discussion at present, are the alleged air pollution by road traffic, owing to abrasion of brake linings of vehicles, and the asbestos content of drinking water, beer and various soft drinks, probably due to the use of asbestos-cement water pipes and of asbestos-containing filters in the manufacture of beverages. It is often stated in support of this hypothesis that asbestos particles can be found in the body of nearly every second adult in the

Table 3 Carcinogenic activity of asbestos in humans

| Asbestos Type | Type and localization | | | Frequency of industrial use in the FRG (%) |
| | Carcinoma in | | Mesothelioma in Pleura and Peritoneum | |
	Lung	GE-Tract		
Chrysotile	+ +	+	(+)	90
Crocidolite	+ +	+	+ +	10
Amosite	+ +	?	?	‹ 1
Anthophyllite	+ +	?	?	‹ 1

general population, mostly in the lung tissue. At present, however, there is no conclusive proof that there exists a causal relationship between these asbestos particles and mesothelioma (*Churg*, 1970). The assumption of air pollution as a result of abrasion of brake linings has also not been confirmed experimentally so far (*Gaensler* et al., 1969; *Smith*, 1965; *Speil* et al., 1969).

The proportionality between the fibrosing process in the lungs on the one hand and the dust concentration and duration of exposure on the other, first established experimentally, has been confirmed by empirical studies on man (*Bohlig* et al., 1960).

There also exists a parallelism between the development of asbestosis and lung cancer. Appropriate industrial hygiene precautions made it possible, however, substantially to reduce exposures and thus the incidence of asbestosis and, in parallel, also the hazard of bronchial carcinoma (*Doll*, 1955; *Knox* et al., 1968). In contrast to the asbestos-induced cancers of the lung and, to a lesser extent, of the gastrointestinal tract, the incidence of mesothelioma is unrelated to that of asbestosis. Thus, of the 80 patients who died of mesothelioma between 1950 and 1967 in Scotland, only 2 had asbestosis. On the other hand, the hazard of mesothelioma varies markedly with the type of asbestos. These tumours develop predominantly after exposure to crocidolite,

also called blue asbestos (*Wagner*, 1971), which makes up only 10% of the total asbestos consumption in Germany (Table 3). In Great Britain the safety rules for handling crocidolite are for this reason 10 times as stringent as those applicable to other types of asbestos, (Table 4) it being borne in mind that a total of 622 cases of mesothelioma have been diagnosed up to 1969 in the United Kingdom alone (*Wagner* et al., 1971).

Any exposure to crocidolite should be avoided as a matter of principle. On the other hand, improvements in the working conditions of asbestos mining, manufacturing and processing industries have drastically reduced the incidence of asbestosis and a lung cancer, so that the US Public Health Service expressed the opinion in 1971 that asbestos can be safely processed in modern industrial plants. This fact, and the Hygiene Standards laid down in Britain, should be borne in mind when discussing the alleged ecological hazard presented by asbestos as an air pollutant owing to abrasion of brake linings.

Table 4 New asbestos regulations of the United Kingdom, May 1970
Industrial Hygiene Standards

Chrysotile, Amosite, Anthophyllite	0.1 mg / m³
Crocidolite	0.01 mg / m³

As far as purely environmental poisons are concerned, i.e., substances unrelated to industrial processes, epidemiological studies have so far yielded few valid data on the kind and extent of the actual health hazards, except for the lung cancer of cigarette smokers and liver cancer owing to food contaminated with aflatoxins. The main reason for this paucity of data is no doubt the small extent of the expected toxic damage.

This makes it necessary to conduct animal experiments because, from these experiments, it is possible to derive quantitative dose-effect relationships which can then be used as a basis for hazard calculations. As cytotoxic effects are dose-dependent, such calculations make it possible to determine threshold concentrations below which cytotoxic hazards need no longer be considered.

These threshold doses are used as points of reference for defining tolerance limits for the prevention of health damage in man.

In the course of the last decade Nature herself has provided us with an example of threshold concentrations in the form of aflatoxins extracted from the yellow mould Aspergillus flavus.

The carcinogenic action of aflatoxins was first described by *Lancaster* et al. (1961). They cause liver cancer in many animal species even in trace concentrations, and have a more potent carcinogenic action than any of the known carcinogenic chemicals (Table 5). They thus illustrate the fact that the most potent toxic agents are of a natural and not of a synthetic origin.

The species most sensitive to aflatoxins is trout. Certain rat strains have also developed liver cancer after being fed a diet containing only 15 ppb aflatoxin B_1. Other animal species were found to be much less sensitive.

Differences in the threshold doses were

Table 5 Hepatocarcinogenicity of aflatoxin B_1 in different species

Species	Concentration in diet (ppb)	Liver cancer
trout	0.4	+
salmon	12	+
rat	15	+
duck	35	+
guinea pig	150	+
mouse	1000	+
pig	1000	+
sheep	1750/1000**)	(+) (1 animal)
monkey	1000*)	(+) (1 animal)
man (Thailand)	0.28 — 40	(+)

*) = first year 10 μg/day i. m., subsequently 200 μg/day for 4.5 years

**) = groundnut meal with 1750 ppb Aflatoxin for 3½ years, afterwards groundnut meal with 1000 ppb Aflatoxin

References:
Alpert et al. 1969
Gopalan et al. 1972
Lancaster et al. 1969
Lee et al. 1969
Lewis et al. 1967
Newberne et al. 1969
Richir et al. 1964
Shank et al. 1962
Wales a. Sinnhuber 1972

found in chronic experiments not only between different species but also between different strains of the same animal species. Thus, Long Evans rats, in contrast to the more sensitive Fisher rats, showed a 20% incidence of liver carcinoma only at an aflatoxin concentration of 100 ppb in the feed, whereas USC rats developed no liver tumours even after being fed for 2 years on feed containing 80 ppb aflatoxin B_1 (Table 6).

There can hardly be a doubt any longer of the existence of a correlation, first postulated by *Oettlé* (1964), between the high incidence of primary liver carcinoma in man in certain areas of Africa, India and South-East Asia and the consumption of food heavily contaminated with afla-

Table 6 Longterm feeding trials with aflatoxin B_1 in rats

Rat strain	Aflatoxin B_1 ppb in diet	Frequency of liver tumors		References
		Carcinoma %	Hepatoma %	
Fisher	15	50	6	Wogan and Newberne 1967
Long Evans	10	0	0	Lee et al. 1969
	100	20	10	
USC	10	0	0	Alfin-Slater et al. 1969
	80	0	0	

toxins (*Alpert* et al., 1968; *Shank* et al., 1972 a, c). For example, a one-year study carried out in two areas of Thailand with a high incidence of primary liver carcinoma, and in a third area with an incidence no higher than that in the USA and Europe, showed that the daily intake rate of aflatoxins with the food was 10 to 14 times as high in the first two areas as in the third, namely, of the order of 70 ng/kg body weight and, in some cases, even over 1000 ng/kg (*Shank*, et al., 1972 b).

It follows that the rate of ingestion of aflatoxins by the inhabitants of the third area studied must be lower than the critical threshold rate.

When assessing the results of animal experiments in terms of health hazards for man, it is necessary to take into consideration not only the dosages but also several other factors which may affect the findings or be relevant to their interpretation. These factors are:

- the dosages used;
- the mode of administration;
- the animal species used;
- the duration of treatment;
- the external experimental conditions;
- the pharmacokinetic and metabolic behaviour of the substances used in the animal species concerned, in comparison with those in man;
- in long-term experiments, the effects

of a possible enzyme induction or enzyme inhibition;
- possible storage in less sensitive tissues of the organism;
- in teratogenicity tests, the time of administration of the substance in relation to the stage of gestation;
- in mutagenicity tests on mammalian systems, the time of the investigation in relation to the end of treatment.

We shall first discuss these factors with the help of some further examples, and we shall then discuss the relevance of animal experiment findings for man with particular reference to dose-effect relationships for some cytotoxic environmental agents.

Dose-effect relationships in teratology

Teratogenic effects are dose-dependent. In testing substances for their teratogenic effects it is necessary, however, to draw a distinction between the toxic effects of the substance concerned on the mother animal, the so-called *maternal toxicity*, and those on the embryo or foetus, the so-called *embryotoxicity*. Only those substances, the embryotoxicity of which is higher than their maternal toxicity, are potentially dangerous from the teratogenic point of view. A classical example of this type of substance is thalidomide.

As far as embryotoxicity is concerned, a

further distinction should be drawn between a *teratogenic effect,* i.e., the induction of malformations and the *embryolethal or foetolethal effect,* i.e., the killing of embryos or foetuses which are then aborted or, in small rodents, usually suffer intra-uterine resorption.

As an example illustrating the dose-dependence of embryotoxic effects we shall discuss the experiments with monomethylformamide, a compound which had earlier been widely used in industry as a solvent.

Monomethylformamide administered to pregnant mice by intraperitoneal injection at a dosage of 0.05 ml/kg/day from the 9th to the 11th, from the 11th to the 13th or from the 13th to the 15th days of gestation inclusive, had no effect on foetal development. A dose of 0.10 ml/kg/day only had a teratogenic effect, manifested by multiple malformations, if it was administered during the most sensitive stage of gestation, namely, between the 11th and the 13th day after conception. Finally, doses of 0.25 mg/kg/day resulted in a loss of weight by the pregnant mice, i.e., had a maternal toxicity effect, and almost all the foetuses were resorbed (Fig. 1).

This series of experiments also shows that the teratogenic effect depends not only on the substance and on the administered dose, but also on the time of administration in relation to the stage of gestation.

Experiments with still lower doses of monomethylformamide showed that even after 10 administrations spread over the entire sensitive stage of gestation the teratogenic effect of this acid amide increased proportionally to the administered dose. By contrast, the herbicide 2,4,5-trichlorophenoxyacetic acid, hereinafter called 2,4,5-T for short, containing less than 0.02 ppm dioxine, caused an increased cleft palate incidence in the offspring only at dosage levels within the maternal toxicity range. It may therefore be stated that, under these experimental conditions, the largely dioxine-free batch of 2,4,5-T which was tested had no teratogenic action (Fig. 2).

The embryotoxic effect of 2,4,5-T is potentiated by dioxine. This requires a minimum concentration of 1.5 ppm dioxine (*Neubert* and *Dillmann,* 1972). Such a

Monomethylformamide (i.p.)

Mouse

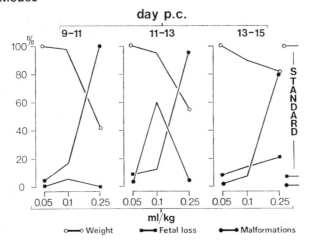

Fig. 1 *Dose and time relationship in teratogenicity trials in mice*

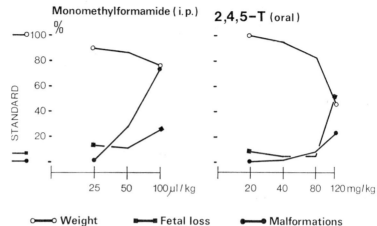

Fig. 2 *Dose response relationship of a strong and a weak teratogenic agent in mice*

potentiation, however, is excluded in practice because, in Germany, 2,4,5-T-containing preparations containing more than 0.1 ppm dioxine are prohibited. It is for this reason that *Roll* (1971), of the Federal Ministry of Health, came to the conclusion that, despite the teratogenic action of 2,4,5-T on some animal species, there is no indication, according to the latest stand of scientific knowledge, of any risk to human embryos and foetuses. *Roll* based his safety calculations on comparing the teratogenic "no effect level" of 20 mg/kg/day found in experiments on the most sensitive animal species (a particularly sensitive mouse strain) with the tolerance limit of 0.05 ppm in cereals laid down in the "Deutsche Höchstmengenverordnung". These considerations are in agreement with findings in man, made in Vietnam, in Globe, Arizona, and in Lapland, luckily all negative.

Lead

Experiments carried out chiefly with inorganic lead compounds showed that these compounds had a teratogenic effect on chicken embryos (*Hammett* and *Wal-*

lace, 1928; *Gray,* 1939; *Catizone* and *Gray,* 1941; *Karnofsky* and *Ridgway,* 1952; *Butt* et al., 1952) and on golden hamsters (*Ferm* and *Carpenter,* 1967; *Ferm* and *Ferm,* 1971) (Table 7), it being noted that the experiments on hamsters entailed intravenous injections of large doses, i.e., a mode of administration at variance with any natural mode of exposure.

In teratogenicity tests on rats, tetraethyl lead caused, even at the lowest doses tested, loss of weight and symptoms of central nervous system poisoning typical of organic lead poisoning. Malformations were not observed, only foetal resorptions and retardation of foetal de-

Table 7 Effect of lead salts on fetal development in Syrian hamsters
Single i. v.-injection on day 8 of pregnancy

Lead salt	Dose mg/kg	Fetal loss (%)	Abnormalities (%)
Lead acetate	50	10	68
Lead chloride	50	5	79
Lead nitrate	25	15	75
Lead nitrate	50	92	8

Table 8 Effect of tetraethyl lead on fetal development in rats. 3 times per os

Dose mg/kg/ day	Gestation days administered	Mortality (%)	Fetal loss (%) *)
Control	9 — 14	0	1.5
2.5	9, 10, 11	0	4
5		0	18.5
10		100	—
2.5	12, 13, 14	0	13.6
5		20	4.5
10		100	—

*) = % of total number of fetuses
   McClain and Becker 1972

velopment, caused by the maternal toxicity of the compound (*McClain and Becker*, 1972) (Table 8).

In infusion experiments with trimethyl lead chloride, this compound crossed the placenta into the foetal compartment only after injection of toxic doses exceeding the binding capacity of the mother's erythrocytes (Fig. 3). This is another reason why embryotoxic effects are unlikely to be caused by organic lead compounds at generally tolerated dosage levels (*McClain* and *Becker*, 1972).

Young of mother mice given toxic doses of lead acetate during the lactation period, of the order of 1200 mg/kg/day admixed to the feed, developed severe damage of the central nervous system (*Rosenblum and Johnson*, 1968). Similar results had been reported in 1915 by C. V. *Weller* after chronic treatment of guinea-pigs with sub-toxic doses of white lead.

Small doses of lead acetate do not affect the reproductive and rearing capabilities of mice. Thus, continuous administration of lead acetate in the drinking water at a dosage of about 200 mg/kg/day for 9 months had no effect on the fertility, gestation, rearing instinct and lactation

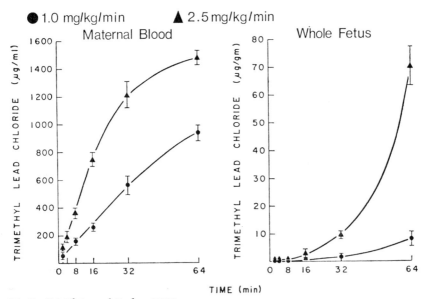

Placental Transfer of trimethyl lead chloride after infusion of

● 1.0 mg/kg/min   ▲ 2.5 mg/kg/min

TIME (min)

Fig. 3 (*McClain and Becker 1972*)

of mother mice, or on the viability of the young (*Leonard* et. al., 1972).
The animal experiment findings confirm the observations on human subjects first reported in 1860 by *Paul*. He had observed numerous abortions by women suffering from chronic lead poisoning, as well as a high rate of infant mortality during the first three years of life. He also discussed a possible connection with chronic lead poisoning of the fathers at the time of conception.

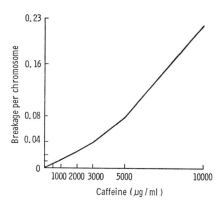

Fig. 5   Breakage induced by Caffeine in HeLa cells (Ostertag, Duisberg et al. 1965)

Dose-effect relationships in mutagenicity

Mutagenic effects are also dose-dependent. Thus, in experiments carried out with triethylene melamine (TEM), the number of dominant lethal mutations increased proportionally to the administered TEM doses. However, 0.035 mg TEM/kg had no mutagenic effect (Fig. 4). This dose was therefore the "no effect level" under the experimental conditions used. Similar dose-effect relationships were also found in dominant lethal mutation tests carried out with other ethylene-imine, nitrogen mustard and sulfonic acid derivatives (*Generoso* et. al., 1972; *Epstein* et al., 1970 a, b, 1972).
As an example of the dose-effect relationship in host mediated assay tests we should mention here experiments carried out with dimethyl nitrosamine. With mice, the mutagenic effect of this compound increased proportionally to the administered dose. The no effect level was at about one-quarter of LD 50 (Table 9).

Fig. 4   (Matter and Generoso 1972)

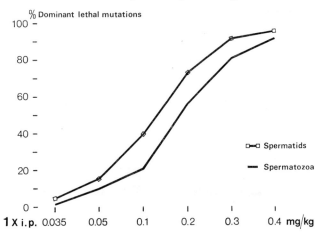

Dominant Lethal Test
with TEM on (101 XC₃H) F₁ Mice ♂

Table 9 Mutagenic action of dimethyl-nitrosamine
Host mediated assay
Indicator bacterium: Salmonella typhimurium G 46 (S 22)
Solvent: Distilled water

Host animal species and strain	Injected volume	Concentration %	Dose mg/kg	Multiple of LD_{50}	Mutation rate
NMRI mice	—	—	—	—	2.18×10^{-8}
	0.1 ml s.c.	0.1	5	x 0.25	2.37×10^{-8}
	per	1.0	50	x 2.5	1.16×10^{-6}
	20 g mouse	10.0	500	x 25	1.55×10^{-6}
Wistar rats	—	—	—	—	1.66×10^{-7}
	1.0 ml s.c.	0.1	10	x 0.25	1.56×10^{-7}
	per	1.0	100	x 2.5	4.4×10^{-7}
	100 g rat	10.0	1000	x 25	8.5×10^{-7}

Hameister and Wahlig 1971

With rats, however, this nitrosamine compound had no definitely positive effect even after injection of doses 25 times as high as the LD 50. This illustrates a difference in species sensitivity, and is a reminder of the fact that the findings obtained by the host mediated assay technique cannot be used uncritically for assessing the hazards for man.

All the in vitro and in vivo cytogenetic investigations carried out at graduated dosage levels have also shown quite clear dose-effect relationships. Thus, for example, the number of chromosome breaks induced in HeLa cell cultures by caffeine was proportional to the caffeine concentration (Fig. 5) and, similarly, the number of aberrant metaphases in the bone marrow of Chinese hamsters, induced by Trenimon®, was proportional to the injected dose (Fig. 6).

It may thus be stated in summary that mutagenicity tests carried out with graduated dosages by the dominant lethal test technique, by the host mediated assay technique and by means of in vitro and in vivo cytogenetic investigations have always shown, firstly, a dose-effect relation and, secondly, a threshold dose below which no genetic aberrations could be detected under the experimental conditions used.

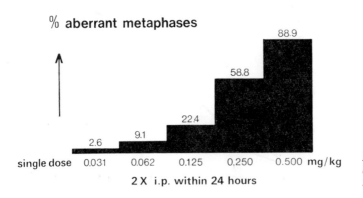

% aberrant metaphases

88.9

58.8

22.4

9.1

2.6

single dose   0.031   0.062   0.125   0.250   0.500 mg/kg

2 X i.p. within 24 hours

Fig. 6   Effect of triaziquone on bone marrow (Chinese hamster) (W. Schmid et al. 71)

Importance of the time at which the investigation is carried out

Optimal time for teratogenicity tests

The thalidomide catastrophe has taught us that the teratogenic action of a substance depends not only on the dose but also on the time of administration. This was a totally new chapter in our understanding of toxic effects.

Thus, for example, it was found that, in mice, the most sensitive stage of gestation in respect of the action of monomethylformamide, a teratogenic compound formerly used in industry as a solvent, is between the 10th and the 13th days after conception. During this period single large doses result in foetal death whereas smaller doses result in multiple malformations. The same doses administered before or after this period have no effect on foetal development (Fig. 7).

Similar observations were made on all other animal species used in teratogenicity experiments.

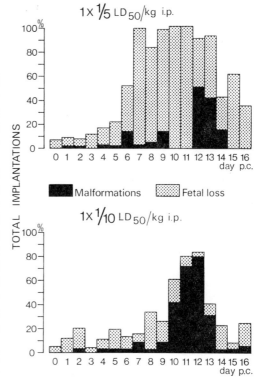

Fig. 7 Teratogenic activity of N-monomethyl-formamide in mice

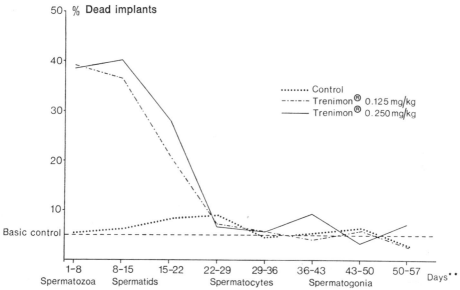

Fig. 8 Dominant lethal test in NMRI mice. * = Sacrifice of untreated mothers between day 10 and 16 p. c. ** = After single i. p. treatment of males

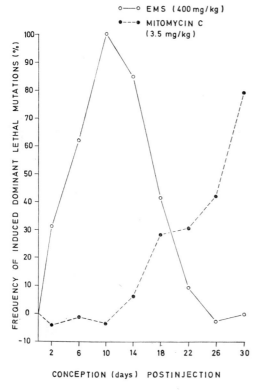

Fig. 9   *Induction of dominant lethal mutations in (101 x C₃H) F₁ mice. Single i. p. injection (Ehling 1971)*

Optimal time for mutagenicity tests

The time elapsed between administration and testing is also decisive for the results of various mutagenicity tests on mammals. Thus, several alkylating agents such as, for example, triaziquone (Fig. 8) or ethyl-methane-sulfonate, cause dominant lethal mutations only in spermatozoa and spermatids. On the other hand there are also compounds such as, for example, mito-mycin C (Fig. 9), which exert a mutagenic action on the prospermatids and primary spermatocytes (*Ehling* 1971).

The data on the optimal time for chromosome preparation after the last dose of the substance being tested also differ. Thus, with Chinese hamsters, the optimum time for testing the mutagenicity of cyclophosphamide and Trenimon® is apparently 6 to 8 hours after administration of the substance (*Schmid* et al., 1971), whereas for dimethylbenzanthracene this time is 144 hours (*Kato* et al., 1969). With mice these optimum testing times are 24 hours for cyclophosphamide, and 48 to 72 hours for 6-mercaptopurine (Table 10). In mice, not only the largest number of

Table 10   Time of maximum aberration rate after compound administration. In vivo cytogenetics: Bone marrow method

Animal species	Compound	Dose mg/kg		Maximum activity hours after administration	References
Chinese hamster	Cyclophosphamide	2 x 64	p. o.	8*	Schmid et al. 1971
	Trenimon (R)	2 x 0.25	i. p.	6*	Schmid et al. 1971
	6-Mercaptopurine	1 x 250	i. p.	48	Frohberg and Bauer 1972
	7,12-DMBA	1 x 4.	i. p.+	144	Kato et al. 1969
Rat	Rubidomycin	1 x 5	i. p.	24	Jensen and Philip 1971
	6-Mercaptopurine	1 x 250	i. p.	48	Frohberg and Schulze Schencking 1973
Mouse	Cyclophosphamide	1 x 200	i. p.	24	Datta and Schleiermacher 1969
	6-Mercaptopurine	1 x 250	i. p.	48	Frohberg and Bauer 1972

+ = μm/animal
* = hours after last administration

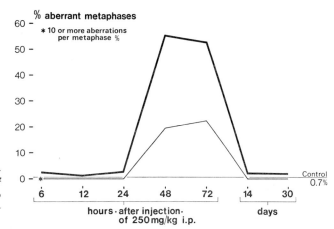

Fig. 10 Time of maximum aberration rate after i.p. injection of 6-mercaptopurine in mice. In vivo cytogenetics: Bone marrow method

chromosomal aberrations but also the most severe aberration types and the largest number of metaphases with multiple aberrations are found 48 to 72 hours after injection of 6-mercaptopurine (Fig. 10).

The optimum time for the investigations is thus determined by the animal species used, by the kind of cells to be examined and by the substance to be tested, because the effect depends on the cell cycle and on the pharmacokinetic behaviour of the foreign substance.

Influence of the mode of administration

Similarly to the principles followed in the testing of drugs or of pesticides, the testing of potential environmental noxae should be based on modes of administration corresponding to the possible modes of human exposure to these noxae, i.e., experimental testing should be limited to administration of these foreign substances by the oral, the dermal or the inhalation routes.

This rule is particularly important in carcinogenicity tests aimed at assessing the potential hazard presented by a given foreign substance. Modes of administration which do not correspond to possible modes of human exposure, and which may result in false positive reactions, should therefore be avoided. This applies in particular to the formerly widely used technique of repeated injections into the subcutis of small rodents, mostly in the same location, and to subcutaneous implantation of solid implants, also with small rodents.

Inappropriate modes of administration may also result in false positive embryo-

Table 11 DOCA. Influence on fetal development of NMRI-mice. 10 times repeated administration from day 6 – 15 p. c.

Single Dose mg/kg	Fetalmortality	Malformationrate %
Laboratory standard value	9.0	1.2
Intraperitoneal		
Control	19.8	2.7
5.0	64.3	2.8
10.0	42.7	2.0
Intramuscular		
Control	11.6	1.7
5.0	5.9	2.9
10.0	12.3	2.8
50.0	9.6	1.8

% = referred to implantations

toxic findings in teratogenicity tests. Thus, for example, repeated intraperitoneal injections of the mineralocorticoid DOCA, which is known with certainty to be non-embryotoxic for humans, resulted in abortions in most experimental animals. The correct mode of administration for DOCA is by intramuscular injection. When this correct technique was used in animal experiments, DOCA was found to have no effect on embryonal development (Table 11).

Differences in the sensitivity of various animals and man to foreign substances

The differences in the sensitivity of different animal species, and of man, to various foreign substances are due to the following reasons:

Firstly, to differences in the inherent sensitivity of the target organs to various exogenous noxae in different animal species;

Secondly, to differences in the absorption, distribution and excretion of foreign substances by different animal species. As a result, noxious foreign substances may reach the target organ or organs in a chemically altered form, or in a high or low concentration owing to slow or rapid detoxication and excretion, or possibly not at all.

The main causes of interspecific differences in sensitivity to exogenous noxae are therefore differences in the pharmacokinetics and in the metabolism. For this reason, as in the case of drugs, toxicological testing of potential environmental poisons should be carried out on animal species whose absorption, metabolism and excretion of these foreign substances are as similar as possible to those of man. In this field, however, there still remains a large amount of work to be done because

we know as yet little or nothing on the metabolism of most potentially noxious substances found in our environment, or even of many of the industrial compounds which we have been using for decades.

The differences in the sensitivity of various animal species to aflatoxin, the most potent carcinogenic agent known so far, have been pointed out already. In this particular instance, however, it should be noted that all animals, including man, develop liver cancer after contact with aflatoxin, the only interspecific difference thus being in the threshold dose required. This is not necessarily the case with other carcinogenic or teratogenic compounds. Thus, in man, chronic arsenic poisoning may lead to skin and lung cancer, and chronic benzene poisoning may lead to leukaemia, i.e., blood cancer. Neither substance, however, depeloped a carcinogenic action in any relevant chronic animal experiments under conditions comparable to possible human modes of exposure.

Another example of interspecific differences is presented by thalidomide, which is certainly teratogenic for man.

Thalidomide caused multiple malformations in certain rabbit strains, and even more so in certain primate species, whereas the results obtained with mice and rats were conflicting, even at doses very much higher than those formerly used clinically. On the other hand the folic acid antagonists aminopterin and amethopterin, also known to be teratogenic for man, were found to be teratogenic for small rodents and rabbits, but not for monkeys. Conversely, acetylsalicylic acid, which is certainly not teratogenic for man, caused malformations in small rodents and also in monkeys.

Glucocorticoids are another example of this kind from the drug sector. These compounds are not teratogenic for man, the malformation incidence of 2.6% re-

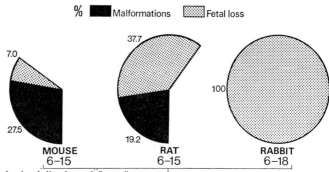

Fig. 11   Teratogenic activity of dexamethasone

corded after high dosage glucocorticoid therapy during pregnancy being within the scatter range of the spontaneous malformation rate for man. These compounds are teratogenic, however, for certain mouse, rat and rabbit strains. In these experiments rabbits, and especially mice, were found to be more sensitive than rats (Fig. 11).

Mice, followed by hamsters, are the two species most sensitive to the teratogenic action of 2,4,5-T. There are, however, no indications that 2,4,5-T with a low

Table 12   Teratogenic activity of 2,4,5-T

Species	Dioxin content	
	< 0.5 ppm	> 0.5 ppm
mouse	±	+
rat	$\emptyset$	±
hamster	+	+
rabbit	—	$\emptyset$
sheep	—	$\emptyset$
reindeer	—	$\emptyset$
monkey	$\emptyset$	$\emptyset$
man	—	$\emptyset$

Collins et al. 1971 a, b
Courtney et al. 1970, 1971
Emerson et al. 1971
Epstein 1970 b
Neubert et al. 972
Reports on 2,4,5-T, 1971 a, b
Sparschu et al. 1971 a, b
Wilson 1972

dioxine content can induce malformations in any other species, including monkeys and man (Table 12).

Geneticists working at Lund expressed in 1971 the suspicion, based on experiments carried out on mice and on Drosophila melanogaster, that 2,4,5-T has a mutagenic action (*Dävring* and *Sunner*, 1971; *Dävring,* 1971, unpublished). However, in experiments on bacteria and in host mediated assay and dominant lethal mutation tests, 2,4,5-T with varying contents of dioxine was found to have no mutagenic action after single intraperitoneal or oral administration or after repeated oral doses (Table 13, 14) (*Buselmaier et al.,* 1972; *Roll,* 1971 a). These negative experimental findings are in agreement with the available records on man. For example, in a group of 52 workers in a 2,4,5-T manufacturing plant, who had been exposed for up to 3 years to 2,4,5-T concentrations corresponding to an intake rate of between 1600 and 8100 mcg/day, the incidence of structural or numerical chromosomal aberrations in the peripheral lymphocytes was no higher than that in a control group of subjects without a history of exposure to 2,4,5-T. Such high 2,4,5-T concentrations in the air are not reached with the use of 2,4,5-T in practice.

The concentrations measured in the use of 2,4,5-T in practice are of the order of

Table 13   2,4,5-T "Mutagenicity"

In vitro studies	
Bacteria	$\emptyset$
Drosophila	+
Host mediated assay	$\emptyset$
In vivo studies	
Dominant lethal test	$\emptyset$
Cytogenetic studies	
in mouse	(+)
in man	$\emptyset$

Table 14   Dominant lethal test with 2,4,5-T in mice

Dose level mg/kg/day	Dioxin content (ppm)	Result	Authors
intraperitoneal			
1 x 100	0.02	$\emptyset$	Buselmaier et al. 1972
per os			
1 x 100	0.05	$\emptyset$	Roll 1971
7 x 150	0.05	$\emptyset$	
10 x 100	1.1	$\emptyset$	

only 0.06 mcg/m³ air. Assuming that a person breathes in about 30 m³ air per day, this concentration corresponds to a 2,4,5-T intake rate of 1.8 mcg/day (*Johnson*, 1970, in the Report on 2,4,5-T submitted to the US Department of Agriculture on 25. 2. 1971).

The 2,4,5-T intake rates to which the aforementioned workers in the 2,4,5-T manufacturing plant had been exposed for a long time, and for which no cytogenetic changes were found, were thus 900 to 4500 times higher than those to which the general population might possibly be exposed. It follows surely that 2,4,5-T presents no genetic hazard for man.

We shall now discuss, on individual examples, whether or not certain other foreign substances in the environment, which have been found mutagenic in some

animal experiments, present a genetic hazard for man at the relevant concentrations.

Lead

Lead acetate caused no manifest chromosomal changes in Chinese hamster cell cultures, whereas in human lymphocyte cultures some findings were positive and some negative (*Obe* and *Sperling*, 1970; *Bauchinger* and *Schmid*, 1972; *Schmid* et al., 1972).

After mice were treated orally for two weeks with a toxic dose of lead acetate of 1200 mg/kg/day, a raised incidence of chromosomal aberrations was found in the bone marrow. However, in mice which had been given lead acetate in the drinking water at a rate of about 200 mg/kg/day for 9 months, the chromosomal aberration rates in the bone marrow and in the spermatocytes were within the normal range (*Leonard* et al., 1972).

A comparison of these two in vivo cytogenetic experiments and of dominant lethal mutation tests (*Kennedy* and *Arnold*, 1971) shows that genetic aberrations were only induced by toxic lead doses, whereas doses which were tolerated by the animals caused no mutagenic effects (Table 15).

Lead-induced chromosomal damage was reported for the first time in 1970 in a group of 8 workers in a lead oxide plant, whose mean blood lead level was 74.7 mcg/100 ml (*Schwanitz* et al., 1970). Raised rates of structural and numerical chromosomal aberrations, in comparison with those in control groups, were also found in 15 further subjects occupationally exposed to lead and presenting biochemically demonstrable signs of damage, and in almost all workers with clinically manifest lead intoxication. By contrast, no chromosomal abnormalities were found in

Table 15   Mutagenicity studies with lead acetate and tetraethyl lead in mice
Route of administration: per os

Compound	Dose level mg/kg/day	in vivo cytogenetics			dominant lethal test	Authors
		duration of treatment (days)	bone marrow	spermato-cytes		
Lead	1200	14	+	—	—	Muro and Goyer 1969
acetate		60	—	—	∅	Kennedy and Arnold 1971
	207	280	∅	∅	—	Leonard et al. 1972
	73	5	—	—	∅	Kennedy and Arnold 1971
Tetraethyl	32 (toxic)	1	—	—	∅	Kennedy and Arnold 1971
lead	6.5	1	—	—	∅	Kennedy and Arnold 1971

+ = positive
∅ = negative
— = not examined

subjects who had overcome a chronic lead poisoning (Table 16), or in lead workers, dustmen, street cleaners and traffic policemen whose blood lead levels were within the normal range (Table 17), this being defined as 15 to 40 mcg/100 ml blood, with a mean of 17 mcg/100 ml (*Goldwater* and *Hoover, 1967*).
The so-called "7 City Study" has shown that no blood lead levels outside the normal range were found in persons living in areas with lead concentrations in the air of between 0.17 and 3.39 mcg/m³ (Fig. 12).

It is highly probable that, in man, lead-induced chromosomal changes occur only after long periods of the blood lead level being raised over 70 mcg/100 ml. It may therefore be assumed that the lead content of the air in our cities presents no genetic hazard for the population. This assumption is also supported by the findings of experiments carried out on volunteers in whom, despite 4 months of continuous exposure to a lead concentration in the air of 10.9 mcg/m³, the blood lead levels only rose to about 35 mcg/100 ml and then returned to the starting values after

Table 16   Chromosomal damage after occupational exposure to lead

	Number of workers			
	Peripheral lymphocytes		Bone marrow	
	positive	negative	positive	negative
without intoxication	0	69	—	—
preclinical intoxication	23	0	—	—
with intoxication	38	3	0	10
18 months after intoxication	0	13	—	—

— = not examined

Bauchinger et al.   1972
Forni and Secchi   1972
Gäth and Thiess   1972
Obe and Sperling   1970
Schmid et al.   1972
Schwanitz et al.   1970

Table 17   Correlation between blood lead concentration and chromosomal damage in humans

Profession	Number	Blood lead μg/100 ml	Chromo-somal damage	Authors
Traffic policemen	29	17.3	∅	Schmidt et al. 1972 Bauchinger et al. 1972
Dustmen and scavenger	152	26.0	—	Lehnert et al. 1970
Industrial }	1	59.0	∅	Schmid et al. 1972
lead workers }	8	74.7	+	Schwanitz et al. 1970

— = not examined, ∅ = negative, + = positive

the end of the exposure period (*Cole* and *Lynam*, 1972) (Fig. 13).

To reinforce this assumption still further, especially with respect to children who are more sensitive to lead than adults, it would be desirable to carry out more intensive cytogenetic studies in connection with the lead tolerance studies being conducted since 1968 in the Meza river valley in Yugoslavia, mainly on women and children, i.e., on persons not occupationally exposed to lead. The reason for this suggestion is that in the Meza valley, because of the presence of modern lead and zinc smelting works, the lead concentration in the air is substantially higher than that in our large cities (*Graovac-Leposavic* et al., 1972).

Despite the fact that benign and malignant kidney tumours have been induced in rats by chronic administration of high, mostly toxic, doses of lead acetate and lead phosphate (Table 18), there are no indications that lead or its compounds have a carcinogenic action on man.

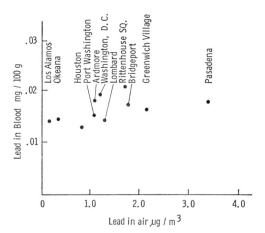

Fig. 12   Lack of a relationship between air lead concentration and blood lead concentration in different US-cities (Cole and Lynam 1972)

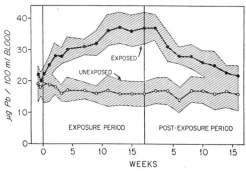

Fig. 13   Mean concentration of lead in the blood of eight volunteers who remained in the study throughout a four month exposure period and 16 week post exposure period (Cole and Lynam 1972)

Table 18   Carcinogenic activity of lead salts in animals

Species	Compound	Dose	Route	Tumor localisation	Reference
Calf	Lead acetate	1 — 3 g/day	p. o.	$\emptyset$	Beijers 1952
Rat	Lead acetate	0.1 %	diet	kidney	van Esch et al. 1962
	Lead acetate	1.0 %	diet	kidney	Boyland et al. 1962
	Lead phosphate	20 mg once a week	s. c.	kidney	Zollinger 1953
	Lead carbonate	10 mg/day	diet	$\emptyset$	} Fairhall and Miller 1941
	Lead arsenate	10 mg/day	diet	$\emptyset$	

Benzene

The situation with benzene is different. It is known that massive and intensive exposure to benzene over several years may induce not only aplastic bone marrow damage and aplastic anaemias and panmyelopathies but also leucoses.

However, besides a prolonged and massive exposure to benzene, this requires individual sensitivity and possibly also additional exogenous factors such as, for example, infections or chronic drug abuse (Fig. 14).

For example, of a total of 154 workers who had been exposed to benzene for 8.9 years on average between 1950 and 1960, only 3 developed aplastic bone marrow disorders, and only 1 developed a neo-plastic bone marrow disorder. Local measurements at specific working locations showed benzene concentrations of between 16 and 1264 ppm (*Loskant*, 1972, personal communication).

Benzene-induced chromosomal changes in man were first observed in 1964 in subjects who had withstood a benzene intoxication (*Pollini* and *Colombi*, 1964 a, b).

According to all the studies published so far, raised rates of chromosomal aberrations in the lymphocytes have been found in all the patients suffering from chronic benzene poisoning, and in about 50% of subjects with a history of exposure to benzene but without clinical poisoning manifestations, on whom cytogenetic investigations were carried out

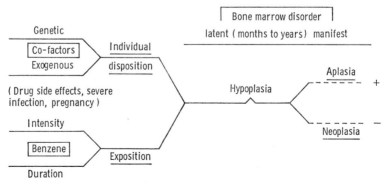

Fig. 14   Genesis and course of benzene-induced myelopathy (Merker 1962)

Table 19 Correlation between benzene atmosphere concentration and chromosomal damage in peripheral lymphocytes of workers

	Benzene concentration (ppm)	Number of workers with chromosomal damage	without chromosomal damage
without intoxication	‹ 15	0	26
	‹ 25	9	0
	25 – 150	32	12
	125 – 532	2	0
	not measured	24	0
with intoxication	‹ 25	2	0
	200 – 1640	1	0
	not measured	28	0
years after intoxication	‹ 15	0	4
	125 – 532	5	3
	not measured	5	0

Forni and Moreo 1967
Forni and Moreo 1969
Forni et al. 1971
Gäth and Thiess 1972
Hartwich et al. 1969
Hartwich and Schwanitz 1972
Khan and Khan 1973
Manu and Popescu 1972
Mente 1970
Pollini and Colombi 1964 a
Pollini and Colombi 1964 b
Pollini et al. 1964
Pollini et al. 1969
Sellyei and Kelemen 1971
Tough et al. 1970
Vigliani and Forni 1966

(Table 19). It might therefore appear that benzene is capable of inducing chromosomal changes not only at high but also at low concentrations. However, scrutiny of the benzene concentrations to which workers, on whom in vivo cytogenetic investigations were carried out, had been exposed, shows that no chromosomal changes have been detected so far in cases in which the benzene concentrations in the air were lower than 15 ppm (Table 19). Excluding concurrent absorption through the skin, chromosomal changes have been found only after many years of exposure on premises with high benzene concentrations in the air.

The few relevant findings available so far thus indicate that a raised incidence of structural and numerical chromosomal aberrations in subjects exposed to benzene may be considered as a sign of a threatening benzene poisoning owing to massive exposure, whereas slight exposure to benzene is unlikely to induce chromosomal changes.

Caffeine

It has often been postulated that, being a purine base, caffeine can become incorporated into the DNA molecule instead of adenine or guanine, and may thus exert a mutagenic effect. The damaging effect of caffeine on plant chromosomes was first reported in 1949 (*Kihlman* and *Levan*, 1949; *Kihlman*, 1952). Caffeine also exerts a mutagenic effect on bacteria and to some extent on Drosophila melanogaster.

Positive results were also obtained in cytogenetic investigations in vitro on Chinese hamster and HeLa cell cultures (*Ostertag, Duisberg* and *Stürman*, 1965; *Bishun, Williams* and Raven, 1973). The addition of 0.25 mg/ml caffeine to human lymphocyte cultures also caused chromosome breaks (*Weinstein* et al., 1972). By contrast, the findings of in vivo cytogenetic investigations on volunteers, who had been given 800 mg caffeine daily for a month, were negative (Table 20). The blood caffeine levels of these test subjects rose by the end of four weeks to 1.3 mg/100 ml (= 0.013 mg/ml) on average, and in only one case to 3.0 mg/100 ml (= 0.03 mg/ml). Even this high blood concentration, however, had no mutagenic effect on human lymphocytes in vitro.

Table 20   Cytogenetic studies with caffeine

In vitro			In vivo		
Dose mg/ml	Type of cells	Result	Dose mg/kg	Type of cells	Result
0.049 and more	chinese hamster cells	+	351 x 1200.0	mouse spermatocytes	ϕ
0.080 and more	HeLa	+			
0.030	{ human	ϕ	28 x 13.0	human lymphocytes	ϕ
0.250 and more	{ lymphocytes	+			

10 cups of coffee contain 900 mg Caffeine $\approx$ 15 mg Caffeine/kg corresponding to a level of appr. 0.013 mg/ml blood in humans. Half life time: 3.5 hours

Kihlmann et al. 1971
Bishun et al. 1973
Weinstein et al. 1972

Adler and Röhrborn 1969
Adler 1970, 1966
Timson 1972
Axelrod et al. 1953

Germ cells were found to be even less sensitive to caffeine than somatic cells. Thus, no increase in the incidence of chromosomal aberrations was found in the spermatocytes of mice kept for one year on drinking water containing 0.5% caffeine, a dosage level corresponding to about 1200 mg/kg/day. The insensitivity of germ cells to damage by caffeine is further illustrated by the negative results of acute and chronic dominant lethal mutation tests on various mouse strains (Table 21), and of specific locus mutation tests on mice (Lyon et al., 1962; Russell et al., 1968). Caffeine also failed to induce gene mutations in host-mediated assays (Legator, 1970).

It may thus be stated in summary that caffeine in high concentrations in vitro can induce chromosomal changes in bac-

Table 21   Dominant lethal tests in mice with caffeine

Single intraperitoneal injection

Dose (mg/kg)	Results
200	ϕ
240	ϕ

Repeated oral administration

Concentration (%) in drinking-water	mg/kg/day	Duration of treatment (days)	Results
0.0023	5.6	245	ϕ
0.01	24.0	245	ϕ
0.1	240.0	56	ϕ
0.5	1200.0	245 and 351	ϕ

Adler 1966, 1968, 1970
Adler and Röhrborn 1969
Epstein 1970

Table 22   Caffeine "Mutagenicity"

In vitro studies	
Bacteria	+
Plants	+
Drosophila	±
Cytogenetic studies	+
Host mediated assay	ϕ
In vivo studies	
Dominant lethal test	ϕ
Cytogenetic studies	ϕ
Specific locus test	ϕ

teria, and plants and, to some extent, in Drosophila and in animal and human tissue culture (Table 22). In all the in vivo investigations, however, carried out so far on man and other mammals, as well as in specific locus mutation tests, caffeine was found to have no mutagenic action (*Adler*, 1970; *Epstein*, 1970; *Röhrborn*, 1972; *Vogel*, 1970).

These studies thus prove that the daily consumption of 10 or more cups of coffee presents no genetic hazard to man. These studies also clearly illustrate the fact that it is neither possible nor permissible to draw from positive in vitro test findings conclusions regarding in vivo hazards for mammals, and even less so for man. This was pointed out in 1971 by the WHO Expert Commission (WHO Techn. Rep. Ser. No. 482, 1971).

DDVP (Dichlorphos)

It is for this reason, despite positive in vitro findings with DDVP on certain bacterial strains (*Voogd* et al., 1972; *Löfroth* et al., 1969), and despite the known alkylating properties of this compound, that the investigators of the National Institute of Public Health in Bilthoven, Holland, came in 1972 to the following conclusion:

"In our opinion the increases of mutation frequency induced by Dichlorphos during our experiments are insufficient for the compound to be regarded as dangerously mutagenic to man" (*Voogd* et al., 1972).

Despite this body of scientific data, statements were published in some of our newspapers early in 1973 to the effect that all further sales of household insecticides containing DDVP should be stopped as a precautionary measure because DDVP has a mutagenic effect on bacteria. Such a sweeping judgment is scientifically unfounded, because the correctness of the

Table 23   DDVP "Mutagenicity"

In vitro studies	
Bacteria	±
Neurospora crassa	φ
Yeast	φ
Cytogenetic studies	φ
Host mediated assay	φ
In vivo studies	
Dominant lethal test	φ
Cytogenetic studies	φ

Table 24   Dominant lethal test in mice with DDVP by inhalation

DDVP-atmosphere (µg/l)	Results
Single inhalation study	
1 x 30 ⎫	φ
1 x 55 ⎬ for 16 hours	φ
Multiple inhalation study	
28 x 2.1 ⎫	φ
28 x 5.8 ⎬ for 23 hours a day	φ

B. J. Dean and E. Thorpe 1972 b

opinion of the Dutch National Institute of Public Health has since been confirmed by experimental proof of the absence of mutagenic effects of DDVP on some bacterial strains, Neurospora crassa and yeasts, and in cytogenetic in vitro studies on human lymphocyte cultures. DDVP also had no mutagenic effects in host mediated assay tests using mice as the host animals and 2 bacterial strains, namely Salmonella typhimurium G 46 and Serratia marcescens (*Buselmaier* et al., 1972) as well as the yeast strain Saccharomyces cerevisiae strain D 4, despite oral administration of 100 mg/kg, subcutaneous injection of 25 mg/kg or inhalation of 99 mcg/litre of Dichlorphos for 5 hours (Table 23) (*Dean* et al., 1972). In dominant lethal mutation tests on male

Table 25   In vivo cytogenetic studies with DDVP by inhalation in mice and Chinese hamsters

Species	DDVP-atmosphere µg/l	Results	
		Bone marrow	Testis
	Single Inhalation Study		
Chinese hamsters	1 x 32 ⎫ for 16 hours	∅	∅
Mice	1 x 72 ⎭	∅	∅
	Multiple Inhalation Study		
Mice	21 x 5 for 23 hours a day	∅	∅

B. J. Dean and E. Thorpe 1972 a

mice DDVP was also negative after single or repeated inhalation exposures throughout the 8-week mating period (*Dean* and *Thorpe,* 1972 b) (Table 24).

In cytogenetic in vivo studies on mice after single or repeated oral administration or inhalation of sub-toxic doses (Table 25), DDVP also failed to induce in the bone marrow or in the testicles a higher incidence of chromosomal aberrations than that found in the controls (*Dean* and *Thorpe,* 1972 a).

When the DDVP strips are used indoors at a density of 1 strip per 30 m³ enclosed space, the average DDVP concentration in the air amounts to 0.04 mcg/litre 1 to 2 weeks after affixing the strips, and drops to 0.01 mcg/litre within 3 months. The DDVP concentrations used in the long-term in vivo cytogenetic studies and in the corresponding dominant lethal mutation tests were thus 100 times higher, and those used in the corresponding acute experiments were 1000 times higher, than the DDVP concentrations in the air in enclosed spaces under practical conditions (*Elgar* and *Steer,* 1972).

It follows that the correct use of DDVP strips does not entail any hazards of genetic damage for man.

References

Adler, I.-D.: Humangenetik *3*, 82 (1966)

Adler, I.-D.: In: Vogel and Röhrborn: Chemical Mutagenesis in Mammals and Man. Springer Verlag, Berlin - Heidelberg - New York 1970., p. 383

Adler, I.-D. and Röhrborn, G.: Humangenetik *8*, 81 (1969)

Alfin-Slater, B., Aftergood, L., Hernandez, H. J., Stern, E., Melnick, D.: J. Am. Oil Chemists Soc. *46*, 493 (1969)

Alpert, M. E., Davidson, C. S.: Am. J. Med. *46*, 325 (1969)

Alpert, M. E., Wogan, G., Davidson, C. S.: Gastroenterology *54*, 149 (1968)

Axelrod, J., Reichenthal, J.: J. Pharm. Exp. Therap. *107*, 519 (1953)

Bauchinger, M., Schmid, E.: Mutation Res. *14*, 95 (1972)

Bauchinger, M., Schmid, E. and Schmidt, D.: Mutation Res. *16*, 407 (1972)

Beijers, J. A.: Tijdschr. Diergeneesk. *77*, 587 (1952)

Bishun. N. P., Williams, D. C., Raven, R. W.: Mutation Res. *17*, 145 (1973)

Bohlig, H., Jacob, G., Müller, H.: Die Asbestose der Lungen. Genese, Klinik, Röntgenologie. 1. Aufl. Verlag G. Thieme, Stuttgart 1960

Boyland, E., Dukes, C. E., Grover, P. L., Mitschley, B. C. V.: Brit. J. Cancer *16*, 283 (1962)

Bridge, J. C.: Annual Report of the Chief Inspector of Factories and Workshops for the Year 1932 Her Majesty's Stat. Off., London 1933, p. 103

Buselmaier, W., Röhrborn, G., Propping, P.: Biol. Zbl. *91*, 311 (1972)

Butt, E. M., Pearson, H. E., Simonsen, D. G.: Proc. Soc. exp. Biol. Med. *79*, 247 (1952)

Catizone, O., Gray, P.: J. exp. Zool. (Philadelphia) 87, 71 (1941)

Churg, J.: Geographical Pathology of Mesothelioma. "Asbestosis Course", New York City, 15.–18. 7. 1970, cit: Woitowitz 1972

McClain, R. M., Becker, B. A.: Toxicol. appl. Pharmacol. 21, 265 (1972)

Cole, J. F., Lynam, D. R.: ILZRO's Research to define lead's impact on man. International Symposium: Environmental Health Aspects of Lead, Amsterdam, October 2–6, 1972

Collins, T. F. X., Williams, C. H.: Teratology 4, 229 (1971 a)

Collins, T. F. X., Williams, C. H.: Bull. Environm. Contamin. Toxicol. 6, 559 (1971 b)

Courtney, K. D., Gaylor, D. W., Hogan, M. D., Falk, H. L., Bates, R. R., Mitchell, I.: Science 168, 864 (1970)

Courtney, K. D., Moore, J. A.: Toxicol. appl. Pharmacol. 20, 396 (1971)

Dävring, L.: unpublished, 1971

Dävring, L., Sunner, M.: Hereditas 68, 115 (1971)

Datta, P. K., Schleiermacher, E.: Mutation Res. 8, 623 (1969)

Dean, B. J., Thorpe, E.: Arch. Toxikol. 30, 39 (1972 a)

Dean, B. J., Thorpe, E.: Arch. Toxikol. 30, 51 (1972 b)

Dean, B. J., Doak, S. M. A., Funnell, J.: Arch. Toxikol. 30, 61 (1972)

Doll, R.: Brit. J. ind. Med. 12, 81 (1955)

Ehling, U. H.: Mutation Res. 11, 35 (1971)

Elgar, K. E., Steer, B. D.: Pesticide Sci. (in press), cit: Dean and Thorpe 1972 a, b

Emerson, J. L., Thompson, D. J., Strebing, R. J., Gerbig, C. G., Robinson, V. B.: Fd Cosmet. Toxicol. 9, 395 (1971)

Epstein, S.: In: Vogel and Röhrborn: Chemical Mutagenesis in Mammals and Man. Springer Verlag, Berlin - Heidelberg - New York 1970, p. 404

Epstein, S.: U. S. Congress: Statement before the Subcommittee on Energy, Natural Resources and the Environment of the Committee on Commerce. April 15, 1970 b.

Epstein, S. S., Arnold, E., Andrea, J., Bass, W., Bishop, Y. Toxicol. appl. Pharmacol. 23, 288 (1972)

Epstein, S. S., Arnold, E., Steinberg, K., MackIntosh, D.: Shafner, H., Bishop, Y.: Toxicol. appl. Pharmacol. 17, 23 (1970 a)

Epstein, S. S., Bass, W., Arnold, E., Bishop, Y.: Science 168, 384 (1970 b)

van Esch, S. J., van Senedren, H., Vink, H. H.: Brit. J. Cancer 16, 289 (1962)

Fairhall, L. T., Miller, J. W.: Pub. Health Rep. 56, 1610 (1941)

Ferm, V. H., Carpenter, S. J.: Exp. Molec. Path. 7, 208 (1967)

Ferm, V. H., Ferm, D. W.: Life Sciences 10/II, 35 (1971)

Forni, A., Pacifico, E., Limonta, A.: Arch. Environm. Hlth 22, 373 (1971)

Forni, A. and Moreo, L.: Europ. J. Cancer 3, 251–255 (1967)

Forni, A. and Moreo, L.: Europ. J. Cancer 5, 459–463 (1969)

Forni, A., Secchi, G. C.: I. Intern. Symposium der Werksärzte der chemischen Industrie, Ludwigshafen 27.–29. 4. 1972

Frohberg, H., Bauer, A.: Arzneim.-Forsch. 23, 230 (1973)

Frohberg, H., Schulze Schencking, M.: Unpublished, 1973

Gaensler, E. A., Addington, W. W.: New Engl. J. Med. 280, 488 (1969)

Gäth, J., Thiess, A. M.: Zbl. Arbeitsmed. Arbeitsschutz 22, 357 (1972)

Gardner, L. U., Heslington, H. T.: Fed. Proc. 5, 221 (1946)

Generoso, W. M., Russell, W. L., Huff, S. W., Stout, S. K.: 2nd Ann. Meet. Europ. Environm. Mutagen Soc., Zinkovy Castle, Pilsen, May 10–12, 1972 Mutation Res. 21, 32 (1973)

Goldwater, L., Hoover, A. W.: Arch. Environm. Hlth 15, 60 (1967)

Gopalan, C., Tulpule, P. G., Krishnamurthi, D.: Fd Cosmet. Toxicol. 10, 519 (1972)

Graovac-Leposavic, L., Djuric, D., Valjarevic, V., Senicar, H., Senicar, L., Milic, S., Delic, V.: Intern. Symposium: Environmental Health Aspects of Lead, Amsterdam, October 2–6, 1972

Gray, P.: Arch. Entwicklungsmech. 139, 732 (1939)

Gross, E.: Z. angew. Chem. 53, 368 (1940)

Hameister, W., Wahlig, H.: unpublished, 1971

Hammett, F. S., Wallace, V. L.: J. exp. Med. 48, 659 (1928)

Hartwich, G., Schwanitz, G.: Dt. Med. Wschr. 97, 45 (1972)

Hartwich, G., Schwanitz, G., Becker, J.: Dt. Med. Wschr. 94, 1228 (1969)

Hueper, W. C., Wiley, F. H., Wolfe, H. D.: J. Indust. Hyg. 20, 46–84 (1938)

Hueper, W. C.: Texas Rep. in Biol. a. Med. 10, 167 (1952)

Hueper, W. C.: Arch. Ind. Health 18, 284 (1958)

Jacob, G., Bohlig, H.: Arch. Gewerbepath. 14, 10 (1955)

Jensen, M. K., Philip, P.: Mutation Res. 12, 91 (1971)

Johnson, J. E.: cit: Report on Status of Knowledge Regarding 2, 4, 5-T, submitted by U.S. Department of Agriculture, 25. 2. 1971

Karnofsky, D. A., Ridgway, L. P.: J. Pharmacol. exp. Therap. 104, 176 (1952)

Kato, R., Bruze, M., Tegner, Y.: Hereditas 61, 1 (1969)

Kennedy, G. L., Arnold, D. W.: EMS News Letter 5, 37 (1971)

Khan, H. and Khan, M. H.: Arch. Toxikol. 31, 39–49 (1973)

Kihlmann, B. A.: Symbolae Bot. Upsalienses 11 (4): 1 (1952 a)

Kihlmann, B. A.: Hereditas 38, 115 (1952 b)

Kihlmann, B. A.: Mutation Res. 12, 463 (1971)

Kihlmann, B. A., Levan, A. Hereditas 35, 109 (1949)

Knox, J. F., Holmes, S., Doll, R., Hill, I. D.: Brit. J. ind. Med. 25, 293 (1968)

Lancaster, M. C.: Cancer Res. 28, 2288 (1968)

Lancaster, M. C., Jenkins, F. P., Philip, J. M.: Nature 192, 1095 (1961)

Lee, D., Wales, J. H., Ayres, J. L., Sinnhuber, R. O.: Cancer Res. 28, 2312 (1968)

Lee, D. J., Wales, J. H., Sinnhuber, R. O.: J. Nat. Cancer Inst. 43, 1037 (1969)

Legator, M. S.: In: Vogel and Röhrborn: Chemical Mutagenesis in Mammals and Man. Springer Verlag, Berlin-Heidelberg-New York 1970, p. 260

Lehnert, G., Mastall, H., Szadkowski, G., Schaller, K.-H.: Dt. Med. Wschr. 95, 1097 (1970)

LeNoir and Claude: Bull. Mém. Soc. Méd. Hôp. Paris, 3me sér. 14, 1251 (1897)

Leonard, A., Linden, G., Gerber, G. B.: Intern. Symposium: Environmental Health Aspects of Lead. Amsterdam, October 2–6, 1972

Lewis, G., Markson, L. M., Allcroft, R.: Vet. Rec. 80, 312 (1967)

Löfroth, G., Kim, Ch., Hussain, S.: EMS Newsletter 2, 21 (1969)

Loskant, H.: Personal communication 1972

Lyon, M. F., Phillips, J. S. R., Searle, A. G.: Z. Vererbungslehre 93, 7 (1962)

Manu, P., Popescu, H. I.: I. Intern. Symposium der Werksärzte der chemischen Industrie, Ludwigshafen 27.–29. 4. 1972

Matter, B. E., Generoso, W. M.: 2nd Ann. Meet. Europ. Environmental Mutagen Society, Zinkovy Castle, Pilsen, May 10–12, 1972

Melick, W. F., Escue, H. M., Naryka, J. J., Mezera, R. A., Wheeler, E. R.: J. Urol. (Baltimore) 74, 760 (1955)

Mente, B.: Inaugural-Dissertation Tübingen 1970

Merewether, E. R. A., Price, C. W.: Report on Effects of Asbestos Dust on the Lungs and Dust Suppression in the Asbestos Industry. HMSO, London 1930

Merker, H.: Med. Klinik 57, 1254 (1962)

Muro, L. A., Goyer, R. A.: Arch. Path. 87, 660 (1969)

Neubert, D., Dillmann, I.: Naunyn-Schmiedeberg's Arch. Pharmacol. 272, 243 (1972)

Newberne, P. M., Butler, W. H.: Cancer Res. 29, 236 (1969)

Nordmann, M., Sorge, A.: Z. Krebsforsch. 51, 168 (1941)

Obe, G., Sperling, K.: "Arbeitsgruppe Blei" der Kommission für Umweltgefahren des Bundesgesundheitsamtes, Berlin, 1970

Oettlé, A. G.: J. Nat. Cancer Inst. 33, 383 (1964)

Ostertag, W., Duisberg, E., Stürmann, M.: Mutation Res. 2, 293 (1965)

Paul, C.: Arch. Générales de Médecine 1, 513 (1860)

Pfeil, E.: (1912) cit.: Oettel, Thiess, Uhl: Zbl. Arb. Med. Arbeitsschutz 18, 298 (1968)

Pollini, G., Biscaldi, G. P. and Robustelli della Cuna, G. Med. del Lavoro 60, 743–758 (1969)

Pollini, G., Colombi, R.: Med. del Lavoro 55, 241 (1964 a)

Pollini, G., Colombi, R.: Med. del Lavoro 55, 641 (1964 b)

Pollini, G., Strosselli, E., Colombi, R.: Med. del Lavoro 55, 735 (1964)

Pott, P.: Chirurgical Observation relative to the Cancer of the Scrotum. Hawes a. Others, London 1775.

Rehn, L.: Langenbecks Arch. Klin. Chir. 1, 588 (1895)

Report on 2,4,5-T. A Report of the Panel on Herbicides of the President's Science Advisory Committee March 1971

Report of the Advisory Committee on 2,4,5-T to the Administration of the Environmental Protection Agency, May 7, 1971

Rhoads, C. P.: Letter to Dr. Paul A. Neal, 7 Dec. 1946, cit.: Hartwell, J. L.; Survey of compounds which have been tested for cancerogenic activity. Publ. Health Service Publ. No. 149, 2. Ed., U.S. Government Printing Office, Washington 1951

Richerand: (1815) cit.: Koelsch, F., Zbl. Arbeitsmed. 8, 161 (1958)

Richir, C., Martineaud, M., Toury, J., Dupin, H.: C. R. Soc. Biol. 158, 1375 (1964)

Röhrborn, G.: Z. Ernährungswiss. Suppl. 14, 54 (1972)

Roll, R.: Bundesgesundheitsblatt 14, 342 (1971 a)

Roll, R.: Fd Cosmet. Toxicol. 9, 671 (1971 b)

Rosenblum, W. I., Johnson, M. G.: Arch. Path. 85, 640 (1968)

Russell, W. L., Cumming, R. B., Kelly, E. M.: Biol. Div. Ann. Progr. Rept. Dec. 31 ORNL-4412, p. 100 (1968).

Schmid, W., Arakaki, D. T., Breslau, N. A., Culbertson, J. C. Humangenetik *11*, 103 (1971)

Schmid, E., Bauchinger, M., Pietruck, S., Hall, G.: Mutation Res. *16*, 401 (1972)

Schmidt, D., Sansoni, B., Kracke, W., Dietl, F., Bauchinger, M., Stich, W.: Münch. Med. Wschr. *114*, 1761 (1972)

Schwanitz, G., Lehnert, G., Gebhart, E.: Dt. Med. Wschr. *95*, 1636 (1970)

Selikoff, I. J., Hammond, E. C., Churg, J.: JAMA *204*, 106 (1968)

Sellyei, M. and Kelemen, E.: Europ. J. Cancer *7*, 83–85 (1971)

Shank, R. C., Cordon, J. E., Wogan, G. N., Nondasuta, A., Subhamani, B., Fd Cosmet. Toxicol. *10*, 71 (1972 b)

Shank, R. C., Siddhichai, P., Subhamani, B., Bhamarapravati, N., Gordon, J. E., Wogan, G. N.: Fd Cosmet. Toxicol. *10*, 181 (1972 c)

Shank, R. C., Wogan, G. N., Gibson, J. B.: Fd Cosmet. Toxicol. *10*, 51 (1972 a)

Smith, K. W.: Ann. N. Y. Acad. Sci. *132*, 685 (1965)

Sparschu, G. L., Dunn, F. L., Lisowe, R. W., Rowe, V. K.: Fd Cosmet. Toxicol. *9*, 527 (1971 b)

Sparschu, G. L., Dunn, F. L., Rowe, V. K.: Fd Cosmet. Toxicol. *9*, 405 (1971 a)

Speil, S., Leineweber, J. P.: Environm. Res. *2*, 166 (1969)

Timson, J.: Mutation Res. *15*, 197 (1972)

Tough, I. M., Smith, P. G., Court Brown, W. M., Harnden, D. G.: Europ. J. Cancer *6*, 49 (1970)

Vigliani, E. C., Forni, A.: Minerva med. *57*, 3952 (1966)

Vigliani, E. C., Forni, A.: J. occup. Med. *11*, 148 (1969)

Voogd, C. E., Jacobs, J. J. J. A. A., van der Stel, J. J.: Mutation Res. *16*, 413 (1972)

Vogel, F.: Alkohol und Coffein. Wiss. Veröffentl. d. Dtsch. Ges. Ernährung *17*, 162 (1970)

Wagner, J. C.: J. Nat. Cancer Inst. *46*, V–IX (1971)

Wagner, J. C., Gilson, J. C., Berry, G., Timbrell, V.: Brit. Med. Bull. *27*, 71 (1971)

Walpole, A. L., Williams, M. H. C., Roberts, D. C.: Brit. J. industr. Med. *9*, 255 (1952)

Wales, J. H., Sinnhuber, R. O., J. Nat. Cancer Inst. *48*, 1529 (1972)

Weinstein, D., Mauer, I., Solomon, H. M.: Mutation Res. *16*, 391 (1972)

Weller, C. V.: J. Med. Res. *33*, 21 (1915)

Wilson, J. G.: Proc. S. Weed Sci. Soc. *25*, 26 (1972)

WHO: Evaluation and Testing of Drugs for Mutagenicity: Principles and Problems. Techn. Rep. Ser. 482, 1971

Wogan, G. N., Newberne, P. M.: Cancer Res. 27, No. 12, Pt. 1,2370 (1967)

Woitowitz, H.-J. Dt. Med. Wschr. *97*, 346 (1972)

Yamagiva, W. K., Ichikawa, K.: J. Cancer Res. *3*, 1 (1918)

Zollinger, H. U.: Virchows Arch. *323*, 694 (1953)

Current Situation with Respect to Environmental Problems in the United States*

Emil M. Mrak

Univ. of California, Davis, USA

Summary The history and the responsibilities of the national Environmental Protection Agency (EPA) are presented, and the difficulties resulting from unclearly defined competences of the states' environmental protection agencies and other institutions for environmental protection are discussed with examples.

Zusammenfassung Die Bildung und Aufgaben der nationalen Environmental Protection Agency (EPA) werden vorgestellt und besonders die Schwierigkeiten durch unklar definierte Kompetenzen der staatlichen environmental protection agencies und sonstiger Umweltschutzämter an einigen Beispielen diskutiert.

This is a broad subject and there is so much that one could cover that he could speak for hours. The assignment, however, does give me leeway, and this I have taken.

Rather than get involved in a technological discussion which is covered so well by the talented people attending this meeting, I plan to discuss the political and administrative problems, relating to improvement of the environment. This is important, for as a result of the rapid development of the intensive interests in environmental control, there are times I feel it has gotten out of hand. We may have been making judgments on the basis of emotions and political expediency rather than by rules of fact, reason and good judgment. We have erred and made mistakes, and I only hope that others will be careful in following our activities.

In time, I am sure we will disentangle the chaotic situation in which we find ourselves now and then, but this will take time, understanding, and perhaps even legislation. We have moved awfully fast. We can gather some facts, we can become limited in our thinking, we can forget interrelationships and even lawmakers. We can be influenced by lay scientists and even the courts. These things can, and in a number of instances have happened.

But first as background material, I should like to tell you briefly about the Environmental Protection Agency. President Nixon appointed a commission to study the situation in respect to the environment. As a result of its recommendations, from various departments in the government a new agency termed the Environmental Protection Agency, or EPA, was

* This paper was presented in part at the International Symposium on the Establishment of Air Quality Standards, Paris, Oct. 1972, organized by the International Academy of Environmental Safety.

created. The departments that contributed personnel, budgets and assignments were primarily Agriculture in the pesticide area, Health, Education, and Welfare – the areas of solid waste, radiation, pesticides, air pollution, and the Secretary's Pesticide Advisory Committee. The Department of Interior was involved in water pollution and this, too, was transferred to the new agency.

In creating this agency, it was felt that the budget should be sufficiently large to be a critical mass. I believe it is in the neighborhood of a billion and a half dollars.

The Agency is scattered through many buildings – over a hundred in Washington and various states in the Union. Although now a single center is under construction. Although the Agency is only a few years old, it has undergone a number of organizational changes. At present, there is an Administrator in charge of the Agency and five assistant Administrators. One of the Assistant Administrators is responsible for the areas of pesticide, radiation, solid waste, hazardous materials, and probably in the future, will also be responsible for matters relating to noise and odors. Thus, you can see how vast the problem is.

A second Assistant Administrator is responsible for air and water. A third one for research and monitoring, a fourth for planning, and the fifth for law and enforcement.

A very interesting laboratory was created for the development of protocols to use in testing for safety. When the Secretary's Commission on Pesticides and Their Relationship to Environmental Health completed its study, it was well realized that adequate methods of testing did not exist. The existing governmental agencies were not particularly interested in developing satisfactory protocols to use in testing for safety.

Industry was at a loss as to what procedures to follow. No matter how careful they might be, it always appeared that someone would come up with a different method, and then they were in trouble. This is what happened when 2,4,5-T was injected into the intraperitoneal cavity using DMSO as a carrying agent. Most certainly this is not the way 2,4,5-T comes into contact with an individual. Then again, monosodium glutamate was injected into the base of the brain of a young primate, and certain adverse observations were made. It almost resulted in the banning of glutamate. There are a number of other cases that I could cite.

In view of this, a National Center for Toxicological Research was established at Pine Bluff, Arkansas, a facility formerly used by the military for the production of biological warfare materials. Its purpose is to develop protocols for testing for safety, determine threshold values, if possible, reliable methods of analyses and of monitoring. I mention the NCTR here because it is a joint venture between EPA and the Food and Drug Administration, which is a part of Health, Education and Welfare. The laboratory is indeed an important one and should fill a great need. It is my hope that cooperation will prevent bureaucratic warfare that could destroy the laboratory.

It is unfortunate that EPA did not have three or four years in which to become organized and congealed. The creation of this vast empire from parts of many existing departments was and still is a difficult one to digest and this, of course, has been the situation. Furthermore, the pressures exerted on EPA by environmentalists and nature conserving groups have been unbelievable. As a result of these pressures, there undoubtedly has had to be actions that were taken faster than would have been under normal conditions. Decisions have been made on the limitations of the use of certain pesticides, water contamination, air pollution by motor cars, elimination of solid waste, dumps, and so forth. These, of course, have not been too popular, although they are perhaps the best that could be done under the circumstances, for criticism continued from both sides – those who were adversely affected, and those that were bent on banning everything.

But, unfortunately, this is not the only point of action and subsequent confusion. The states, too, are busy creating various types of environmental protection agencies. Illinois has an environmental protection agency, and it has already been very active in certain areas. As a matter of fact, it made quite a study of the use of nitrate fertilizers with the view of limiting their use by farmers. This, to me, appears to be going pretty far, especially when we do not have sufficient information to make good judgments. As a matter of fact, subsequent investigations have indicated quite clearly that the real contamination of streams with nitrates results primarily from animal wastes. These studies have resulted in some very curious observations with respect to the protein value of these animal wastes. By proper treatment of swine and sheep waste, it is possible to recover a certain amount of high quality protein and use it in refeeding. These are just indications of what is going on in some of the states. In other states, we find pesticide restrictions and they may or may not coincide with the federal restrictions. Then again, there is the matter of odors whether they come from a feedlot or a factory – they can and do create environmental problems.

In California, we do not have an environmental protection agency, but we certainly have segments of our State government interested in the environment – twenty-nine to be exact. The legislature has been trying to create an environmental protection agency, but bringing this about is almost an impossibility because of the vested interest in the various existing State agencies, in local government, and in industry. The existing situation in California, at times, seems almost impossible. I would like to give you a few examples of the untenable, political and administrative situation that we have experienced in some instances. To me, it is quite chaotic.

There is a simple problem of disposing of empty agricultural pesticide containers. There is concern on the part of many people that the empty pesticide containers might be harmful if left in the open. Children might be poisoned by contact with some of the pesticides, or perhaps even by imbibing them. Wildlife might be susceptible to the poisoning, likewise farm animals, and so it goes. As a result, the State legislature has passed a law requiring the State Department of Agriculture to work out methods of disposing of these containers. It is also indicated that until methods of disposal are worked out, the containers must be kept in a secure place that is fenced in. As a result, the empty containers have been accumulating on farms in California for over two years, and they are reaching rather monstrous proportions. The Department of Agriculture has looked into the matter and has learned a great deal as a result of this – they have learned that there are unbelievable roadblocks, and that it really has become what we term a "hot potato".

There are six State agencies directly involved in the handling of empty pesticide containers. The Public Health Department must be assured that the way they are handled will not be harmful to the population. Then there is an Air Pollution Agency that is concerned with contamination of the air. If we leave them in the open, there might be vaporization, or if we heat the containers then we would put materials in the air. The Water Pollution Agency is likewise concerned about leakage from the container and also pollution of streams and lakes or even underground water. The Wildlife Agency, of course, is concerned about protecting wildlife. The surprising one relates to the Highway Patrol. The Federal Transportation Agency has issued a regulation to the effect that open containers cannot be hauled over the highways. If they are once used, of course, they have been opened. The Highway Patrol enforces the regulation of the Federal Transportation Agency so here we have a difficult one.

There is talk about using what is termed "Class 1" dumps or landfills where harmful materials can be disposed of. However, there are regional planning groups and local control of such dumps, and, as a result, there are very few of them in the State of California. Furthermore, if they are to be disposed of at these dumps, they must be hauled over the highways, and this is the problem. But this is not all.

It would be possible, perhaps, to go out in some desert lands, owned by the government, and use sanitary landfills to dispose of the containers, but then this requires permission from the Bureau of Land Management, a federal agency, and this is not esay. Then, again, the Environmental Protection Agency has an ever-watchful eye to see that the environment is not spoiled.

The University of California Experiment Station is working on methods of handling the containers so that when emptied into spray rigs, they may be thoroughly washed and presumably in a condition that will permit them to be hauled and disposed of easily, if only the various agency will permit it.

The Western Agricultural Chemicals Association has worked out a method of washing at the time of emptying and has actually issued a bulletin on it, but the procedure has not been generally accepted. Its use will require some training of the people carrying it out.

Industry is also involved in attempting to work out soluable containers made of some sort of plastic material and there are others considering mechanical disposal systems. The result is that empty pesticide containers are accumulating on the farms, and unless there is legislative action, I do not see us getting out of the maze.

Another situation that has caused problems between the state and federal governments relates to the use of pesticides. California has very strict regulations on the use of pesticides, and perhaps has the best monitoring system in the country, if not in the world, insofar as their use on farms is concerned. But, there are special needs, not only in the State as a whole, but in parts of the State, and when federal regulations are made at the federal level, these are not always compatible with local situations. It is indeed hard to generalize, yet this is what has been done to a large extent. This has really caused problems.

There are certain areas of pesticide use that are hard to bring under control, and these are primarily home gardeners and pest control operators who treat buildings and various structures to protect them against termites, fungi, rodents, etc.

There is great confusion now on who should be concerned with the so-called "reentry time" of workers after the chemicals have been applied in an agricultural area. The federal Environmental Protection Agency is interested, and likewise a new agency, the National Safety and Occupational Health Administration. At our State level, there has been concern on the part of both the Departments of Agriculture and Public Health. A bill has been passed in the legislature now assigning joint responsibility to Public

Health and Agriculture for the development and administration of safety regulations for the worker. I must say I am not at all certain this will work out because labor is using this, not only for the protection of the individual, but as a political tool.

The fruit and vegetable processing industry in certain areas of California was recently confronted with edicts that would almost stop operation. Fruit and tomato waste were deposited in certain areas near the city of San Jose, but people objected to the odors. It was necessary, therefore, to move into other areas, but this was not easy because of local regulations. It was necessary to bring together various local, state and even federal governmental agencies to work out a program and this was done. It was perhaps one of the most successful, collaborative developments we have experienced.

More recently, the California Water Pollution Agency has indicated to the City of Sacramento that it must reduce the BOD in its sewage, much of which results from cannery wastes discharged into the city sewage system. If it were necessary to discontinue this, the canneries would have to close down. On the other hand, the agency threatened to fine the City of Sacramento six thousand dollars a day if BOD was not reduced. I am not certain that this has been settled yet, although the canneries are still operating.

Now, I should like to discuss an entirely different matter that relates to our environment in California and, as I see it, really relates to clean air. Specifically, I am referring to environmental problems that relate to open lands, State and National parks, recreation areas, etc. One year, recently, over two hundred thousand people were turned away from state parks in one day in California. Another forty-eight thousand could not even be accommodated overnight. The projections for the needed construction of new camping sites, picnic areas, boat-access parking spaces and hiking and riding trails are tremendous.

These needed developments might be brought about, but unfortunately they involve some serious political problems. A helpful step would be to coordinate the efforts of all suppliers of recreational facilities, including 16 federal and 13 state agencies, 58 counties, 396 cities, and 650 special districts. I mention this to indicate how complicated the regulation of the environment can be, and this only relates to the use and creation of parks which should be simple processes.

There seems to be confusion as to the difference between a State Park, set aside for its uniqueness in flora, fauna, geology, archaeology, and so forth, and an area set aside for recreation. Unfortunately, tremendous political pressures continue to threaten the preservation of the natural values by encouraging intensive development of existing state parks as a substitute for funding new acquisitions.

There has been a suggestion that ordinary land adjacent to some of these unique areas be purchased and used for camp sites and so forth. But, unfortunately, many nembers of the legislature did not share this view and generally have been unwilling to vote funds for the acquisition of lands unless the land to be purchased has unique or outstanding values.

The use of these areas by large numbers of people is not the only problem now confronting us. Our thinking has not kept pace with new technological developments. Creation of the so-called off-road recreational vehicles, such as jeeps, dune buggies, all-terrain vehicles, power trail bikes, and snow mobiles has indeed created new problems, and certainly the maintenance of clean air. Present day parks and recreational areas are not equipped for their use and control. The result is they have become extremely destructive.

This is something the Environmental Protection Agency, at least at the state level, must consider and I hope very soon. I doubt if it is being considered by our national Environmental Protection Agency. We, in California, feel there must be breathing space for all Californians and a wholesome activity for their leisure time. With limited resources, therefore, comprehensive planning and equitable zoning on a statewide basis is the only viable solution.

The provision of adequate recreational facilities for all is not a frill. Without such amenities and committing ourselves simply to survival, is indeed a barren prospect.

The National Park Service has become interested in an institute that was originally established by citizens becoming involved in the use of parks as open-air laboratories and, too, their preservation for the present and future generations. At present, the institute is giving serious consideration to the frailties of ecosystems, as related to their use by man, horses and so on. How many of these animals or people can a small mountain lake tolerate? Then, too, how many people can the floor of Yosemite Valley tolerate. How many automobiles, or should they be excluded, and, if so, how can we transport people around the park? These are matters now under serious consideration and certainly involve environmental protection and, of course, water and stream pollution, wildlife and all fauna and flora.

I have given you just a few examples of the critical situation that is facing us in California because of political and administrative frailties. There are many other cases I could cite. For example, there are local agencies at odds with the national Environmental Protection Agency on the contamination of the Mississippi River, likewise the coast of Maine. I think, however, I have said enough. The question now is, what to do about it? We must think differently, we must cross the walls of the tiny empires and have complete coordination and cooperation. If this is not done, the whole movement, in my opinion, will fail.

As scientists, we must become aware of the political and administrative weaknesses as well as scientific detail. We can talk and discuss matters ad ifinitum, but if we do not consider the implementation of our findings in an effective, logical manner, involving good judgment, then we will get no place. I must say, too, that we must consider the sociological aspects, whatever this means. It seems to be a byword with the Environmental Protection Agency, and apparently should take into consideration economic factors, people's welfare, and so on as well as the environment.

One of our early distinguished citizens by the name of Samuel Adams once said, we must have chaos for out of choas comes order. We certainly do have political and administrative chaos, so I am looking forward to order coming out of it, hoping that Sam Adams was right that out of this chaos will come order.

The Role of Biochemical Criteria in the Establishment of Air Quality Guides*

John C. Gage

Department of Environmental Health, University of Lund, Lund, Sweden

Summary Diagnostic biochemical tests are extensively used to assess the health status of men exposed to atmospheric contaminants, and also in experimental toxicology on animals. Such tests have not, however, played a large part in the establishment of air quality guides; the reasons for this are discussed.

Zusammenfassung Biochemische Diagnosetests werden intensiv eingesetzt zur Untersuchung des Gesundheitszustandes von Menschen, die Luftverschmutzungsstoffen ausgesetzt sind, und auch in tierexperimentellen toxikologischen Untersuchungen. Diese Tests haben jedoch keine große Rolle bei der Festlegung von Luftqualitätsrichtlinien gespielt; die Gründe hierfür werden diskutiert.

Biochemical measurements have been made for a number of years on men exposed to toxic chemicals in the course of their work to ensure that they are not suffering, or not likely to suffer, from occupational disease. In addition to the value of these biochemical criteria in occupational hygiene, they are also used in experimental toxicology, to study the nature of the effects of chemicals on animals and on man. These measurements are made on urine, blood or expired air, and sometimes on other body fluids or tissues. There are two distinct types of tests which serve different purposes. Firstly, there are the clinical diagnostic tests aimed at detecting early signs of pathological or functional changes. Secondly, there are those tests which provide a measure of the extent of exposure; these are based on the assumption that if a concentration of a toxic substance in air can be regarded as safe for human exposure, then concentrations of the chemical, or of its metabolites, may exist in tissues and body fluids which can also be regarded as free from risk. Such a test implies that a man may be used as a sampling instrument to provide an assessment of his integrated exposure.

We have now to consider to what extent these biochemical criteria can play a useful part in the establishment of air quality guides. We can obtain an indication of the extent to which they have been used in this way in connection with occupational exposure by an analysis of the detailed documentation of the American threshold limit values. Table 1 lists those compounds for which tests designed to disclose manifestations of biological effects have played a part in establishing

* This paper was presented in part at the International Symposium on the Establishment of Air Quality Standards, Paris, Oct. 1972, organized by the International Academy of Environmental Safety.

Table 1

Compound	Biochemical measurement
Organophosphorus pesticides	Cholinesterase inhibition
Aromatic amines	Methaemoglobinaemia
Alkoxyethanols	Haemoglobinuria
Cadmium	Proteinuria
Carbon tetrachloride	Urobilinogen and serum iron
Dimethyl hydrazine	Anaemia
Carbon monoxide	Carboxyhaemoglobin
Lead	Urinary coproporphyrins

the threshold limit value, that is, the tests have provided information which has enabled an inference to be drawn on the concentration in air that is not likely to produce harmful effects. Some of these tests reveal changes that are absolutely indesirable, so that any positive reaction would be regarded as an indication of an unsatisfactory condition. In this category would probably be included the proteinuria of cadmium poisoning and the haemoglobinuria associated with the alkoxyethanols. A second group of tests measure effects that are not necessarily unacceptable, as they indicate an interference with a function for which there is a large reserve capacity in the body, and a "pre-toxic" state of interference can exist which does not imply that the subject's health is at risk. A good example of this is the presence of carboxyhaemoglobin in the blood after exposure to carbon monoxide. Here the establishment of the threshold limit value has required knowledge of the atmospheric concentration of carbon monoxide associated with an acceptable level of carboxyhaemoglobinaemia. Another example is the relation between the atmospheric concentration of organophosphorus and carbamate pesticides and the extent of inhibition of blood cholinesterase.

Table 1 does not, of course, imply that no other biochemical tests have been made on these and other substances. Many tests have been made in the clinical diagnosis of occupational disease and in experimental investigation into the mechanisms of toxic actions, but these do not appear to have contributed to the establishment of threshold limit values. Notable examples are the extensive investigations of the action of lead on haem synthesis, and of the chlorinated hydrocarbons on the liver. In some cases, extensive clinical investigations have not been supported by the adequate measurements of the extent of atmospheric contamination that are necessary for the formulation of a threshold limit value.

Table 2 lists the substances for which a determination of a chemical or of its metabolites in a biological sample has been used in the establishment of a threshold limit value. Again, this does not imply that no other investigations have been made into the tissue storage, metabolism and excretion of chemicals in connection with biochemical investigations into their mode of action. In general, the main use of both types of test in occupational hygiene is to relate the measured value to the presence or absence of occupational disease without reference to the extent of exposure; they lead to the establishment of a "biological threshold limit".

It would not be appropriate for me to discuss here in detail the various biologi-

Table 2

Compound	Measurement
Arsine	Arsenic in urine
Benzene	Phenol in urine
Fluorides	Fluoride in urine
Trichloroethylene	Trichloroacetic acid in urine

cal threshold limits that have been recommended by national and international bodies. They have been considered internationally by the various committees of the International Association of Occupational Medicine, by the International Union of Pure and Applied Chemistry and will shortly be considered by the Ecotoxicology Group of SCOPE. These criteria play an important role in occupational hygiene, but they do not appear to have contributed much to the establishment of quality guides for toxic substances in air. Have they a greater potential, and should they be more widely employed in the formulation of air quality standards both for occupational exposure and for the wider aspects of community air pollution? Let us consider some of the difficulties.

Table 3 presents a scheme relating the atmospheric concentration with (a) the appearance of biochemical evidence of toxic effects, (b) "pre-toxic" biochemical effects, and (c) biochemical evidence of absorption.

The first of these forms the basic procedure for the establishment of air quality guides for toxic substances, by associating the presence or absence of toxic effects with the duration of exposure to known atmospheric concentrations. The evidence may be derived from observations on man or by animal experimentation. As the guides are intended for use in the control of human exposure, it is to be expected that information from human sources would be the most valuable, but this presents difficulties. As we are not concerned primarily with the diagnosis of disease but with the establishment of a no-effect threshold concentration, it is very desirable that an adequate epidemiological procedure should be used for collecting the information. This requires unequivocal diagnosis, and the selection of an appropriate control group to permit a statistical analysis, and a knowledge of the extent of exposure to the air-borne contaminant. This last presents a problem, as not only may the survey of the atmospheric contamination be inadequate, but there may be other routes of absorption than by inhalation. In epidemiological surveys, diagnostic biochemical criteria may be of value as they can provide an objective assessment of the health status of an individual that is not liable to subjective error.

Animal experimentation is not subject to the same errors as is information from human sources. The experimental conditions can be defined, an adequate control group selected and any appropriate tests can be made. Biochemical tests are

Table 3

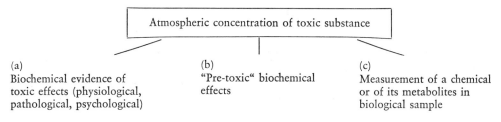

(a)	(b)	(c)
Biochemical evidence of toxic effects (physiological, pathological, psychological)	"Pre-toxic" biochemical effects	Measurement of a chemical or of its metabolites in biological sample

being increasingly used in toxicological investigations and are of great value in elucidating the mechanism of a toxic action, but they do not often provide the best means of assessing the threshold. Other factors, such as weight gain and behaviour, may be more sensitive. The drawback of animal experimentation lies in the difficulty of applying the results with certainty to man. The species difference resides in quantitative and qualitative differences in the rates of absorption, metabolism and excretion, and in differences in the sensitivity of receptor sites. It is possible to undertake biochemical investigations to compare the metabolism in the experimental species with that in man, so that the results can be applied with more certainty to man. This is frequently undertaken nowadays in the toxicological investigation of food additives, though I am not aware of it being applied to occupational toxicology. A knowledge of the mechanism of the toxic action in the experimental animal may also enable us to predict the activity at the receptor sites in man with more certainty, but I suspect that our knowledge of species variation in sensitivity is not yet sufficiently advanced for this to be of much assistance.

We have further difficulties when we attempt to derive air quality guides from the measurement of pre-toxic states or of the concentrations in tissues or excreta. In occupational hygiene such measurements are used to decide whether men are at risk from their environment, without attempting to define the environmental conditions. We refer measurements under (b) and (c) in Table 3 directly to the presence or absence of toxic effects. When we measure carboxyhaemoglobin in blood or trichloroacetic acid in urine, we do not do this to calculate the concentrations of carbon monoxide or of trichloroethylene in air,

so that we may decide whether these are safe concentrations or not. We do this because we know from theoretical considerations or from practical experience that if established biochemical threshold limits are exceded, we may expect trouble. The limit for carboxyhaemoglobin has been based mainly on the consideration that this is the maximal reduction of the oxygen-carrying capacity of the blood which should be tolerated; the limit for trichloroacetic acid in urine has been based on epidemiological studies on men exposed to trichloroethylene. In order to derive an air quality guide from a criterion of this nature, it would be necessary to undertake experiments on man to discover the atmospheric exposure corresponding to 10% carboxyhaemoglobin in blood, or of 100 mg/l trichloroacetic acid in urine. It might be thought that such a direct determination would not be necessary when the excretion of a chemical or of its metabolites in urine is measured, and that one would calculate the integrated exposure directly from the excretion. I know of no case where this is possible, usually the excretion in urine is only a small and variable proportion of the total intake. There is a further difficulty in applying the results of measurements of the type indicated by (b) and (c) in Table 3; inhalation may not be the only route of absorption. The major risk to agricultural workers handling organophosphorus insecticides arises from skin absorption and for many years such workers have been protected by imposing a limit of 30% for the inhibition of their blood cholinesterase activity. It is not certain whether the same limit would be appropriate for men exposed only to air-borne chemicals of this type. The same problem exists in attempting to apply such biochemical measurements to the general population exposed to industrial air contamination, for much of their intake may be ingested due to deposition of the pollutants on food and water supplies.

To sum up, biochemical investigations have a useful but limited role in the establishment of air quality guides. They are valuable in experimental toxicology to study the qualitative and quantitative effects on chemicals, and they provide an objective test of the health status of men exposed to toxic chemicals. Biochemical measurements of events that are not themselves toxic manifestations, but which may be related to such effects, can be used with safety in experimental studies of environmental conditions on man, but they have a limited use in the derivation of air quality guides, unless the guide is presented in terms of the measured quantity. With a few substances, where inhalation is the only route of absorption, this might be possible. For example, a standard for carbon monoxide in air might be prescribed in terms of the blood carboxyhaemoglobin of men exposed to it, but this hardly seems to be practicable if the aim of air quality guides is to enable engineers and others to keep the environment safe.

Fundamental Biochemical Aspects of Air Pollution*

F. Korte

Institut für ökologische Chemie der TU München, and Gesellschaft für Strahlen- und Umweltforschung mbH, München, West Germany

Summary   Biochemical reactions are classified and the specific and unspecific enzyme reactions of toxication and detoxication of foreign substances, respectively, are presented on the example of some model substances. The mixed-function oxidases, enzymatic reductions of foreign compounds, and conjugation reactions are especially discussed.

Zusammenfassung   Biochemische Reaktionen werden klassifiziert und die spezifischen und unspezifischen Enzymreaktionen der Toxikation bzw. Detoxikation von Fremdstoffen werden an einer Reihe von Modellsubstanzen vorgestellt. Besonders diskutiert werden die mischfunktionellen Oxidasen, enzymatische Reduktionen von Fremdstoffen und Konjugationsreaktionen.

An average adult man needs 10 kg air per day, while he consumes ca. 1.5 kg of food and 2 kg of water. Man can live some weeks without food, some days without water, but only some minutes without air. Due to the obligatory, continuous consumption, polluted air might lead to serious adverse effects, such as discomfort, untoward symptoms like sensory irritation, alteration of physiological functions, insidious or chronic disease, shortening of life, acute sickness, or even death.

If we want to discuss the fundamental aspects of such effects, we need first of all a definition of the term "air pollutant". Although the term "air" is somewhat hard to define, since the composition of uncontaminated air is continuously varying, I would like to divide pollutants into 3 groups: inorganic gases, organic vapors, and particulates. The inorganic gases classified as air pollutants are: ozone, nitrogen oxides, sulfur dioxide, hydrogen sulfide, and carbon monoxide, although normal constituents of air. Other contaminants, like molecular halogens or hydrogen halides are not usually called air pollutants; they are an occupational rather than an environmental problem.

Air pollutant organic vapors are aldehydes, ketones, ketenes, peroxides, organic sulfur compounds, and the peroxyacyl nitrates, which are formed by photochemical reaction of olefins and nitrogen oxides in the smog from automobile exhausts.

The particulates include inorganic and organic mists and solids. A striking example of unexpected air pollution by a highly toxic product of an organic reaction is the death of a monkey during a si-

* This paper was presented in part at the International Symposium on the Establishment of Air Quality Standards, Paris, Oct. 1972, organized by the International Academy of Environmental Safety.

mulated flight test in a satellite cabin[1]. Since some of the symptoms were suggestive of dichloroacetylene poisoning, a sample of air from the cabin was analysed. Besides a number of chlorinated hydrocarbons, 0.1 ppm dichloroacetylene was detected, and it could be demonstrated that it was formed from trichloroethylene present in 0.3 ppm concentration upon reaction with lithium hydroxide which was used as a CO_2-absorber.

This, of course, is an isolated incident, but it demonstrates at what low levels certain contaminants can be hazardous. In this lecture, I shall use the term "air pollutant" for such substances as may be encountered in ambient air in concentrations which produce some adverse effect on man, animals or plants. Obviously, the threshold levels for this classification are greatly dependent on the rate at which a harmful substance is converted or degraded in the organism; a contaminat which is rapidly converted to less toxic products may be tolerated at relatively high concentrations, whereas highly persistent compounds may be harmful at very low levels. The knowledge of both the rate of conversion and the mode of action in different organisms could enable us to predict the threshold levels beyond which contaminants become harmful and hazardous pollutants. To achieve this such knowledge must be the basic aim of any biologic-chemical approach to the pollution problem.

Biochemical processes may be classified as
A.) Enzyme reactions and transport mechanisms of physiological compounds,
B.) Specific and unspecific reactions for the toxication or detoxication on incorporated xenobiotics or unwanted compounds derived from pathological changes of metabolism.

In this lecture, I shall put more emphasis on the latter class which seems to be essential for the degradation of organic vapors, especially those compounds which are highly active in very low concentrations and which, so far, have hardly been discussed as air pollutants. The effects and the mode of action of inorganic gases will be discussed later in special lectures. Inorganic gases seem to affect mainly the processes of energy production. Judging on the basis of our present knowledge, there are to be considered mainly physiological effects in the pulmonary region, like decreased respiratory function or permeability changes of alveolar membranes which result in a lower amount of available oxygen and in irritation of eyes and nose. In the case of carbon monoxide, oxygen transport is reduced by addition of CO to the O_2-carrying hemoglobin, the complexing power of CO for hemoglobin being 210-fold greater than that of O_2.

An additional effect is the reduction of the dissociative capacity of oxyhemoglobin by carboxyhemoglobin, so that with HbCO, less oxygen is available for tissue respiration at a given HbO level than without it. The time of exposure to CO seems to be a critical factor, because time is required for equilibration between CO in the lungs and in blood. At normal breathing rates, 7–8 hours are required to reach blood saturation at CO air levels from 50 to 100 ppm[2].

Intensive studies have been carried out concerning the mode of action of ozone. Stokinger and Coffin[2] have compiled and correlated the results. Changes in pulmonary functions are produced in animals and man following short exposure to ozone concentrations of a few ppm. Repeated exposure revealed rapid development of tolerance not only against O_3 but also against acute O_3 injury; the most effective antagonists are sulfhydryl- and disulfide compounds and iodine, which are known to be free radical scavengers. Based upon these findings, a free radical mechanism was proposed as the mode of ozone action. Ozone is a bi-free radical, so it can initiate free radical chain reactions. Ozone seems to affect the sulfhydryl part of enzymes, the chain reaction ending in formation of disulfide links and thus inhibition of the enzyme.

One of the more important compounds for reducing capacity, glutathion, is affected in a similar way: an in vitro study showed that ozone oxidises glutathion to its disulfide, cystein, and cysteic acid. Tolerance development seems to be connected with the ability to maintain or mobilise sulfhydryl and gluathion. This requires an increased production of NADPH which in turn is a product of the pentose phosphate pathway. Consequently the development of resistence has been ascribed, at least partly, to the activation of the pentose phosphate cycle.

The reactions for internal regulation and those for the detoxidation of xenobiotics (enzymes of group b and c of my preceding classification), apparently are closely related: very similar enzyme systems are involved in the biosynthesis and metabolism of hormones as well as in the conversion of lipophilic foreign substances, whereas the highly specific enzyme systems of intermediary metabolism (group a) seem to play a minor part in the conversion of persistent xenobiotics. However, these enzymes might be involved in some conjugation reactions.

Since I feel that in the majority the same enzyme-systems are involved as in other cases, you will allow me to concentrate on the enzyme systems of group c) which effect the detoxication mainly of lipophilic compounds by introduction of polar functional groups to increase water solubility. The more important reactions, direct oxidation and hydration have been studied mainly for drugs and pesticides, but there is some good evidence that they may be extended to all kinds of unpolar xenobiotics. One group of enzymes I have in mind are the mixed function oxydases which effect the introduction of oxygen into organic molecules.

Primary processes in the metabolism of xenobiotics usually result in the introduction of polar functional groups in unpolar parent compounds. The main reactions are direct oxidation, hydration, and reduction.

Direct oxidation is achieved by unspecific or mixed function oxydases which are found in the microsomal fraction of mammalian liver homogenates; in the intact liver they are located in the endoplasmic reticulum. These oxydases are involved in the biosynthesis of steroids and aminoacids as well as in the conversion of heme to biliverdin and in the ω-oxidation of fatty acids.

Some of these enzymes are capable of attacking xenobiotics. It has not been established whether this is due to their low specificity or to their ability of quick adaptation to foreign substrates.

For the direct oxidation of organic molecules, molecular oxygen must be activated. This can be effected by binding the oxygen molecule to free ligand positions of metal complexes, and most of the mixed function oxydases contain iron (II) or copper (I) complexes as reactive sites. In some bacterial oxydase flavoproteins are utilized instead of metal complexes.

The best known and most frequently encountered mixed function oxydases contain iron bound in cytochrome P_{450} as oxygen-activating component. Cytochrome P_{450} is a hemoproteide which forms a carbonmonoxide compound with a maximum of light absorption at 450 nm. This is what the name P_{450} comes from.

This is rather unusual, as all other known CO-compounds of iron-porphyrin complexes absorb near 420 nm.

Cytochrome P_{450} has been found in mammals[2], insects[3], yeasts[4,5], and bacteria[6–8].

In almost all cases an interaction in hydroxylation was attributed to its presence, thus it may be regarded as the most important prosthetic group in mixed function oxydases.

According to the proposed mechanism, the cytochrome component of the enzyme complexes with molecular oxygen to form an "activated oxygen" intermediate. One atom of the activated oxygen molecule is then transferred to the substrate, and the other is reduced to water.

Hydroxylation of substituted aromatic compounds follows clearly the rules of electrophilic aromatic substitution; intramolecular rearrangement of chlorine, bromine, tritium or deuterium which is familiar to the organic chemists as NIH-shift (because it was first discovered in the National Institute of Health) leads to the suggestion that arene oxide is an intermediate of the reaction.[9, 10] The suggestion that the active oxygen is added to the π-system is confirmed by the formation of epoxides from isolated double bonds. Based upon this evidence, an oxenoid structure has been postulated for the active oxygen.[11]

After the oxygen transfer, the oxydized enzyme must be reactivated by some reducing agent. All mixed function oxydases with cytochrome P_{450} seem to require NADPH or NADH for this purpose. Some oxydases which contain other prosthetic groups are reduced by ascorbic acid or tetrahydropteridins, as for example dopamine-β-monooxygenase or phenylalanine-4-monooxygenase. The reducing agents are not always very specific, or may even be interchanged in related systems.

By attachment of carbon monoxide to the free ligand position of the iron-porphyrin complex, enzymes with cytochrome P_{450} are inhibited. They can be reactivated in vitro by irradiation with light of 450 nm which dissociates the CO complex. This specific reaction may be utilized to verify the presence of cytochrome P_{450}.

The question arises whether the mixed function oxydases responsible for the direct oxidation of xenobiotics are entirely unspecific. Induction experiments showed that there is at least a certain group specificity. Pretreatment of animals with drugs or other foreign substances results in an increase of mixed function oxydase activity. Barbiturates mainly increase the oxidation of aliphatic substrates, whereas pretreatment with polycyclic hydrocarbons strongly increases the hydroxylation of aromatic compounds.[12, 13]

Since most of the information on mixed function oxydases originates from work with mammals, our knowledge of similar systems in other organisms is relatively poor. Ray demonstrated that a carbon monoxide binding pigment similar to cytochrome P_{450} is present in microsomes from the housefly and other insects.[15] He found that the epoxidation of aldrin by housefly microsomes is inhibited by carbon monoxide, and that this inhibition can be reversed by light-irradiation.

Heslop[16] demonstrated the presence of a P_{450}-type cytochrome in microsomes from the larvae of Ploida interpunctella and Acarus siro. Price and Kuhr[17] reported oxidation of carbaryl and aldrin in a fraction obtained from the fat body of blowfly larvae which contained cytochrome P_{450}.

In plants, mixed function oxydases with cytochrome P_{450} seem to be involved in the biosynthesis of gibellerins. In the endosperm of developing seeds of Echinocystis macrocarpa, the enzymatic oxidation of kaurene to kaurenoic acid, a gibellerin precursor, requires NADPH and oxygen, a P_{450}-type difference spectrum was demonstrated, and there is a light-reversible inhibition of the reaction by carbon monoxide.[18-20]

Microorganisms, too, have been demonstrated to contain cytochorome P_{450}. Cells of Pseudomonas putida contain a soluble hydroxylase which can be induced with camphor and converts this substrate into the 5-exo-hydroxy-derivative, the conversion requiring NADH, molecular oxygen, a flavoprotein, putidaredoxin, which is a non-heme iron protein, and a soluble cytochrome P_{450}.[21] A similar system appears to effect the ω-oxidation of fatty acids in Pseudomonas oleovorans,[22] and there is a report of a rather unstable dimethylamine oxydase system in Pseudomonas aminovorans that requires NADH or NADPH for the conversion of dimethylamine into methylamine and formaldehyde, a typical conversion effected by mixed function oxidases.

Epoxidation of double bonds does not result in a marked detoxication of xenobiotics, since the epoxides are only little more polar than the corresponding unsaturated compounds, and there is consequently no substantial increase of excretion. In the class of cyclodiene insecticides, the epoxides are sometimes even more toxic than the original dienes.

Enzymatic hydration has been found to be the mechanism of epoxide detoxication. In 1964, we isolated trans-6,7-dihydroxy-dihydroaldrin from the urine of rabbits which had been treated with dieldrin.[23] Brooks isolated a solubilized cyclodiene epoxide hydrase from livers of pigs, rabbits and rats, and from some insects, which hydrates dieldrin and heptachlor epoxide in vitro. The hydration of heptachlor epoxide in vivo has not been found so far. The hydration of endrin, the endo-endo stereoisomer of dieldrin, seems to be impossible for steric reasons. Jerina and his group [24-27] studied the enzymatic oxidation of benzene and naphthalene. They found benzene oxide and naphthalene-1,2-epoxide to be the primary intermediates which are converted into the corresponding trans-dihydrodiols by an epoxide hydrase in rabbit liver microsomes. Chemical rearomatisation to form phenols, accompanied by NIH-shift, competes with the enzymatic hydration for the arene oxides: competitive blocking of naphthalene-1.2-oxide hydrase by styrene oxide results in increased formation of 1-naphthol.

Reductive conversion is another pathway of detoxication. The best examples of enzymic reduction of xenobiotics are those effected by the so-called "nitroreductase" enzymes which appear to be present in most living organisms and are responsible for the reduction of aromatic nitro-groups, and by the azo-reductases responsible for the reduction and cleavage of azo-compounds. Mammalian liver and kidney contain both microsomal and soluble enzymes that can reduce nitro-groups under anaerobic conditions in the presence of NADPH or NADH, and oxygen normally inhibits the conversions.

The replacement of chlorine by hydrogen in the conversion of DDT into DDD has been described for a number of biological systems. This reductive dechlorination was shown to be effected by dilute solutions of reduced iron-porphyrin complexes.

After the introduction of functional groups into the molecule of a xenobiotic, its excretion can be greatly increased by conjugation to more hydrophilic compounds. Most of our knowledge on conjugation reactions has been derived from drug metabolism studies in mammals. From these investigations certain generalisations have been estabilshed which appear to be of evolutionary origin and can doubtless be extended to xenobiotics. Conjugation with sugars, for example, takes the form of glycosides in plants, bacteria, mollusca, and insects, but in most vertebrates the mechanism has modified to give glucuronides instead, glucuronic acid being activated by uridine diphosphate. The conjugation, using coenzyme A, of foreign acids with endogenous aminoacids to form peptides, also differs between species. Conjugation with glycine to form hippuric acids occurs in all terrestrial animals. In addition, anthropods form conjugates with arginine, reptiles and birds with ornithine, and man and primates employ glutamine, the amino acid employed being related to the mode of nitrogen metabolism of the species.

The conjugation of glutathione to xenobiotics often involves its direct interaction with the unchanged molecule, and might therefore be regarded as a primary process, whereas the gluathione conjugation of aromatics requires their preceding oxidation to areneoxide intermediates by mixed function oxidases, and must be regarded as a secondary process. Different S-transferases effect the transfer of glutathione to various xenobiotics, with two groups of reactions involved: first, the addition of GSH to double bonds and epoxides by glutathione-S-alkene- and S-epoxide transferases, and second, the substitution by GSH catalyzed by S-alkyl-, S-aralkyl-, and S-aryl-transferases, replacing for example the halogens of methyl iodide, benzyl chloride, or chloronitrobenzene, respectively. Glutathione conjugation is certainly involved in the metabolism of the hexachloro-cyclohexane isomers which results in γ-pentachlorocyclohexene and in 2,4-dichlorophenylglutathione for lindane. Whereas the lindane metabolism consumes glutathione, the dehydrohalogenation of DDT to DDE requires it as a catalyst, GSH-levels remaining unchanged during the reaction. An interesting hypothesis was deduced from the findings of Dinamarca et al[28] that the housefly DDT-ase consists of an aggregation of monomers with a molecular weight of about 30,000 each. Enzyme activity towards DDT appears in aggregates having a minimum molecular weight of 90,000 and is maximal in the tetramer, which appears to be the native enzyme. Aggregation of the monomers is induced by DDT but not by GSH, although the latter is required for activity and to stabilize the tetrameric form of the enzyme. Dinamarca postulated that the enzyme is present in vivo in an inactive form which becomes active in the presence of DDT. If this idea proved correct, it might be that susceptible insects possess monomeric forms of DDT-ase but lack the ability to produce highly active forms of the enzyme by aggregation. Thus, selection for DDT resistance could involve selection of those insects in a population which had high ability to produce active enzyme aggregates in the presence of DDT. The effect of DDT would then appear similar to that of enzyme induction insofar as active enzyme would appear in its presence, but ought also to be demonstrable in vitro, since it seems to be a physical effect of DDT on existing proteins.

Reconsidering the discussed enzymatic mechanisms, one comes to the conclusion that all organisms utilize well-established pathways for the conversion and detoxication of xenobiotics. This is often connected with the stimulation of the enzymatic systems involved, in particular the mixed function oxydases. Street[29] reported pronounced reduction of the tissue storage and increased rate of excretion for aldrin, dieldrin, endrin, chlordene, and heptachlor in rats, when he fed them cyclodiene insecticides simultaneously with DDT, associating this effect with induction of microsomal enzyme activity. On the other hand, this induction also results is an accelerated degradation of steroid hormones, as was shown by Welch et al [30] for estradiol-17β, testosterone, progesterone, and deoxycorticosterone in rat liver microsomes with DDT and chlordane. Thus, the positive effect of accelerated detoxication of foreign substances is paralleled by an undesired influence on the equilibrium of hormonal regulation.

At this point of the discussion, the question of adaptation by prolonged contact arises. Will man and the various species of his living environment be able to develop efficient defense mechanisms against the continuous impact of xenobiotic substances? Can enzyme systems be sufficiently induced to eliminate all the pollutants taken up by inhalation or ingestion? Can the sensitive equilibrium of internal hormonal regulation, which is disturbed by enzyme induction, be restored, perhaps by an increased production of hormones? If an adaptation is possible, and there is some evidence for this assumption, how much time will the different species need for it?

Since answers for these urgent questions may come from profound and relevant studies of comparative metabolism. The compilation and intercomparison of the knowledge about the various enzyme systems and transport mechanisms in the biosphere must be carried out with the aim to acquire a general understanding. From a broader knowledge we will hopefully some day be able to predict on the basis of theoretical considerations, which risks arise from the presence of environmental pollutants, inorganic gases, as well as highly bioactive organic molecules.

Literature

[1] Raymond A. Saunders: "Another Incident of Dichloroacetylene Contamination Proceedings of the 5th Annual Conference on Atmospheric Contamination in Confined Spaces 1969, p. 289—292 AMRL-TR-69-130

[2] Herbert E. Stokinger, D. C. Coffin: "Biologic Effects of Air Pollutants" in "Air Pollution", 2nd Ed., Vol. I, Editor A. C. Stern, Academic Press 19

[2a] M. Klingenberg, Arch. Biochem. Biophys. 75, 376 (1958)

[3] S. E. Lewis, C. F. Wilkinson, J. W. Ray, Biochem. Pharmacol. 16, 1195 (1967)

[4] A. Lindenmayer, L. Smith, Biochem. Biophys. Acta 93, 445 (1964)

[5] J. M. Lebeault, E. T. Lode, M. J. Coon, Biochem. Biophys. Res. Commun. 42, 413 (1971)

[6] C. A. Appleby, Biochem. Biophys. Acta 172, 71 (1969)

[7] M. Katagiri, B. N. Ganguli, I. C. Gunsalus, Fed. Proc. 27, 525 (1968)

[8] G. Gardini, P. Jurtshuk, J. Biol. Chem. 2452789 (1970)

[9] J. W. Daly, G. Guroff, D. M. Jerina, S. Udenfriend, B. Witkop, Hoppe-Seylers Z. Physiol. Chem. 349, 1000 (1968)

[10] L. Nover, Pharmazie, 7, 361 (1969)

[11] G. A. Hamilton, J. Amer. Chem. Soc. 86, 3391 (1964)

[12] H. Remmer, Arch. Exp. Pathol. Pharmkol. 235, 279 (1959)

[13] A. H. Conney, J. J. Burns, Nature 184, 363 (1959)

[15] J. W. Ray, Pest Infestation Research 1967 p. 70 H. M. Stationary Office, London (1967) J. W. Ray, Biochem. Pharmacol. 16, 99 (1967)

[16] Heslop, unpublished, in G. T. Brooks, Pathways of Enzymatic Degradation of Pesticides in "Environmental Quality and Safety" Editors F. Coulston, F. Korte, Vol. I 1972 Thieme / Academic Press

[17] G. M. Price, R. J. Kuhr, Biochem. J. 112, 133 (1969)

[18] C. D. Upper, C. A. West, J. Biol. Chem. 242, 3285 (1967)

[19] D. T. Dennis, C. A. West, J. Biol. Chem. 242, 3293 (1967)

[20] P. J. Murphy, C. A. West, Arch. Biochem. Biophys. 133, 395 (1969)

[21] M. Katagiri, B. N. Ganguli, I. C. Gunsalus, J. Biol. Chem. 243, 2543 (1968)

[22] J. A. Peterson, D. Basu, M. J. Coon, J. Biol. Chem. 241, 5162 (1966)

[23] F. Korte, H. Arent, Life Sci. 4, 2017 (1965)

[24] D. M. Jerina, J. Daly, B. Witkop, P. Zaltzman-Nirenberg, S. Undenfriend, Arch. Biochem. Biophys. 128, 176 (1968)

[25] D. M. Jerina, J. Daly, B. Witkop, P. Zaltzman-Nirenberg, S. Undenfriend, J. Amer. Chem. Soc. 90, 6525 (1968)

[26] D. M. Jerina, H. Ziffer, J. W. Daly, J. Amer. Chem. Soc. 92, 1056 (1970)

[27] D. M. Jerina, J. Daly, B. Witkop, P. Zaltzman-Nirenberg, S. Undenfriend, Biochemistry, 9, 147 (1970)

[28] M. L. Dinamarca, I. Saavedra, E. Valdes, Comp. Biochem. Physiol. 31, 269 (1969)

[29] J. C. Street, Enzymatic Oxidation of Toxicants, P. 197. E. Hodgson, Ed. North Carolina State University at Raleigh (1968) Library of Congress Catalogue Card No. 68—63363

Residues in Animals During Chronic Exposure to Dieldrin

F. Moriarty

Monks Wood Experimental Station, Abbots Ripton, Huntingdon, U. K.

Summary Theory, and most of the relevant experimental data, suggest that chronic exposure to a harmless concentration of an organochlorine insecticide leads to a steady state concentration in the body. The few long-term experiments that have been made suggest that in fact, after 18 months or so, there may often be a second phase of increasing concentrations. If this is a real possibility, it poses an additional hazard from chronic exposure to pollutants.

Zusammenfassung Die Theorie und die meisten relevanten experimentellen Daten deuten darauf hin, daß die chronische Aufnahme einer harmlosen Konzentration eines insektiziden Chlorkohlenwasserstoffs zu einer Sättigungskonzentration im Körper führt. Die wenigen Langzeitexperimente, die bisher durchgeführt wurden, zeigen, daß etwa nach 18 Monaten häufig eine zweite Phase der Konzentrationssteigerung eintreten kann. Wenn dies allgemein möglich ist, stellt es eine zusätzliche Gefahr der chronischen Aufnahme von Chemikalien aus der Umwelt dar.

Introduction

A great deal of attention has been paid to the size of residues that animals acquire during exposure to the persistent organochlorine insecticides. The first view to attract much support suggested that these compounds accumulate and concentrate along food chains. This has now, at least to some extent, been replaced by compartmental analysis. This form of analysis has a relatively long history, but has been applied only recently to pesticide studies, by Robinson and his colleagues (Robinson & Roberts, 1968). This analysis provides a much more appropriate model (Moriarty, 1972): it emphasises, not a species' position in the food web, but the species' rates of uptake and elimination for each pollutant.

The Mrak report (1969) deduced that, according to the theory of compartmental analysis, an animal with a constant exposure to an organochlorine insecticide should eventually reach and maintain a steady concentration of insecticide in its tissues. This report also concluded that the published experimental results for mammals were consistent with this prediction. Thus the concentration c in a specific tissue at any time t after the start of exposure can be expressed as

$$c = C_\infty (1 - e^{-kt})$$

where C_∞ is the steady state concentration at t_∞ and kg is the rate constant of elimination. It can be illustrated graphically as follows:

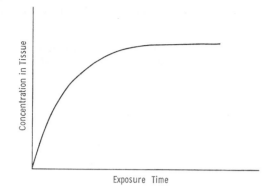

The steady state concentration is presumed to occur when the rate of elimination has increased until it equals the rate of uptake.

When there is some residue already present in the tissue before exposure starts, the equation can be rewritten as

$$c = C_\infty - Be^{-kt}$$

which can be illustrated graphically as follows:

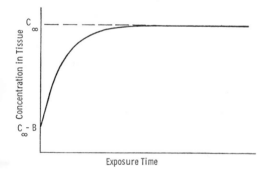

I want now to discuss the evidence for one aspect of this relationship: the maintenance, indefinitely, of a constant concentration once the steady state has been reached.

Experimental evidence

Most of the experimental evidence is in reasonable agreement with the concept that a steady state is established during chronic exposure to sublethal doses (Moriarty, in preparation). It is not surprising to find that this steady state can be disturbed by various factors, such as ageing (Hayes, 1965) or subsequent exposure to a second insecticide (Deichmann, MacDonald & Cubit, 1971). Much more study is still needed of the effects of these additional factors (Brown, 1970).

One factor that has received scant attention so far is the effect of the passage of time, as distinct from the effect of ageing, on the steady state. Quaife, Winbush & Fitzhugh (1967) examined the evidence for and against the idea that a state of equilibrium can be attained between intake and tissue storage for aldrin and dieldrin. They enumerated several desirable features of any critical experiment. These included a long exposure period, which should cover a significant part of an animal's life time, and which should also include a prolonged period after growth has stopped. In most published experiments animals have been exposed for relatively short periods of time, rarely for more than six months. However, there have been two fairly recent experiments in which dieldrin was fed daily for two years.

1) Observations on man

Thirteen adult male volunteers ingested known amounts of HEOD (the main component of dieldrin) daily, for two years (Table I). Blood samples were analysed at intervals for HEOD. There were four dose rates during the first 18 months, which were allocated randomly to the volunteers (Hunter & Robinson, 1967). The pre-exposure concentrations of HEOD found in blood and fat samples taken from the volunteers were consistent with a random allocation (Table I). The dose rates were altered for the last 6 months, when, unfortunately, the controls started to ingest HEOD too. The

Table I Doses of HEOD given to 13 adult men (data from Hunter & Robinson, 1967, and Hunter, Robinson & Roberts, 1969).

| Subject No. | Dose rate (μg HEOD/day) | | Concentration of HEOD in tissues before **dosing** began (pp 10^9) | | Concentration in whole blood after 18 months of dosing (pp 10^9) |
	First 18 months	Next 6 months	Whole blood	Adipose tissue	
1	0	211	1.9	366	2.6
2	0	211	1.2	95	2.3
7	0	—	1.6	262	2.3
10	0	211	2.2	114	1.7
3	10	211	1.7	222	
5	10	211	1.7	236	
8	10	211	0.6	33	
4	50	50	2.2	232	
12	50	50	2.3	402	
13	50	50	0.7	63	
6	211	211	0.9	145	
9	211	211	1.4	199	
11	211	211	1.6	270	

concentration of HEOD in the controls' blood samples had not altered appreciably during the first 18 months (Table I), and presumably this state of affairs would have continued.

All of the volunteers were healthy throughout the study. Numerous tests of physiological function were made, and, although the relevance of some of these tests to any sublethal effects of HEOD is obscure, there was no consistent difference between control and dosed individuals, and all results were within the range of variation found in healthy men.

I shall confine my attention to those six volunteers given either 50 μg or 211 μg HEOD/day for the entire two years. Hunter & Robinson (1967) concluded that, after 18 months' exposure, the increase with time in the blood's concentration of dieldrin was consistent with the compartmental model. However, when the results for the final 6 months are also considered, the situation appears quite different (Figs. 1 & 2).

Hunter, Robinson & Roberts (1969) concluded that, for the men who ingested 50 μg HEOD/day, there was no significant change in the concentration of dieldrin in the blood during the final 6 months. In other words, a steady state existed. For men ingesting 211 μg HEOD/day there was a slight increase during months 18–21, but little change after that. I doubt whether their data support these conclusions (Figs. 1 & 2). Hunter et al. (1969) fitted their data to the relationship

$$c = C_\infty - Be^{-kt}$$

which we have already discussed. However, each observation was first weighted in inverse proportion to its value, because "the variation between successive days in the concentration of HEOD in the blood tended to increase as the concentration in the blood increased". The weighting was achieved by using logarithms of the concentrations, when the model becomes

$$\log_{10}c = \log_{10}(C_\infty - Be^{-kt})$$

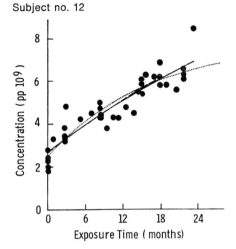

Subject no. 12

Fig. 1   *Concentration of HEOD in the blood of three adult men ingesting 50 μg HEOD/day (data from Hunter & Robinson (1967) and Hunter, Robinson & Roberts (1969))*

· · · · · · · , *curve calculated by Hunter et al. using logarithms;*

——————— , *curve calculated from the two years' data;*

— — — — , *curve calculated from the first 18 months' data.*

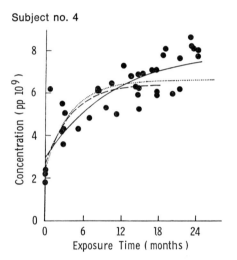

Subject no. 4

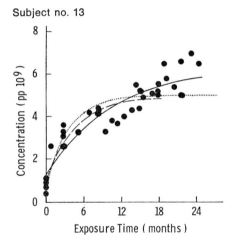

Subject no. 13

The important result of this modification is that, when the parameters for this equation are estimated from the experimental data, less weight is attached to the samples with relatively high concentrations of HEOD.

No direct evidence is given of this relationship between concentration and the accuracy of its estimate. A rough test can be made by calculating the standard deviations for groups of samples that were taken during short time intervals of not more than 4 days (Table II). Such a test suggests that for the three subjects on the lower dose rate the variance is not affected by the mean. For the higher dose rate the standard deviation does tend to increase with the mean, but it is difficult to decide what might be the appropriate transformation to produce a constant residual variation.

The parameters have been re-estimated, by the least squares method, without this weighting. The difference between the curves fitted with and without weighting is of minor importance for subjects 12, 9 and 11. Use of weighted observations does give very different results however

Subject no. 6

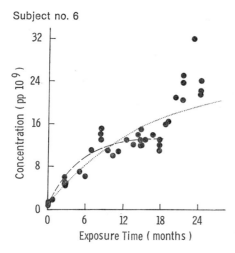

Fig. 2 *Concentration of HEOD in the blood of three adult men ingesting 211 µg HEOD/day (data from Hunter & Robinson (1967) and Hunter, Robinson & Roberts (1969)).*

........, *curve calculated by Hunter et al. using logarithms;*

————, *curve calculated from the two years' data;*

— — —, *curve calculated from the first 18 months' data.*

Subject no. 9

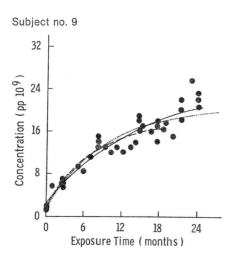

Subject no. 11

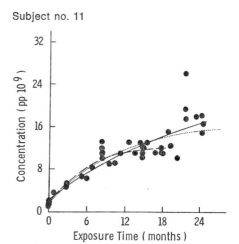

with subjects 4 and 13 (Fig. 1). When logarithms are used, the asymptotic value is virtually attained within 18 months, and the curve appears to pass through the last 6 months' values too low down; where no weighting is used the asymptotic value is not reached within the two years, and a more equal balance exists between points above and below the line for the last six months. With subject 6 it was not possible to obtain estimates of the parameters unless logarithms were used. The data (Fig. 2) do in fact suggest that the best-fitting line for the analytical results from subject 6 should have a point of inflexion, which is incompatible with the model. I would suggest, from these comparisons, that the original analysis with logarithms attaches too little weight to the data obtained during the last six months.

However, the really interesting question is not what constitutes the best estimate of the asymptotic value (C_∞), but whether the data suggest that a steady state is achieved and maintained. If there

Table II Means, and standard deviations of single estimates, for concentration of HEOD in blood (pp 10^9 w/v).

Period of time during which blood samples were taken (days after start of exposure)	Number of samples	Subject number					
		4	12	13	6	9	11
0	5	2.2±0.3	2.3±0.4	0.7±0.3	0.9±0.2	1.4±0.3	1.6±0.4
78 — 82	5	4.5±0.8	3.7±0.7	3.0±0.4	5.0±0.6	6.2±0.6	4.8±0.3
246 — 250	5	6.1±0.0	4.5±0.3	4.3±0.2	14.0±1.0	14.0±0.7	11.4±1.1
442 — 445	4	6.1±0.7	5.9±0.3	5.0±0.4	13.0±1.4	17.3±1.5	11.3±1.0
533 — 535	3	6.4±0.6	6.3±0.6	5.3±0.3	11.3±1.5	16.3±2.1	11.3±0.6
645 — 648	3	7.5±1.2	6.3±0.3	5.6±0.9	23.2±2.4	20.1±1.9	20.1±4.5
729 — 731	3	7.9±0.2	—	—	22.7±1.3	21.9±1.3	16.5±1.6

were no significant change in concentration during the last six months, the estimates of C_∞ derived from the first 18 months' data should be similar to estimates derived from the whole 2 years' data (Table III).

Several features are noteworthy:

a) subject 12: the amount of HEOD in the blood appears to rise steadily all the time. This means, if the model be correct, that the concentration is still well below the asymptotic value, whose estimate has therefore a large standard error.

b) subject 6: no estimates could be calculated for the two years' data. We have already discussed why.

c) for all four remaining subjects (4, 13, 9 and 11) the estimates for C_∞ are

Table III Estimates of the parameters for the equation $c = C_\infty - Be^{-kt}$ for data on the concentration of HEOD in the blood of men during chronic exposure. c is the concentration of HEOD in the blood, C_∞ is the asymptotic value, t is exposure time. Data taken from Hunter & Robinson (1967) and from Hunter, Robinson & Roberts (1969).

	Data for first 18 months					
Exposure	50 μg HEOD/day			211 μg HEOD/day		
Subject number	4	12	13	6	9	11
C_∞ ± standard error (pp 10^9)	6.4±0.3	15.3±19.7	4.9±0.2	13.7±0.8	18.3±1.3	12.7±0.7
B ± standard error (pp 10^9)	3.8±0.4	12.6±19.6	4.0±0.3	13.3±0.9	16.6±1.3	11.3±0.8
k ± standard error (x 10^{-3}/day)	8.14±2.67	0.61±1.11	7.34±1.51	6.62±1.31	4.29±0.86	5.42±1.04
	Data for entire 2 years					
C_∞ ± standard error (pp 10^9)	8.0±0.7	14.3±11.3	6.4±0.6	—	26.0±3.4	25.6±9.3
B ± standard error (pp 10^9)	5.0±0.7	11.6±11.2	5.1±0.5	—	23.6±3.2	23.3±8.9
k ± standard error (x 10^{-3}/day)	3.12±1.12	0.66±0.78	3.13±0.84	—	2.01±0.55	1.34±0.82

higher when based on the two years' data. The estimates for C_∞ are not normally distributed, so the standard confidence tests cannot properly be used.

One could argue that the data, excluding those for day 0, are best fitted by a linear regression. The principal reason why the model can be fitted is the relatively rapid rise in concentration that occurred during the first few days. Certainly one cannot say with any confidence for any of these 6 subjects that a steady state concentration has been reached and maintained.

An alternative argument, which is exemplified by the next set of data, would be that something like a steady state is approached within 18 months, after which there is a second relatively rapid rise in the amount of HEOD in the blood:

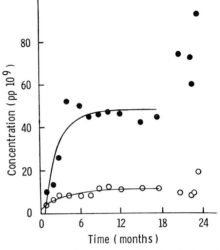

Fig. 3   Amounts of HEOD in the blood of male beagle hounds dosed orally with either 0.005 mg dieldrin/kg body weight/day (O———O) or 0.05 mg dieldrin/kg body weight/day ●———●) (data from Walker, Stevenson, Robinson, Thorpe & Roberts (1969)). The curves indicate the least squares solution for the compartmental model when applied to the first 18 months' data.

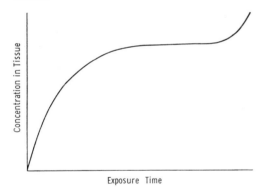

2) Observations on beagle hounds

Five male and five female dogs were selected for both of two dose rates: HEOD was ingested daily, for two years, at the rate of either 0.005 or 0.05 mg dieldrin/kg body weight. Control groups received capsules with olive oil (Walker, Stevenson, Robinson, Thorpe & Roberts, 1969).

The results for the higher dose rate do suggest that initially a steady state is established (Figs. 3 & 4). There is a si-

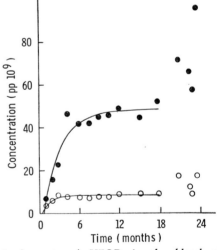

Fig. 4   Amounts of HEOD in the blood of female beagle hounds dosed orally with either 0.005 mg dieldrin/kg body weight/day (O———O) or 0.05 mg dieldrin/kg body weight/day (●———●) (data from Walker, Stevenson, Robinson, Thorpe & Roberts (1969). The curves indicate the least squares solution for the compartmental model when applied to the first 18 months' data.

milar trend with the lower dose rate too, although individual values deviate rather more from the estimated curve (Figs. 3 & 4). The last four values, estimated during the final six months, do strongly suggest that the steady state is not maintained indefinitely, but that a second increase in concentration occurs after a sufficiently long exposure. The dogs' health, behaviour and body weight were unaffected by the dieldrin throughout the experiment.

Discussion

Both of these experiments suggest that, after a steady state has been reached, continued exposure can result in a second increase in the amounts of HEOD in the blood. If this be true, three possible explanations come to mind:
1) this is an ageing effect. This seems unlikely for the experiment on men, whose ages ranged, at the start of the experiment, from 32–52 years. In the beagles the steady state was disrupted rather abruptly, which suggests a sudden change.
2) A significant, but unappreciated, factor changed during these experiments. This possibility can never be eliminated completely.
3) The second increase is the direct result of a long exposure.
It is not possible, at this stage, to choose with certainty between these possibilities. I know of only two other long term experiments with organochlorine insecticides. Both experiments used DDT. In the first, rhesus monkeys were fed DDT at concentrations of 5 and 200 ppm in the diet for seven and a half years (Durham, Ortega & Hayes, 1963). These dose rates are equivalent, roughly, to dosages of 0.1 and 4 mg DDT/kg body weight/day. Samples of abdominal fat were removed at intervals, and showed that the maxi-

mum concentration of DDT was reached within 6 months. There was no subsequent second increase in concentration. In fact there was a decrease during the last few years. It is difficult to tell from the published data whether or not this was a real decrease, because there were fewer animals towards the end of the experiment.

In the second experiment, human male volunteers ingested DDT daily for 21.5 months (Hayes, Dale & Pirkle, 1971). Fat samples were analysed after 0, 12.2, 18.8, and 21.5 months' exposure. The data are too few to deduce anything about the steady state.

The available evidence suggests that, at least for dieldrin, chronic exposure can result in a second rise in concentration after the initial steady state has been established. It is unlikely that this is due to the organism getting older. Although it is important to know whether this second increase is a direct response to continued exposure, or is caused by environmental changes, the result of immediate practical significance is that a second increase can occur in reasonably "normal" situations.

I do not wish to imply, from current data, that this has happened in practice in man: the evidence suggests that the size of our residues of organochlorine insecticides corresponds to the amount of insecticide to which we have been exposed (Abbott, Collins & Goulding, 1972). But it is important that we find out whether many pollutants can induce second increases in tissue concentrations during prolonged exposure.

Acknowledgments: I am most grateful to Mr. D. E. Walters, of the Agricultural Research Council's Statistics Group, University of Cambridge, for advice and for the computation. I would also like to thank Mrs. Pauline Lunniss for her assistance in preparing this paper.

References

Abbott, D. C., Collins, G. B. & Goulding, R. (1972). Organochlorine pesticide residues in human fat in the United Kingdom 1969–1971. *Br. med. J.* 553–556.

Brown, S. S. (1970). Kinetics of drug absorption, distribution, biotransformation, and excretion. In: "Foreign compound metabolism in mammals. Vol. I" The Chemical Society, London. 98–129.

Deichmann, W. B., MacDonald, W. E. & Cubit, D. A. (1971). DDT tissue retention: sudden rise induced by the addition of aldrin to a fixed DDT intake. *Science, N. Y.* 172, 275–276.

Durham, W. F., Ortega, P. & Hayes, W. J. (1963). The effect of various dietary levels of DDT on liver function, cell morphology, and DDT storage in the rhesus monkey. *Archs int. Pharmacodyn. Thér.* 141, 111–129.

Hayes, W. J. (1965). Review of the metabolism of chlorinated hydrocarbon insecticides especially in mammals. *A. Rev. Pharmac.* 5, 27–52.

Hayes, W. J., Dale, W. E. & Pirkle, C. I. (1971). Evidence of safety of long-term, high, oral doses of DDT for man. *Archs envir. Hlth.* 22, 119–135.

Hunter, C. G. & Robinson, J. (1967). Pharmacodynamics of dieldrin (HEOD). I. Ingestion by human subjects for 18 months. *Archs envir. Hlth.* 15, 614–626.

Hunter, C. G., Robinson, J. & Roberts, M. (1969). Pharmacodynamics of dieldrin (HEOD). Ingestion by human subjects for 18 to 24 months, and postexposure for eight months. *Archs envir. Hlth.* 18, 12–21.

Moriarty, F. (1972). The effects of pesticides on wildlife: exposure and residues. *Sci. Total Environ.* 1, 267–288.

Mrak, E. M. (1969). Report of the secretary's commission on pesticides and their relationship to environmental health. U.S. Dept. of Health, Education, & Welfare, pp. 677 + xvii.

Quaife, M. L., Winbush, J. S. & Fitzhugh, O. G. (1967). Survey of quantitative relationships between ingestion and storage of aldrin and dieldrin in animals and man. *Fd Cosmet. Toxicol.* 5, 39–50.

Robinson, J. & Roberts, M. (1968). Accumulation, distribution and elimination of organochlorine insecticides by vertebrates. Society of Chemical Industry, Monograph No. 29, 106–119.

Walker, A. I. T., Stevenson, D. E., Robinson, J., Thorpe, E. & Roberts, M. (1969). The toxicology and pharmacodynamics of dieldrin (HEOD): two-year oral exposures of rats and dogs. *Toxic. appl. Pharmac.* 15, 345–373.

Comparative Aspects of the Metabolism of Pesticides

C. H. Walker

Dept. of Physiology & Biochemistry. The University Whiteknights Reading, U. K.

Summary Since very early times living organisms have been exposed to compounds which play no part in their normal metabolism. Such compounds are termed "foreign compounds" or "xenobiotics" and may enter organisms in a variety of ways – by ingestion with food or water, or passage across the skin, integument or respiratory surface. Owing to the differences in metabolism that exist between species a normal metabolite to one organism is not infrequently a foreign compound to another. For example, many plant metabolites such as atropine, curare, and muscarine are both foreign and toxic to mammals. Indeed, a fair proportion of the foreign compounds of natural origin absorbed by animals have considerable intrinsic toxicity. It can be argued, therefore, that there has been a need for effective mechanisms for eliminating foreign compounds from the animal body since the early history of life on earth. The evolution of detoxification mechanisms is to be anticipated and the present form of these mechanisms in different groups and species may reflect particular features of the diet and habitat to which these groups and species have been exposed.

Experiments with vertebrates have already demonstrated the existence of sophisticated and efficient mechanisms for facilitating the removal of a wide range of drugs from the body. Thus, there is evidence that rather non-specific systems have evolved in response to the selective pressure of foreign compounds in the environment. One suggestion has been that certain mechanisms concerned with the metabolism of liposoluble compounds have evolved from systems originally concerned with the removal of endogenous steroids, for there are close similarities between steroids and liposoluble foreign compounds with regard to both metabolism and excretion. However, too little is known about the comparative aspects of the subject to make any detailed statements about the probable course of evolution. The possible influence of different habitats and diets upon the development of systems for metabolism and excretion of foreign coupounds cannot be assessed in the absence of further evidence. In general comparative studies of the elimination of foreign compounds are at an early stage of development.

With the development of the chemical industry a great variety of new organic chemicals has been released into the living environment. Sometimes, as in the case of antibiotics administered to farm animals, or pesticides applied in the field, introduction has been deliberate with a definite purpose in mind. Sometimes, as with polychlorinated biphenyls and polycyclic aromatic carcinogens, this has not been so. The compounds have turned up as waste products and their appearance in the environment has been the result of inadequate disposal arrangements. Whatever the source of these polluting substances, the versatility of living organisms in metabolising and excreting many of them has been remarkable. It has become clear that living organisms have certain systems which are able to cope with a wide range of foreign compounds, both man made and naturally occurring, and that these vary between species, strains, sexes and age groups.

Thus, it is evident that a proper comparative investigation of the physiological and biochemical systems involved in the elimination of foreign compounds should be an integral part of a rational approach to such practical problems as the selective toxicity of pesticides and the persistence of pollutants in the environment.

Zusammenfassung   Lebende Organismen sind schon von jeher Verbindungen ausgesetzt gewesen, die in ihrem normalen Stoffwechsel keine Rolle spielen. Diese Verbindungen nennt man „Fremdstoffe" oder „Xenobiotika". Sie können auf verschiedenen Wegen in den Organismus gelangen, durch Aufnahme mit Lebensmitteln oder Wasser, Durchdringen der Haut oder über die Atemwege. Aufgrund der Metabolismusunterschiede, die unter den Spezies bestehen, kann ein normaler Metabolit eines Organismus häufig ein Fremdstoff für einen anderen Organismus sein. So sind z. B. viele Pflanzenmetaboliten wie Atropin, Curare und Muscarin für Säugetiere sowohl Fremd- als auch Giftstoffe. Tatsächlich ist ein ziemlich großer Anteil der Fremdstoffe natürlichen Ursprungs, die von Tieren absorbiert werden, stark toxisch. Daher kann man sagen, daß wirksame Mechanismen zum Abbau von Fremdstoffen im Tierkörper schon seit frühester Entwicklungsgeschichte notwendig waren. Es ist also damit zu rechnen, daß Detoxikationsmechanismen entwickelt werden, deren heutige Form in verschiedenen Gruppen und Arten besondere Merkmale der Ernährung und Gewohnheiten reflektieren könnte, denen die betreffenden Gruppen und Arten ausgesetzt waren.

Versuche mit Wirbeltieren zeigten, daß hochentwickelte und wirksame Mechanismen bestehen, die Entfernung von einer großen Anzahl von Fremdstoffen aus dem Körper zu erleichtern. Es ist also erwiesen, daß unspezifische Systeme aufgrund des selektiven Drucks von Fremdstoffen in der Umwelt entwickelt wurden. Als Erklärung wurde vorgeschlagen, daß gewisse Mechanismen, die im Zusammenhang mit dem Metabolismus fettlöslicher Verbindungen stehen, aus Systemen entstanden sind, die ursprünglich für die Entfernung endogener Steroide verantwortlich waren, da große Übereinstimmungen bestehen zwischen Steroiden und fettlöslichen Fremdstoffen, sowohl hinsichtlich des Metabolismus als auch der Ausscheidung. Es ist jedoch zu wenig bekannt über vergleichende Aspekte dieses Gebietes, um detaillierte Aussagen über den möglichen Ablauf der Evolution machen zu können. Der mögliche Einfluß der verschiedenen Lebensräume und Ernährungsgewohnheiten auf die Entwicklung von Systemen für Metabolismus und Ausscheidung von Fremdstoffen kann nicht bestimmt werden, solange keine weiteren Belege vorliegen. Vergleichende Untersuchungen über den Abbau von Fremdstoffen sind noch in den Anfängen ihrer Entwicklung.

Mit der Entwicklung der chemischen Industrie ist eine Vielzahl neuer organischer Chemikalien in die belebte Umwelt gelangt. Manchmal, wie zum Beispiel bei der Verabreichung von Antibiotika bei der Tierhaltung, oder bei der Anwendung von Pestiziden in der Landwirtschaft, war die Anwendung absichtlich, mit einem definierten Ziel. In manchen Fällen, wie z. B. bei polychlorierten Biphenylen und polyzyklischen aromatischen Karzinogenen, war dies nicht der Fall. Als Abfallprodukt war ihr Auftreten in der Umwelt das Ergebnis unangebrachter Vernichtungsmethoden.

Was auch immer die Quelle dieser Verschmutzungsstoffe sein mag, die Fähigkeit der lebenden Organismen, viele von ihnen zu metabolisieren und auszuscheiden, war sehr bemerkenswert. Es zeigte sich, daß lebende Organismen gewisse Systeme haben, die in der Lage sind, eine große Anzahl von Fremdstoffen ohne Schaden aufzunehmen, sowohl jene Fremdstoffe, die vom Menschen hergestellt sind, als auch jene, die natürlich vorkommen, und diese Systeme sind unterschiedlich in Spezies, Stämmen, verschiedenen Geschlechtern und Altersgruppen.

Eine vergleichende Untersuchung der physiologischen und biochemischen Systeme, die zur Eliminierung von Fremdstoffen in Organismen angewandt werden, sollte deshalb in die Versuche zur Lösung praktischer Probleme, wie z. B. der selektiven Toxizität von Pestiziden und der Persistenz von Verunreinigungsstoffen in der Umwelt, integriert werden.

Introduction

Before considering physiological and biochemical systems in more detail, it is worthwhile saying a little about the way in which they operate against xenobiotics. In the first place, a distinction can be made between compounds that are polar and water soluble, and compounds of pronounced liposolubility. In the case of vertebrates, water-soluble compounds are normally excreted with relative ease via the bile and/or urine. On the other hand liposoluble compounds are not readily excreted, but tend to partition into fatty tissues (e.g. fat depots, brain tissue). Fat depots function as inert storage depots in which the compounds are not usually metabolised and from which they tend not to be rapidly removed.

Notwithstanding their retention in fatty tissue there is good evidence that there is a turnover of liposoluble molecules in the body i.e. an equilibrium exists between molecules in different compartments of the body.[1] Because of this, even molecules that have passed into depot fat may be brought into contact with enzymic systems (notably in the liver) in the course of time. Commonly, liposoluble compounds are attacked oxidatively, hydrolytically or hydratively, and this nearly always leads to the production of metabolites that are more polar and water soluble than the parent compounds. Where the metabolites possess hydroxyl groups, they may be rendered more water soluble still by conjugation with endogenous molecules such as glucuronic acid or peptides. Once water soluble metabolites or conjugates have been formed they do not show much tendency to move back into hydrophobic storage areas, but are readily excreted into the bile or urine. Thus the rate at which a liposoluble compound is excreted by a vertebrate animal is influenced by the rate at which it can be broken down into water soluble metabolites and conjugates. Both the structure of the compound and the metabolic capacity of the species are important in determining what this rate is in any particular instance.

It should be added that the metabolic capacity for any individual animal is not necessarily constant. It is possible for liver enzymes to be induced in response to various liposoluble compounds in the body, and this represents an important defence mechanism against such substances. Induction leads to greatly enhanced oxidative activity towards many foreign compounds and is usually accompanied by proliferation of the smooth endoplasmic reticulum, and liver hypertrophy. Where an animal is being chronically dosed with a liposoluble compound, induction can be associated with a marked increase in the rate of elimination. This was demonstrated in an experiment by Gilbert & Golberg[2] where rats were dosed chronically with butylated hydroxytoluene (BHT). Over the first two days of dosing the BHT concentration rapidly rose, in the depot fat. Subse-

quently, however, liver enzymes were induced, and the concentration in depot fat fell to about half of the maximum level.

In the simplest situation where induction does not occur the rate of disappearance of a liposoluble compound from an animal may be conveniently measured as a "biological half life".[3] This involves the determination of residue concentration in one or more tissues at different times after dosing. In the case of adipose tissue, plotting the log of the concentration against time, gives a straight line relationship, and the time at which the concentration falls to 50% of the original can be estimated. The determination of the half lives of certain organochlorine compounds in adipose tissue has given some idea of the degree of persistence that is possible in different species. In fat for example dieldrin has a half life of 10.3 days in the male rat' and approximately 47 days in the pigeon.[3] The half life for dieldrin in human blood has been estimated at 369 days.[4]

A knowledge of the connection between metabolic fate and toxic action is important in understanding (1) the evolution of enzymic systems for metabolising foreign compounds in different species and strains and (2) the basis for the selective action of pesticides. The metabolic transformation of pesticides is usually a detoxifying process, but this is not always the case. There are some instances where it leads to an enhancement of toxicity. For example the organophosphorus insecticides parathion and malathion are oxidised to paraoxon and malaoxon, both of which are much more powerful anticholinesterases than the parent compounds. At this stage it is worthwhile considering the question of detoxification in a little more detail. A metabolic conversion may be regarded as a detoxification so far as the whole animal is concerned when one of the following conditions is met.

1. When the metabolite has less intrinsic toxicity than the parent compound i.e. when it is less effective at the site of action.

2. When the metabolite has less toxic effect than the original compound because the distribution within the body is different. For example the transformation of a liposoluble poison into water soluble metabolites can lead to rapid excretion with the consequence that there is little or no contact with the site of action.

It should be emphasised that (2) does not necessarily mean that the metabolite has less intrinsic toxicity than the parent compound. Indeed there are certain cases where the reverse seems to be true. In interesting investigations of the action of dieldrin upon the nerves of the German cockroach (Blatella germanica)[5] and the American cockroach (Periplaneta Americana)[6] it was suggested that the actual toxic agent is aldrin transdihydrodiol produced by hydration of the insecticide. On the other hand this compound is considerably less toxic than dieldrin when administered to the mouse, especially when given orally, and is also the main excreted metabolite of dieldrin in the rabbit where its formation appears to represent an effective detoxifying step. Apparently this particular metabolic conversion may be either detoxifying or activating depending upon where it takes place. The production of aldrin transdihydrodiol in the liver seems to lead to its rapid excretion whereas its generation in the neighbourhood of its site of action (the nerve membrane) may produce strong toxic action.

Differences in the ability to metabolise and excrete foreign compounds have been found between species, strains, sexes and age groups. With regard to enzymic attack, some of the sharpest contrasts have been found between conjugative and hydrative systems in different species. On the other hand mixed function oxidases seem to be universal in the animal kingdom and the differences between species, sexes, strains and age groups to be quantitative rather than qualitative. In the case of insects the development of resistance to insecticides is often associated with an increased ability to metabolise the toxicant in question.

Dealing now with differences in excretion, vertebrates vary considerably in their preferred excretory routes for particular foreign compounds or metabolites. Sometimes excretion is largely via the urine or via the bile; sometimes there is a balance between the two routes. This subject together with the less well resolved problem of excretion in insects will receive more attention later on.

The aim in drawing up this review has been to focus attention upon the processes recognised in living animals that are concerned with the removal of foreign compounds, with particular reference to the comparative aspects of the subject. So far as possible the case has been argued for pesticides, but in a number of instances drugs and other compounds are used as examples. This has been unavoidable, because drugs have been much more widely investigated than pesticides, and some of the more important principles rest upon work with drugs alone. More attention has been given to variations between species, than to variations between sexes, strains and age groups.

The review is divided into the following sections: –

1. *Enzymic systems involved in the metabolism of foreign compounds.*

This deals especially with *in vitro* studies, and draws attention to the location of the enzymes, and also to comparative aspects of the subject.

2. *Excretion of foreign compounds by vertebrates and insects.*

3. *The comparative metabolism of pesticides.*

Individual pesticides are taken as examples. Where possible, an attempt is made to give a picture of the metabolic fate of a compound in different animals, and how this involves the interplay of different systems.

4. *Conclusion. The practical significance of comparative metabolism.*

Here the relevance of comparative metabolism to environmental persistence, selective toxicity, synergism and resistance is briefly reviewed.

Enzymic Systems which Metabolise Foreign Compounds

According to R. T. William's the transformation of most foreign compounds takes place in two distinct stages: –

Phase 1   Phase 2

Foreign compound → Metabolite → Conjugate
                   activation   deactivation
                   or deactivation
                        Endogenous
                        substrate

There are, however, certain departures from this scheme. Sometimes unchanged foreign compounds are conjugated directly and foreign compounds or metabolites are excreted without being conjugated. The first phase (or primary process) may be an oxidation, a hydration, a hydrolysis or a reduction and the metabolite so formed may be more or less toxic than its precursor. In the case of liposoluble compounds the metabolites formed by oxidation, hydrolysis or hydration are nearly always more water soluble than the parent compound and

are therefore excreted more rapidly. The second phase (or secondary process) nearly always leads to increased water solubility and diminished toxicity. Typically the phase 1 and phase 2 reactions described here take place in the livers of vertebrates, but some enzymes e.g. esterases are well represented in other tissues as well. The picture in insects is less well understood.

Phase I Reactions

Mixed function oxidations

Mixed function oxidation is probably the most important primary process for the metabolism of foreign compounds in vertebrates and insects. This system is so named because it brings about a splitting of molecular oxygen which leads to the incorporation of one atom into a foreign substrate and the other into water.[8]

$$XH + NADPH + H^+ + \overset{*}{O_2} \rightarrow$$

$$X\overset{*}{O}H + NADP^+ + H_2\overset{*}{O}$$

Some examples of mixed function oxidation are presented in Fig. 1 to give some idea of the wide range of reactions that can be mediated by this system.

Typically, mixed function oxidations are carried out by microsomal fractions from a variety of sources. Of special note is the microsomal fraction from vertebrate liver homogenates which is derived from the smooth and rough endoplasmic reticulum. This shows particularly strong mixed function oxidase activity, especially in the material from the smooth endoplasmic reticulum. Active microsomes can also be prepared from lung, kidney, and adrenal tissue of vertebrates,[9, 10] although it should be noted that mitochondria are included in the adrenal microsomal fraction and the mixed function oxidase system here is particularly concerned with

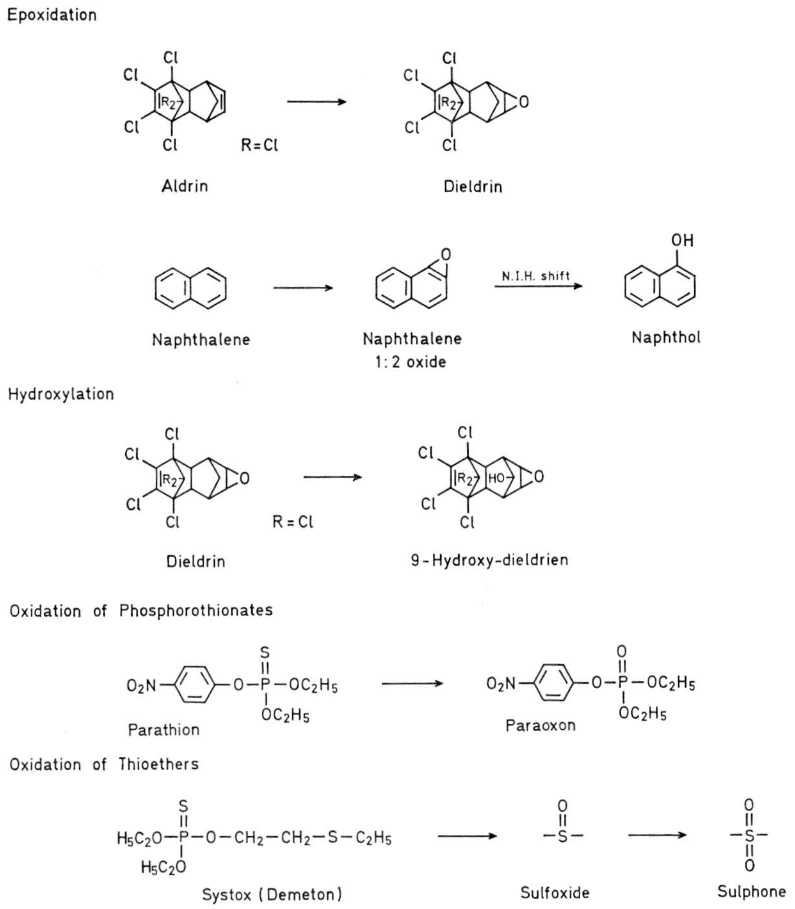

Epoxidation

Aldrin → Dieldrin (R=Cl)

Naphthalene → Naphthalene 1:2 oxide → (N.I.H. shift) → Naphthol

Hydroxylation

Dieldrin → 9-Hydroxy-dieldrien (R = Cl)

Oxidation of Phosphorothionates

O_2N—⟨⟩—O–$\overset{S}{\underset{OC_2H_5}{P}}$–$OC_2H_5$ → O_2N—⟨⟩—O–$\overset{O}{\underset{OC_2H_5}{P}}$–$OC_2H_5$

Parathion → Paraoxon

Oxidation of Thioethers

H_5C_2O–$\overset{S}{\underset{H_5C_2O}{P}}$–$O$–$CH_2$–$CH_2$–$S$–$C_2H_5$ → $-\overset{O}{S}-$ → $-\overset{O}{\underset{O}{S}}-$

Systox (Demeton) → Sulfoxide → Sulphone

Fig. 1   Some typical mixed function oxidations

the metabolism of endogenous steroids.[10] Much of the early work upon mixed function oxidation by insects was with microsomes derived from homogenates of the whole body. Only relatively recently has attention been paid to the activity of different tissues and organs from insects and some of the values have been surprisingly high compared with those for whole insect preparations.[11]

The following insect tissues have been found to possess relatively high oxidative activity: – the fat body of the locust *(Schistocerca gregaria)* [12], cockroach *(Blaberus giganteus)* [13] and blowfly larva

(Calliphora erythrocephala) [14], the mid gut of the southern army worm *(Prodenia eridania)* [15] and the malpighian tubules of the house cricket *(Acheta domesticus)*.[16] The fat body of the cockroach and the mid gut of the southern army worm had much of their oxidative activity in the microsomal fraction.

Most, but not all, mixed function oxidation systems which metabolise foreign compounds depend upon an unusual pigment – cytochrome P_{450} – for complexing both the substrate and molecular oxygen.[17] Estabrook has proposed a general scheme for the involvement of

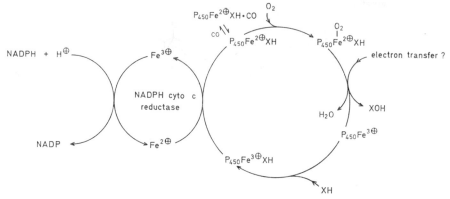

Fig. 2   *Proposed Scheme for Mixed Function Oxidation After Estabrook*

cytochrome P_{450} in hydroxylation reactions (Fig. 2).[18]

There is considerable uncertainty about the details of this scheme, especially with regard to the form(s) in which oxygen exists after binding to cytochrome P_{450}, and the mechanism of electron transfer from NADPH to cytochrome P_{450}.[18]

NADPH reduces a flavoprotein (NADPH cyto c reductase) which in turn reduces cytochrome P_{450} from the ferric to the ferrous state. The substrate binds with cytochrome P_{450} before this happens, and oxygen is subsequently taken up by the enzyme-substrate complex in the ferrous state. It appears that interaction occurs with an electron donor [Perhaps to produce a hydroperoxide ($-O_2^{2-}$) or superoxide (O_2^-) complex], before one atom of oxygen is transferred to the substrate and the other incorporated in water. The oxidised substrate and water are released and cytochrome P_{450} returns to the ferric state.

Mixed function oxidases of this type are characterised by their dependence upon NADPH and molecular oxygen and their sensitivity to carbon monoxide (it binds to cytochrome P_{450}) and methylenedioxyphenyl compounds such as sesamex and piperonyl butoxide.[19]

Different drugs sometimes show contrasting binding properties and it has been argued from this and other evidence that there are different forms of cytochrome P_{450} existing within the same microsomal system.[20] If this is so the differences are likely to be minor, perhaps involving small variations in membrane environment or cytochrome P_{450} structure or both.

The mixed function oxidase system of the liver can be powerfully induced by a wide variety of liposoluble foreign compounds.[21] This process, which may be seen as a physiological defence mechanism, is usually accompanied by liver hypertrophy and proliferation of the smooth endoplasmic reticulum (SER). The increase in the SER ensures that there is an elevated cytochrome P_{450} content in the liver as well as in the microsomal fraction as a whole, for the cytochrome P_{450} content of the SER exceeds that of the RER.

Microsomal oxidase activity can vary considerably between age groups and sexes. Male rats and quail show considerably greater hepatic microsomal aldrin epoxidase activity than do females of these two species.[15, 25] In the case of the rat this difference is also evident in *in vivo* and *in vitro* experiments using other compounds e.g. barbiturates.[21] Aldrin epoxidase activity in microsomes from the malpighian tubules of the house cricket increases sixfold during the week following the final moult.[16] Newborn mice, rats, guinea pigs and rabbits are deficient in oxidase activity, but activity begins to appear within a few days of birth.[49] Maximum activity is reached in about 30 days in rats and about 8 weeks in humans. Findings such as these emphasise the care that needs to be taken in making comparisons between species with regard to the metabolism of xenobiotics.

To date there has been little evidence of qualitative differences between species with regard to mixed function oxidases.[23] One example appears to be the hydroxylation of coumarin to umbelliferone by 10,000 g supernatants of liver homogenate, a reaction which does not occur in rats and mice although it proceeds readily in a number of other vertebrates.[24] Apart from this, there are some examples of quantitative differences in microsomal activity which require further discussion. Brodie and Maickel [22] measured rate of NADPH oxidation by hepatic microsomes from different species.[21] The results need treating with caution since they do not give direct measurement of microsomal oxidase activity. It was found that mammals and birds had much higher activity than did fish or amphibia with reptiles occupying an intermediate position. More useful results have come from the direct measurement of the epoxidation of aldrin to dieldrin.[11, 15, 25] Most vertebrates were found to have much higher activities than the trout, which is in general agreement with the work of Brodie and Maickel (Table 1). The female quail was unusual amongst the higher vertebrates in showing a very low activity. The relatively weak oxidase activity shown by housefly microsomes in comparison with verte-

Table 1   Aldrin epoxidase activity in different species

Mammals (Liver)	Activity $m\mu$ moles/min/mg protein x 10^3	
Rabbit	344†	
Rat	274†	
Rat (male)	84	
Rat (female)	21	22*
Pig	273	
Mouse (male)	78	
Mouse (female)	176	
Birds (Liver)		
Quail (male)	108	
Quail (female)	9	
Feral pigeon (male)	78*	
Fish (Liver)		
Rainbow trout	6	
Insects		
Housefly (whole) (Musca domestica)	41	
Housefly (whole) (Musca vicina)	25	
Blowfly (whole) (Phormia regina)	3	
Southern army worm (gut) (Prodenia eridania)	2145	

* Microsomal protein by Lowry method
† Protein estimation by micro kjeldahl method
   All other protein estimations by Biuret method
After Krieger and Wilkinson[15]

brates may help to explain certain observations made *in vivo* which will be discussed later.

Potter and O'Brien [26] have cast some doubt upon the distinction between mammals and birds as against reptiles, fish and amphibia. Comparing the oxidation of parathion to paraoxon (P=S → P=O) in a number of species they found no consistent difference between aquative and terrestrial vertebrates. This evidence is inconclusive, however, because only the final quantity of paraoxon was measured and no allowance was possible for the amount that had been hydrolysed. In general it seems to be true that fish have relatively weak mixed function oxidase activity in comparison with land vertebrates.[25]

Studies upon metabolites excreted by various animals have revealed striking interspecific differences with regard to hydroxylation reactions which are evidently carried out largely or entirely by mixed function oxidation. Aniline, for example, can be hydroxylated in the ortho or the para positions. In a comparative study, both metabolites were excreted in the urine of all the species investigated although in differing proportions.[27] Five rodent species, the rabbit and the hen carried out mainly para hydroxylation, whereas three carnivores (the cat, the dog and the ferret) showed either a preference for ortho hydroxylation or a balance between the two forms of attack.

The surprisingly high epoxidase activity shown by microsomes prepared from the mid gut of the southern army worm compared with those made from the whole body highlights a particular problem in studies with insects.[15] The reason for this was that the epoxidase was being inhibited in whole insect preparations by a proteinase originally present in the gut contents. Clearly, comparative *in vitro* studies with insects can be meaningless unless done on separate tissues. Even with preparations from individual tissue there is reason for caution since it is always possible to bring the microsomes into contact with inhibitors which would not have affected the endoplasmic reticulum *in vivo* in a comparable way.

This is a suitable point at which to draw attention to some of the limitations of comparative *in vitro* studies of this type as a means of predicting events in the whole animal. The rate at which metabolism occurs in the animal is not simply related to the activity found *in vitro*. It is influenced by such things as the availability of cofactors, the presence of inhibitors, whether or not enzyme induction occurs, and the extent to which the substrate is brought into contact with the systems that can degrade it (fat storage, for example, can limit metabolic rate). Furthermore, *in vitro* studies for vertebrates are mainly upon liver preparations which leaves the metabolism by other tissues or gut microflora as an open question. On the technical side, mixed function oxidase are not very stable, and it is questionable how well their original activity is represented in microsomal preparations derived from different species. Again, the temperature at which assays are conducted is critical e.g. trout liver microsomes are more active at 26° C than at 37° C. Nevertheless the measurement of microsomal activities has given useful basic information on the potential that different species have for mixed function oxidation of various foreign compounds. These and other activity measurements have some predictive value with regard to *in vivo* metabolism if used with caution.

Esterases and Amidases

The esterases, phosphatases and amidases dicussed here are only those which have been shown to metabolise foreign compounds. Sometimes these are enzymes which have a known role for metabolising endogenous compounds; in most cases no such role has been identified. Representatives of the first two groups are found both in the soluble and membrane-bound states.

Esterases are very widely distributed in nature and vary greatly in character and activity between species and between tissues. The picture is complicated by the fact that any particular reaction may be mediated by different enzymes in different tissues.[28] The classification of esterases has rested primarily on their substrate specificity and their sensitivity to inhibition, but this has sometimes been misleading since different esterases can show the same properties when studied in this way. With more critical investigation the complexity of this subject is becoming apparent, and much still remains to be done in this field.

Phosphatases too are diverse in character and present similar problems of identification, but have not been as well investigated as esterases.[29]

Of the esterases, two classes are of particular interest in the present context – the aryl esterases and the aliesterases. Aliesterases (β esterases) catalyse the hydrolysis of both aliphatic and aromatic esters but not choline esters. An imidazole group and a serine hydroxyl group are present at the active centre, but there is no complementary anionic site.[30] In contrast to lipases they act selectively upon water soluble esters rather than fat soluble esters.

The carboxyesterase which degrades the organophosphorus insecticide malathion in rat and human liver preparations and in rat serum, has been identified as an aliesterase.[31, 29] Activity towards this substrate is generally much higher in vertebrates than in insects, and this appears to be the basis of the very useful selective toxicity shown by malathion.

A striking interspecific difference was found in an investigation of plasma esterases. Aliesterases were absent from the plasma of human, monkey, dog and pig, but accounted for most of the esterase activity in the plasma of lower vertebrates. It may be that aliesterases have been replaced by cholinesterases during the course of the evolution of the vertebrates.

Aryl esterases preferentially catalyse the hydrolysis of aromatic esters, especially those containing acetate. There is evidence that a sulphydryl group of the enzyme interacts with a double bond of the substrate to form a thiol-ester intermediate.[32] These enzymes are selective for esters where the double bond of the alcohol moiety is in the α position relative to the ester linkage. For this reason certain aliphatic esters with the double bond correctly situated (e.g. vinyl acetate) can be hydrolysed by aryl esterases. By contrast with aliesterases, aryl esterases are not effectively inhibited by organophosphate. Indeed some organophosphates are hydrolysed by them.

Organophosphate insecticides can be hydrolysed by phosphatases in all mammals, insects and plants, and this is usually the major degradative pathway. However, the enzymes involved have not been properly characterised and it is not clear what their relationship is to the phosphatases concerned with normal metabolism. Hydrolytic attack is not restricted to P-O-C bonds; -P-S-C and P-F bonds can also be cleaved.

The hydrolytic degradation of paraoxon provides a good example of this type of enzyme. There are at least three different enzymes in rat liver which can hydrolyse paraoxon, each showing a different pH optimum and different ion sensitivity. In a comparative study of paraoxon hydrolysis in samples of mammalian serum, the rates of degradation were placed in the following order: – rabbit > ferret > sheep > rat > guinea pig > goat, human > horse > mouse.[34] Rabbit serum was about eight times more active than mouse serum.

Amidase activity has been studied in connection with the degradation of dimethoate.[29] By contrast with the systems discussed above, the enzyme involved is found almost exclusively in the liver.

Epoxide hydration

Another microsomal enzyme that has proved to be important in the metabolism of foreign compounds is an epoxide hydrase. This enzyme mediates the cleavage of epoxide rings by the addition of the elements of water to form trans 1,2 diols.[35] It operates in the absence of cofactors, is not dependent upon NADPH or molecular oxygen, and is not very sensitive to methylenedioxyphenyl inhibitors such as piperonyl butoxide and sesamex, features which distinguish it clearly from mixed function oxidases. Microsomal epoxide hydrase has one thing in common with the latter system however – it can convert liposoluble foreign compounds into more water soluble metabolites which are readily excreted in either the free or conjugated form. The range of substrates that it can metabolise is fairly wide including octene oxides,[36] styrene oxide, cyclohexane oxide, benzene oxide,[37] phenanthrene 9:10 oxide, dibenz (a, h) anthracene 5,6 oxide[38] and a number of chlorinated cyclodiene epoxides with insecticidal activity.[26] These epoxides are hydrated fairly rapidly with the exception of the insecticides dieldrin and heptachlor epoxide.[39, 40, 41] It is of considerable interest that a dieldrin analogue HEOM which differs from the commercial insecticide only in lacking an endomethylene bridge across the non-chlorinated ring is rapidly metabolised by microsomal epoxide hydrase.

In the guinea pig, rat and rabbit, hydrase activity towards arene oxides was found to be high in the liver, low in the kidney and absent from most other tissues.[42] The activity in liver homogenates was located mainly in the microsomal fraction.

Microsomal epoxide hydrase can display stereo selectivity towards its substrates. Brooks et al [40] have shown that pig and rabbit liver microsomes are only able to hydrate up to 50% of HCE, an asymmetric analogue of dieldrin, and that both the residual substrate and the diol show optical activity. They conclude that only the (+) enantiomer of HCE can be readily hydrated by the enzyme.

Some, but not all, of the epoxide hydrase can be isolated from microsomes by treating with deoxycholate, and fractionating with ammonium sulphate.[43] There is evidence that two forms of the enzyme exist. Although most methylenedioxyphenyl compounds have little effect upon epoxide hydrase activity, some epoxides are quite strong inhibitors. Investigating the effects of inhibitors upon the hydration of styrene oxide, Oesch et al. [44] found that p nitrophenylglycidylether and 1:1:1 trichloroepoxypropane were effective inhibitors. The former inhibitor was competitive, the latter uncompetitive. Other studies have shown that relatively high concentrations of SKF 525A, triorthocresyl phosphate and triphenyl phosphate are also inhibitory.[11]

The epoxide substrates discussed up to this point are relatively stable compounds. Attention has also been focussed upon relatively unstable epoxide intermediates formed during the hydroxylation of aromatic compounds. An example of this is provided by the metabolism of naphthalene. This compound is oxidised to the unstable epoxide naphthalene 1,2 oxide, which undergoes transformation in two distinct ways – (1) by rearrangement to a 1 naphthol involving the migration of a hydrogen atom (NIH shift) (Fig. 1) and (2) by conversion to a trans diol by epoxide hydrase attack.[45, 11] In accordance with this, the competitive blocking of hydrase activity by styrene oxide causes increased production of 1 naphthol from naphthalene. There is also evidence that epoxides are intermediates in the microsomal hydroxylation of benzene, phenanthrene, dibenz (a, h) anthracene and dibenz (a) anthracene.[46] This may have a

Table 2   Comparative epoxide hydrase activity towards HEOM in male vertebrate liver preparations

Species	Microsomal hydrative activity μg diol/mg protein/min	% Hydration * Microsomes	Homogenate 11,000 g supernatant
Mammals			
Pig 11	31.35†	—	—
Rabbit+	14.50	98	96
Rat	1.80	94	94
Birds			
Rook (Corvus frugilegus)	—	92	85
Jackdaw (Corvus monedula)	0.48	90	—
Fowl (Gallus domesticus)	—	65	—
Quail (Coturnix coturnix)	0.019	16	11
Fulmar (Fulmarus glacialis)	—	13	—
Pigeon (Columba livia)	0.0016	4	6

Incubation temperature: 37° C for mammals, 42° C for birds
Incubation time: 30 mins, pH 7.4
Substrate: 40 μg HEOM
Protein determinations by Lowry's method

*   Each incubation contained material prepared from 0.2 g liver
†   pH 8.4 incubation at 30° C
+   Female gave similar activity

bearing on the carcinogenic activity of some of these polycyclic aromatic compounds. It now seems likely that unstable epoxide intermediates derived from certain of these substances are able to alkylate DNA. At the same time it should be borne in mind that unstable epoxides are suitable substrates for hydration so their availability for alkylation may be dependent upon epoxide hydrase activity.

One other conversion affected by epoxide hydrase deserves mention – the conversion of squalene 2,3 oxide into lanosterol. The juvenile hormones of some insects are analogous to squalene 2,3 oxide, and it is possible that the enzyme has a role in their synthesis.[40]

Epoxide hydrase activity in liver homogenates and microsomes has proved to be extremely variable between species. Usind HEOM as a substrate, and measuring activity as μg trans diol/mg mi-

crosomal protein/minute, the rabbit, pig and rat showed much greater activity than the pigeon and quail, with the jackdaw occupying an intermediate position (Table 2).[47, 48] The rabbit showed nearly 10,000 times more activity than the pigeon under the same assay conditions. A similar picture was found when comparing the amounts of trans diol produced under standard assay conditions in supernatants and microsomes from different species. Overall the mammals exhibited considerably more activity than the birds although the rook and the jackdaw, two members of the corvidae, approached the mammals in activity.

Hydrase activity has also been measured using HCE, another dieldrin analogue. In this case both oxidation and hydration were allowed to proceed and the balance between the two was studied (Table 3, Fig. 2).[39, 48] Once again the rabbit and the

Table 3 Comparative metabolism of HCE by male vertebrate liver microsomes

Species	% Substrate metabolised	
	by hydration	by oxidation
Mammals		
Pig [39]	30	30
Rabbit	10	60
Rat [39]	1	40
Birds		
Rook	12	50
Jackdaw	3	80
Quail	2	60
Fulmar	2	70
Pigeon	0	90

Incubation at pH 7.4
Mammals – 30 mins at 37° C
Birds – 90 mins at 42° C

pig gave the most active microsomes and the pigeon the least active microsomes (no measurable conversion to the trans diol). The only significant departure from the investigation with HEOM came in the position occupied by the rat which showed the lowest measurable activity – but it should be noted that there were different assay conditions for mammals as opposed to birds. A longer incubation time for the rat liver microsomes should have increased the amount of hydration relative to oxidation since the former system is more stable than the latter.

Phase II Reactions — Conjugations

The excretion of many liposoluble foreign compounds (or their metabolites) is aided by coupling them with appropriate endogenous molecules, to form water-soluble conjugates. Although certain endogenous molecules are widely used for this purpose throughout the animal kingdom there are nevertheless some

marked interspecific differences in conjugation reactions. Indeed, the differences between species are more striking than are those found with primary metabolic transformations such as oxidations and hydrolyses. The preferred endogenous molecule seems to depend upon what is available in the species in question,[49] a point we shall be returning to later.

As with other aspects of the comparative metabolism of foreign compounds, conjugations have been better studied with drugs than with pesticides. The conjugations that will now be discussed in some detail are those that are known to have a significant role in the elimination of pesticides. Thus the systems involved in the production of ethereal sulphates, methyl derivatives and certain peptide-conjugates will only be mentioned in passing although they are of recognised importance in the metabolism of drugs.

Glucuronide formation

Glucuronide formation is the most common type of conjugation recognised in mammals and is mediated by a number of glucuronyl transferases [49] (cf insects which form glucosides but not glucuronides). It is important not only in the removal of foreign compounds but also of endogenous substances such as steroids and catecholamines. It seems that foreign and endogenous compounds sometimes share the same glucuronyl transferase.

The products of glucuronide conjugation are β D glucosiduronic acids in which attachment to the foreign molecule is made through the C_1 atom.[50] A free carboxyl group at the C_6 position contributes to the polarity of the molecule. Conjugation does not take place with free glucuronic acid but with UDP glucuronic acid. There are two known routes for its synthesis.

1. UDP glucose + NAD → UDP glucuronic acid + NADH
UDP glucose dehydrogenase
2. UDP-L Iduronic → UDP glucuronic acid (UDPGA)
epimerase

The transfer of glucuronide from UDPGA to foreign substrates (aglycones) is mediated by a group of enzymes called glucuronyl transferases which are located in the endoplasmic reticulum.

UDP glucuronic acid + ROH → UDP + R-O-glucuronic acid
(β glucuronide)
UDP glucuronyl transferase

It is doubtful whether any glucuronyl transferases have been isolated from the endoplasmic reticulum in a completely pure state for they are very much a part of the membrane structure, and quickly lose activity when attempts to isolate and purify them are made.[50]

O-, H-, and S-glucuronyl transferases are known, all of which bring about addition of glucuronic acid with displacement of a labile proton from the substrate. The groups with which glucuronic acid may interact are hydroxyl, carboxyl, amino, imino and sulphydryl. It now appears that there are a number of similar enzymes with overlapping specificities. This view is supported by the existence of qualitative differences between species and strains. Gunn rats, for example, are unable to synthesise a number of common O-glucuronides but can produce N glucuronides.[51] Some species seem to be deficient in certain glucuronyl transferases. The cat, for example, is unable to form certain common glucuronides although it does not lack UDP-glucuronic acid in the liver and there are glucuronides that it can synthesise.[49] Also some primates including man, the rhesus monkey and the baboon can form the N-glucuronide of sulphadimethoxine whereas the rat, rabbit, dog and guinea pig evidently cannot.[52]

All mammals, birds and reptiles so far studied possess UDP glucuronyl trans- ferase activity, as do adult forms of those amphibians that are predominantly terrestrial.[49, 50] On the other hand amphibians that are predominantly aquatic do not show any activity. The situation in fish is variable – some species show weak glucuronyl transferase activity, others show none at all. In general, this is in good agreement with the theory that species living entirely in an aquatic environment do not depend upon metabolic conversion of liposoluble compounds to promote excretion.

Dorough has made the interesting suggestion that glucuronyl transferases are closely associated with mixed function oxidases in the microsomal membrane.[53] Hepatic glucuronyl transferases have a further point in common with mixed function oxidases. They are also induced by liposoluble compounds such as 3,4 benzpyrene and 3-methyl cholanthrene.[50]

Glutathione conjugation

Glutathione conjugation is another important process for the elimination of pesticides, and has been the subject of a recent review by Boyland.[55] The enzymes that can catalyse the interaction between glutathione and foreign compounds are termed glutathione-S-transferases and are typically found in the supernatants of liver homogenates after high speed centri-

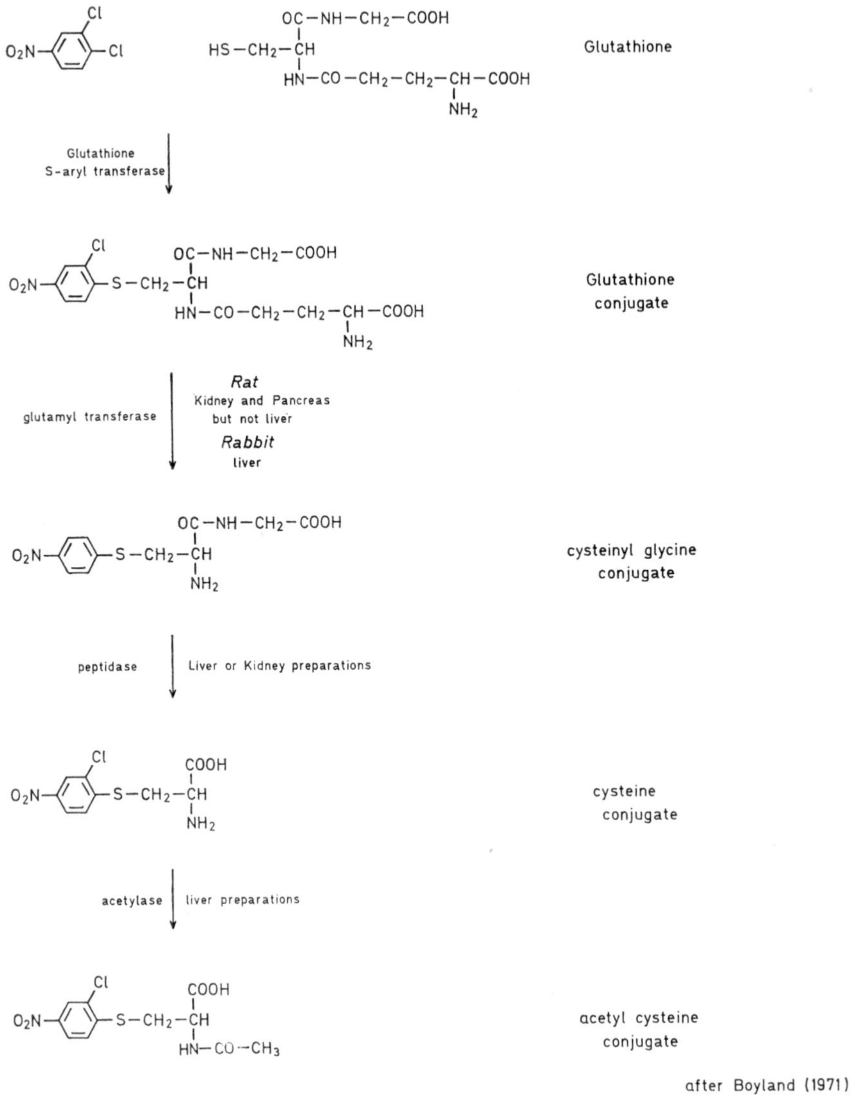

Fig. 3   *The formation of the acetyl cysteine conjugate of 1, 2 dichloro 4 nitro benzene*

fugation (usually 70,000 g for 1 hour). Ten different glutathione-S-transferases have already been characterised which is somewhat surprising since in theory a single enzyme able to atcivate glutathione is all that is required. This points to the enzymes having the function of bringing glutathione and substrate together by binding them to active sites.[55] The original function of the enzymes is obscure. All of the known reactions catalysed by them involve foreign compounds and not endogenous substances. It has been suggested that they protect cellular nucleophiles by removing foreign electrophiles that may attack them.

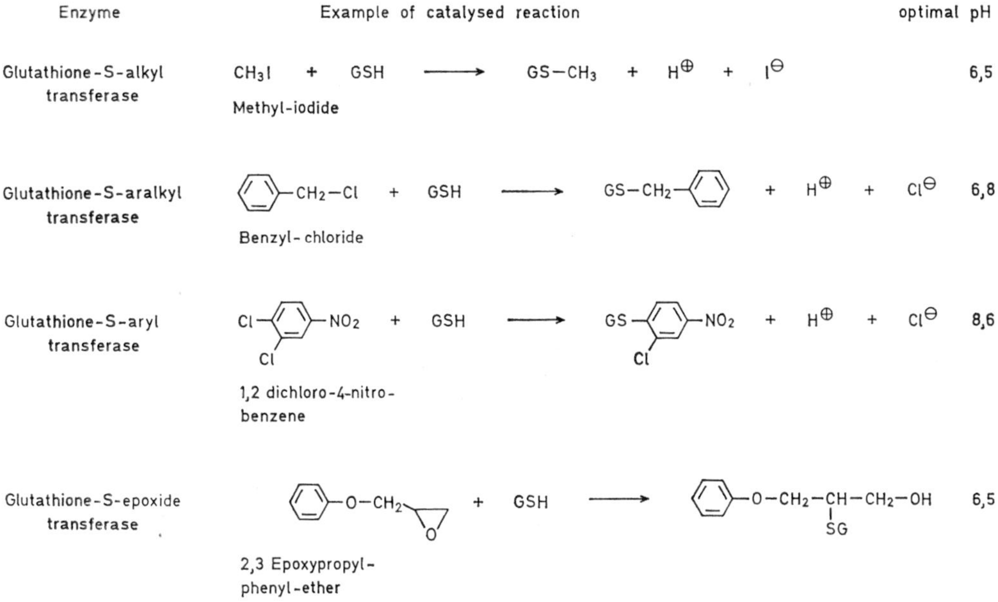

Enzyme	Example of catalysed reaction	optimal pH
Glutathione-S-alkyl transferase	CH_3I + GSH $\longrightarrow$ $GS-CH_3$ + $H^{\oplus}$ + $I^{\ominus}$ Methyl-iodide	6,5
Glutathione-S-aralkyl transferase	benzyl$-CH_2-Cl$ + GSH $\longrightarrow$ $GS-CH_2-$benzyl + $H^{\oplus}$ + $Cl^{\ominus}$ Benzyl-chloride	6,8
Glutathione-S-aryl transferase	$Cl-$benzene$(Cl)-NO_2$ + GSH $\longrightarrow$ $GS-$benzene$(Cl)-NO_2$ + $H^{\oplus}$ + $Cl^{\ominus}$ 1,2 dichloro-4-nitro-benzene	8,6
Glutathione-S-epoxide transferase	phenyl$-O-CH_2-$(epoxide) + GSH $\longrightarrow$ phenyl$-O-CH_2-CH-CH_2-OH$ with SG 2,3 Epoxypropyl-phenyl-ether	6,5

Fig. 4   *Some glutathione-S-transferases*

Glutathione conjugates are not usually excreted unchanged by vertebrates. The excreted forms are usually acetyl-cysteine derivatives produced by further metabolism. The generally accepted pathway for the formation of acetyl-cysteine conjugates is given in Fig. 3 taking the conjugate of 1,2 dichloro-4 nitrobenzene as an example. The complete conversion of such a conjugate to its acetyl-cysteine derivative has been demonstrated in rabbit liver. A somewhat different [56] situation has been reported for the rat where γ glutamyl transferase activity was not found in the liver although it was present in the kidney where conversion of a glutathione conjugate to its cysteine derivative was demonstrated.

By contrast with vertebrates, insects excrete the unchanged glutathione conjugate and/or its cysteine derivative rather than the acetyl cysteine derivative.[57]

Some of the better characterised glutathione-S-transferases are detailed in Fig. 3. Broadly speaking they may be divided into: –

1. Enzymes that catalyse the addition of the whole glutathione molecule to the substrates e.g. glutathione-S-epoxide transferase;

2. Enzymes that catalyse the addition of glutathione to the substrate with attendant loss of labile hydrogen from the -SH group e.g. glutathione S aryl-, S alkyl- and S aralkyl-transferases.

Glutathione-S-epoxide transferase can catalyse the conjugation of a number of epoxides including 2,3 epoxy propylphenyl ether, styrene oxide, and various epoxides of polycyclic aromatic hydrocarbons. It now appears that unstable epoxides produced by mixed function oxidation of polycyclic aromatic compounds such as benz(a) anthracene and dibenz(a, h) anthracene may be intermediates in the production of glutathione conjugates.[58]

Substrates handled by glutathione-S-aryl

transferase include *p*-chloronitrobenzene, *p* dichlorobenzene and the fungicide tetrachlorodinitrobenzene (TCNB). Distribution studies on glutathione-S-aryl transferase have demonstrated its presence in a wide range of vertebrates and insects. Evidence from studies with 3,4 dichloronitrobenzene (DCNB) and 2, 3, 5, 6 tetrachloronitrobenzene indicates that the enzyme exists in more than one form. For example, glutathione-S-aryl transferase activity towards these substrates was inhibited by certain phthaleins, sulphophthalein and dicarboxylic acids in sheep liver homogenates but not in the case of grass grub preparations.[59] Again sulphobromonaphthalein was a competitive inhibitor for the enzyme in rat liver supernatants, but an uncompetitive inhibitor for the enzyme in pigeon liver homogenates, when the substrate was DCNB.[60] In an investigation of hepatic glutathione-S-transferase activity in the livers of nine different vertebrates, Boyland and Chasseaud[61] found more variation in glutathione-S-aryl transferase activity than in the activities of certain other glutathione conjugating enzymes. The highest glutathione-S-aryl transferase activities were found in the female dog and the male guinea pig, and these were some forty times higher than the value found for adult humans.

Glutathione-S-alkyl transferase can tackle a wide range of substrates e.g. alkyl bromides, β propiolactone, and certain organophosphate insecticides. Aglutathione-S-transferase is also involved in the metabolism of the insecticide γ BHC in both insects and vertebrates, although current evidence suggests that a different form exists in insects than in mammals. In insects, direct conjugation of BHC with glutathione is thought to occur, leading to dehydrochlorination and the production of the aromatic conjugate S-2,4 dichlorophenyl glutathione. [62, 11] The rat and the rabbit on the other hand seem to lack this type of activity and couple glutathione to pentachlorocyclohexene derived from γ BHC by dehydrochlorination. [63]

Generally speaking there is considerable variation in glutathione-S-transferase ac-

Table 4   Glutathione S Transferases in different species

Species	Activity in dialysed supernatants of liver homogenates				
	No. of Specimens Sex	Activity μ moles thiol lost/min/g liver			
		Alkyl	Aryl	Aralkyl	Epoxide
Guinea Pig	2 M	1.3	1.3	7.4	2.1
Pigeon	6 M	10.7	0.4	3.3	1.0
Rat	> 30 F	3.0	0.5	2.3	2.1
Dog	1 M	0.4	1.1	1.1	0.8
	1 F	0.6	1.6	2.1	1.0
Mouse	20 M	3.5	1.2	1.9	3.0
Hamster	5 M	1.7	0.2	1.9	1.7
Rabbit	1 M	1.1	0.7	1.1	0.3
Human	1 F	0.8	0.04	0.5	0.4
Ferret	2 M	0.4	0.5	0.3	0.8

M = Male
F = Female
After E. Boyland and L. F. Chasseaud[61]

tivity between species, but as yet no clear trends based on groups or habitat are discernable. The different enzymes within this group show different distributions from one another as can be seen in Table 4. For example guinea pig liver has relatively strong glutathione-S-aralkyl transferase activity but relatively weak glutathione-S-alkyl transferase activity. Brooks suggests that interspecific variations with respect to enzymes of this group may provide a basis for the selective toxicity of pesticides.[11]

Interspecific Differences in Enzymes Which Metabolise Foreign Compounds

Clear cut interspecific differences have been recognised in the operation of certain conjugation systems that have not been discussed so far. Peptide conjugation is a good example. All terrestrial animals so far investigated can form glycine conjugates [64, 49] Birds and reptiles can also form ornithine conjugates whereas amphibia cannot. An explanation for this has been advanced on evolutionary grounds. It is suggested that ornithine conjugation developed some 200 million years ago after amphibia had split off from the branch of the evolutionary tree that was to give rise to reptiles and birds. There appears to be a relationship between urinary nitrogen metabolism and ornithine conjugation.[64, 65] For example, the onset of conjugation in the hens egg coincides with the commencement of uric acid synthesis. Arachnida and myriapoda are unusual in showing arginine and to some extent glutamine conjugation in addition to glycine conjugation.[49] Conjugation with arginine predominates and its use may be connected with the plentiful supply of arginine in these groups.

A further example of an absolute interspecific difference comes with glycoside formation. Glucuronides are formed by most mammals, birds, reptiles and amphibia, but not by fish (fish possess the necessary conjugating enzyme but lack UDP-glucuronic acid). Insects and molluscs form glucosides but not glucuronides.

The development of conjugation mechanisms in the mammalian embryo follows an interesting sequence that may correspond to the course of evolution:–[65]

Early embryo
   Acetylation, ethereal sulphate synthesis
Half developed
   Glycine and ornithine conjugation
Just before birth
   Glucuronide conjugation

To summarise, conjugating systems vary more between species than do primary processes such as oxidation and hydrolysis, and in some instances these differences are qualitative. Attempts have been made to explain qualitative differences upon evolutionary grounds. There is evidence that fish and certain other aquatic vertebrates are deficient in enzymes which can render liposoluble compounds more water soluble. Brodie and Maickel[21] argue that systems which can metabolise foreign compounds in this way may have been evolved in response to the movement from water to land. Whereas aquatic vertebrates can excrete liposoluble substances directly, by diffusion across the skin or gills into the surrounding water, terrestrial vertebrates must first render them water soluble so that they may be excreted via the urine or bile.

The Excretion of Foreign Compounds by Vertebrates and Insects

It should be emphasised that the processes concerned with the excretion of foreign compounds have been much more thoroughly investigated in vertebrates than they have been in insects. Accordingly this account of excretion by insects is inevitably fragmentary and tentative.

In insects and land vertebrates the elimination of both endogenous and exogenous waste products is tied up with the problem of conservation of water. Many water-soluble waste products are removed by a filtration process leading to the production of hypertonic urine after reabsorption of water. In vertebrates, blood is filtered through a glomerulus, and water and certain useful substances are reabsorbed during passage of the filtrate down the kidney tubule. The malphighian tubules of insects produce what is essentially an ultrafiltrate of haemolymph. Water and useful solutes are reabsorbed later from the hind gut after urine has been discharged into it. Sometimes insects excrete toxic substances simply by storing them in suitable tissues, e.g. the deposition of uric acid in the urate cells of the fat body in the cockroach and *Nemeritis canescens*. Insects and land vertebrates other than mammals combine urine and faeces before final elimination from the body. This occurs in the hind gut of insects, but in the cloaca of vertebrates. Mammals on the other hand eliminate urine separately from faeces, a process that involves considerable water loss from the body. Freshwater fish contrast with the foregoing vertebrates in having no problem of water conservation and producing hypotonic urine (cf marine fish).

By contrast with urinary excretion, biliary excretion is confined to vertebrates. Often it provides the principal excretory route for a foreign compound. Excretion of foreign compounds can also take place in milk, sweat, eggs, and the secretions of the gastrointestinal lining. These routes will not be discussed further here, but will be considered from the comparative point of view later in this section.

Urinary and biliary excretion by vertebrates will be considered first, to be followed by an account of excretion by insects and a short discussion.

Urinary Excretion by Vertebrates

The following account will refer in the first place to mammals; special features shown by other groups will be considered later.

The filtration of blood through the glomerulus of the kidney leaves behind most of the plasma proteins together with any foreign compounds that are tightly bound to them. Many water soluble compounds up to a fairly high molecular weight pass through into the tubular lumen at a similar concentration to that originally present in the blood. Throughout subsequent passage down the kidney tubule (especially in the distal region) there is passive transfer of liposoluble molecules across the wall, between the glomerular filtrate and the blood stream.[49] In the case of most weak acids and bases, the non-ionised forms are sufficiently liposoluble to move in this way; the extent to which non-ionised forms exist is determined by the pH of the filtrate which can change markedly with movement down the tubule. Thus, there can be a changing pattern of passive excretion and absorption of such substances as the filtrate moves along the kidney tubule. The reabsorption of water and useful solutes also takes place during this movement. Water removal can, of course, increase the concentration of liposoluble compounds in the lumen, thereby encouraging them to diffuse across the wall into the blood in an attempt to restore equilibrium. Thus, the situation in the kidney tubule is complex and dynamic. One important point, however, requires stressing. Water soluble foreign compounds, e.g. glucuronides and aryl sulphate conjugates, do not tend to be reabsorbed into the blood, but are usually moved into the bladder with the urine, and this provides an effective mechanism for eliminating them from the body. A possible complicating factor, however, is the existence of enzymes in urine that can break down conjugates. It has been shown, for example, that β glucuronidase exists at a relatively high concentration in rat urine.[66] If this is active within the kidney tubules, the release and subsequent reabsorption of non polar aglycones is to be anticipated.

In the proximal tubules of the kidney there are also active transport systems which bring about excretion. Two different systems have been recognised – one for strong organic acids and another for strong organic bases. These systems can deal with both endogenous and exogenous foreign compounds so that, for example, hippuric acid and probenecid, choline and hexamethonium are excreted by the same systems. This provides a further mechanism favouring the elimination of water-soluble metabolites and conjugates with the urine.

There are a number of special features shown by different groups of vertebrates. Freshwater fish, for example, do not concentrate their urine to make it hypertonic. Reptiles, amphibians and birds and certain fish discharge their urine into the cloaca where it is combined with the faeces whereas mammals void urine and faeces independently. The extent to which discharge into the cloaca can lead to reabsorption of materials present in the urine does not appear to have been investigated.

In general, the influence of these interspecific differences in urinary excretion upon the elimination of foreign compounds deserves closer study than it has so far received.

Biliary Excretion by Vertebrates

It is only relatively recently that the importance of this excretory route has come to be recognised.[67] As with urine a wide range of water soluble foreign compounds are excreted in the bile and prominent amongst these are glucuronide, peptide and aryl sulphate conjugates. The process is remarkably similar to that concerned with the removal of endogenous steroids such as the bile salts and hydrophilic metabolites of testosterone and oestradiol.

The subsequent fate of conjugates after they have been released within the gut is of importance. If they are not broken down, they usually pass out of the body with the faeces. On the other hand many conjugates are degraded in the gut, usually by microbial attack. When this results in the release of a relatively liposoluble molecule, reabsorption usually occurs. Frequently this leads to the compound being returned to the liver, reconjugated and re-excreted, a process known as "enterohepatic circulation". In some cases reabsorption can lead to the compound being excreted in the urine.[67] Another problem with biliary excretion is that a compound may be further metabolised in the gut. In the case of chloramphenicol glucuronide for example, hydrolysis occurs followed by further metabolism. The metabolites so formed are thyrotoxic.[68] Thus, it is clear that the degree to which a compound is excreted in the bile can have an important bearing upon its ultimate fate (and therefore upon the toxic effects of it or its metabolites) within the animal. Interspecific variations in this respect can have important implications with regard to comparative metabolism.

In a study of the excretion of 16 different organic anions in the rat, rabbit and guinea pig, Hirom et al found that there was a connection between the molecular weight and the preferred excretory route.[69] In all three species, molecules having molecular weights below 300 were excreted mainly in the urine; those with values above 500 were excreted mainly in the bile. For molecules having intermediate molecular weights there were however marked differences between species. There appeared to be a molecular weight threshold, above which appreciable biliary excretion occurred ($> 10\%$). These thresholds were put at the following values: rat 325 ± 50, guinea pig 400 ± 50 and rabbit 475 ± 50. Other studies suggest that the dog and the hen have a relatively low threshold similar to that of the rat, whereas the rhesus monkey has a relatively high threshold comparable to that of the rabbit.[70]

Above the threshold molecular weight, considerable variations in the extent of biliary excretion were found between compounds having similar molecular weights in the case of the female rat. For example, the chain length of sulphonamides had an effect on this. It was suggested that the effect was due to differences in stereochemistry or differences in polarity or a combination of the two.[71]

It may be that these species differences in threshold molecular weight are the consequence of a selective filtration process.[72] It has been suggested that a "primary" form of bile is first produced and that this is later subjected to a selective reabsorption process whereby small molecules are removed to produce "secondary bile". Recent experiments involving retrograde biliary infusion in the rat lend support to this idea.[72] If this analysis is correct, then the threshold molecular weight is probably determined by pore size, and the importance of differences in stereochemistry should be easy to explain. It may also explain the existence of electrochemical potential gradients for certain foreign compounds between bile and liver blood which have hitherto been attributed to active transport.

Urinary Excretion by Insects

The uptake of simple ions and water by the malpighian tubules has been fairly well investigated in a number of insects including *Carausius morosus*, *Calliphora erythrocephala* and *Rhodnius*. There is evidence in all the three named insects for active transport of Na^+ and K^+, and passive movements of water across either or both the basal cell membrane and the apical cell membrane. There are also certain contrasts between *Rhodnius* and the other two species e.g. with regard to the movement of Cl^-, where only the former species can carry out active transport. These and other matters concerned with insect excretory systems have been comprehensively reviewed by Maddrell.[73]

Evidence is much more scanty for the uptake of organic molecules by malpighian tubules. Simple organic substances of low molecular weight such as sucrose, glycine and urea appear to enter by passive diffusion in Carausius, and their concentration in the urine often approaches but does not exceed that in the bathing fluid. By contrast certain acid dyestuffs of greater molecular weight than the foregoing substances (> 400) are concentrated by the malpighian tubules of a wide range of insects. The process evidently involves active transport and is not linked to fluid secretion.[74] Increasing the pH from 6.5 to 7.5 increases uptake pointing to transport of the anionic form.

The urine from the malpighian tubules runs into the hindgut of the insect, which is divided into two sections – the ileum and the rectum. In the hindgut selective reabsorption of water and small molecules occurs. The hindgut is lined with a fairly thick cuticle which is impermeable to large molecules. In the locust it has been estimated that the cuticle is impermeable to molecules greater than 5–6 Å in radius. It would appear that it serves a protective function by preventing the reabsorption of potentially toxic molecules exceeding 300–500 in molecular weight.[73]

Against this background the work of Cohen and Smith on the metabolism and excretion of *p* nitrobenzyl chloride by the locust *(Schistocerca gregaria)* is of considerable interest.[51] Glutathione conjugation yielded S (*p* nitro benzyl) glutathione as the major metabolite within the insect, and this appeared in the excreta. Some hydrolysis occurred in the malpighian tubules and hindgut to produce the corresponding cysteine conjugate. Both conjugates were found in the excreta. Other studies using γ BHC have shown that its principal transformation product is S-2,4 dichlorophenylglutathione in the locust, housefly, grass grubs (*Costelytra zealandica*), mature blow flies (*Lucilia sericata*) and also in cattle tick (*Boophilus decolopatus*).[62, 75]

γ BHC is converted into water soluble metabolites more rapidly in resistant houseflies than in normal ones, and this is correlated with a more rapid rate of excretion thereby providing a reasonable explanation of the resistance phenomenon.[76] Other evidence strongly suggests that these metabolites are in fact glutathione conjugates[59] or derivatives thereof. It seems that the production of water soluble glutathione conjugates is a very effective detoxication mechanism for organohalogen compounds in insects. These compounds, or their cysteine derivatives, do not appear to be effectively reabsorbed across the cuticular lining of the hindgut. The process is similar to that encountered in mammals where there are many examples of acetyl cysteine conjugates derived from glutathione conjugates being excreted via the urine.

Discussion

Mammals contrast with other vertebrates and insects in eliminating urine independently of faeces. This would appear to be advantageous because elimination is then direct, with less chance of further metabolic transformation with the attendant risks of reabsorption and the production of toxic metabolites. By the same token the existence of high molecular weight thresholds for biliary excretion in species like the rabbit and guinea pig may be an indication of relatively efficient elimination of compounds having molecular weights of less than 450. The limited evidence available indicates that insects as well as mammals tend to eliminate water soluble substances of relatively high molecular weight in the faeces, but for a different reason; the cuticular lining of the hindgut prevents their reabsorption after being taken into the gut with urine. The significance of other excretory routes which have some importance from the comparative point of view now requires brief mention. In the case of mammals and birds, the female possesses an excretory route not available to the male. Liposoluble substances such as DDT and dieldrin are readily excreted in the fat of milk and in the yolk of eggs. In certain cases, e.g. the fowl and the cow, these additional routes for excretion in the female are of some importance.

Another effective mechanism of excretion has been reported for DDT resistant larvae of the mosquito (*Aedes aegypti*). When the peritrophic membrane lining of the gut is rejected by the larva, it carries with it a considerable quantity of bound DDT. Finally fish and amphibia are able to excrete many liposoluble substances into surrounding water by passive diffusion across the gills and skin. It has been argued that these groups are not therefore as dependant as land vertebrates upon the conversion of liposoluble to water soluble compounds to promote excretion – the liposoluble compounds can usually be excreted in their unchanged forms.[22]

The Comparative Metabolism of Pesticides

The organochlorine insecticides

As a group, the organochlorine insecticides are noteworthy for their high liposolubility and their correspondingly low water solubility. They tend to be stored in the fatty tissues of the body. If they are not readily metabolised to more water soluble metabolites and conjugates, they can show considerable biological persistence. Their ability to persist is reflected in their biological half lives, which are discussed elsewhere in this review. Thus the comparative metabolism of organochlorine insecticides is not simply of interest in relation to selective toxicity and the identity of terminal residues; it is also tied up with the question of the persistence of the original liposoluble molecule at different points in ecosystems, a problem that does not arise with readily biodegradable compounds such as the organaphosphate insecticides. The organochlorine insecticides may be conveniently divided into three groups: – the cyclodiene insecticides; DDT and related compounds; isomers of benzene hexachloride.

The *cyclodiene insecticides* include the commercially produced compounds aldrin, dieldrin, heptachlor epoxide, endrin, chlordane, toxaphene, isodrin and telodrin, and the dieldrin analogues HCE and HEOM which have only been used experimentally. The last two compounds are included here because they are readily biodegradable and show some promise as tools for comparative studies

upon the enzyme systems involved in the degradation of cyclodiene compounds.

Surveys conducted in Britain between 1960 and 1965 showed dieldrin and heptachlor epoxide to be widely distributed in the living environment with relatively high concentrations in the eggs and tissues of certain predatory birds from both terrestrial and aquatic environments.[77, 78]

Marked interspecific variations in dieldrin metabolism have been found between the male rat [Carworth Farm E strain (CFE)], the male mouse [Carworth Farm No. 1 strain (CF1)] and the rabbit (Fig. 5).[79, 80] In both rats and mice the main excreted metabolite was 9-hydroxy dieldrin accounting for approximately 50% and approximately 70% respectively of the total excreted radioactivity. The rabbit, on the other hand, excreted predominantly aldrin transdihydrodiol ($>$ 80% total excreted radioactivity) [80, 81] which is only a minor metabolite in the other two species. In addition only the rat excreted a pentachloroketone ($<$ 10% total excreted radioactivity). Both rats and mice excreted relatively small amounts ($<$ 10% of total excreted radioactivity) of the dihydrochlordene-6,7 dicarboxylic acid.

A striking feature of these results is that the rabbit excretes mainly a hydration product whereas the rat and mouse excrete mainly oxidation products (as do rhesus monkeys and humans).[82] The slow hydration of dieldrin to aldrin transdiol by hepatic microsomal epoxide hydrase has been demonstrated by Brooks et al. for the rabbit and pig. The formation of 9-hydroxy dieldrin in 10,000 g supernatants of rat liver homogenate appears to be a mixed function oxidation since it is NADPH-dependent and sesamex sensitive and the pentachloroketone is formed under similar conditions, although the conversion appears to be insensitive to sesamex.

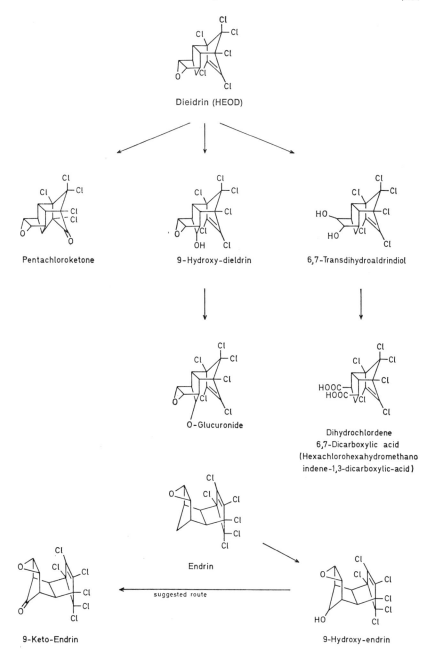

Fig. 5 The metabolism of dieldrin and endrin. All of these transformations can be carried out by male rats.

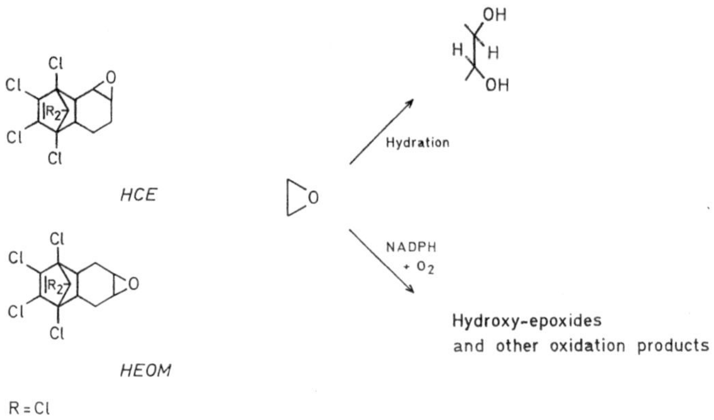

Fig. 6 Metabolism of HCE and HEOM

It is interesting to compare these findings with results obtained *in vitro* using the dieldrin analogues HCE and HEOM (Fig. 6). As we have seen epoxide hydrase activity towards HEOM is about six times greater in the rabbit than in the male rat.[47, 83] With HCE metabolism by hepatic microsomes, oxidation predominates over hydration in the rat, but the two systems show similar activity in the rabbit.[39, 83] Thus, the balance of oxidation and hydration exhibited by liver microsomes of the rat and the rabbit towards dieldrin analogues anticipates the differences in dieldrin metabolism shown by the two species *in vivo*. This holds out some promise for *in vitro* studies of this kind for the prediction of primary metabolism of cyclodiene compounds by different species *in vivo*.

The rat also differs from the rabbit in readily converting aldrin trans diol into dihydrochlordene 6,7 dicarboxylic acid, a change that hardly takes place at all in the rabbit.[84] This acid is the most important hydrophilic metabolite of aldrin in higher plants.[85]

The rat and the mouse also contrast with the rabbit respecting the preferred route of excretion of dieldrin metabolites. When rats were injected intravenously with C^{14} labelled dieldrin the rate of faecal excretion of radioactivity was about five times greater than the rate of urinary excretion,[79] which was in keeping with the relatively high rate of biliary excretion found in this specie.[86, 82] In other experiments male CFE rats, male CF1 mice and rabbits[79] were dosed orally with dieldrin. From three days after the discontinuation of dosing until the end of collection (when significant quantities of unabsorbed dieldrin were not likely to occur in the faeces), the ratios of urinary radioactivity:faecal radioactivity were as follows: – rabbit 134, CFE rats 0.17, CF1 mice 0.1.

The main excreted metabolite in rat bile is probably the glucuronide of 9-hydroxy dieldrin (M.Wt. = 573)[82] which is well over the average threshold molecular weight for biliary excretion by the rat.[69] On the other hand aldrin transdihydrodiol (M.Wt. 399) which is the main excreted metabolite in rabbit urine[80] comes well within the equivalent threshold value for this species.[69] Thus the contrasts reported here between the rat and the rabbit are explicable on the grounds of threshold molecular weights. If this analysis is correct it then appears that a metabolic difference between the species is crucial in determining the excretion route. If 9-hydroxy dieldrin glucuronide had been the main metabolite in the rabbit, then biliary excretion should have predominated.

Table 5   Excretory routes for metabolites of organochlorine insecticides in the rabbit and the male rat [48, 80, 81, 84, 86, 87]

Compound	Male rats					Rabbits				
	C^{14} excreted in urine / C^{14} excreted in faeces and urine	% Total dose excreted	Principal Excreted Metabolite	% Total excreted C^{14} as principal metabolite	Molecular weight	C^{14} excreted in urine / C^{14} excreted in faeces and urine	% Total dose excreted	Principal Excreted Metabolite	% Total excreted C^{14} as principal metabolite	Molecular weight
Dieldrin	0.18	19%	9 hydroxy dieldrin (faeces); 9 hydroxy dieldrin glucuronide? (bile)[82]	c 70%	397; 573	0.99 †	—	aldrin transdihydrodiol	c 85%	399
Heptachlor	0.08	14%	5 hydroxy heptachlor epoxide	c 80%	406	> 0.5	23%	5 hydroxy heptachlor epoxide	c 80%	406
Trans Chlordan	—	—	—	—	—	0.75 †	—	1 hydroxy 2 chloro dehydro-chlordene	—	392
Endrin	< 0.01	> 50%	9 hydroxy endrin[88]	—	397					
HCE	0.16	35%	Hydroxy HCE	c 60%	385	0.99	c 95%	Hydroxy HCE partially conjugated	45%	385 and 385 +

Unless otherwise stated, doses given by injection
† Insecticide administered orally. The ratio of urinary to total excretion was estimated as follows:
(1) Dieldrin — using only data from the period 2—30 days after dosing had ceased
(2) Chlordane — by not including unchanged chlordane excreted in faeces. Only hydrophilic metabolites were counted

Essentially the same pattern of excretion has also been observed with trans chlordane, heptachlor[87] and HCE[83] — see Table 5. In all cases the favoured route of elimination of the main metabolites is the urine in the rabbit but the faeces in the rat; this appears to be in agreement with the proposed threshold molecular weights for biliary excretion. The main faecal metabolites in the rat all have molecular weights exceeding 325, and in view of the likelihood of their being conjugated, these are to be regarded as minimum values so far as biliary excretion is concerned. With the rabbit, on the other hand, the molecular weights of the main urinary metabolites come within 475.

It is not clear, however, to what extent the metabolites in the urine represent the forms transported to the kidney in the blood. It is possible that conjugated forms are transported in the blood which are broken down in the kidney during excretion.

A notable feature of dieldrin elimination by the male rat is that there are different principal metabolites of dieldrin in the urine and bile. The main urinary metabolite is the pentachloroketone, whereas the main biliary metabolite is a glucuronide of 9-hydroxy dieldrin. This could fit in with the idea of a threshold molecular weight for biliary excretion, although the explanation may be that the keto metabolite is produced by the kidney and not by the liver.[82] The pentachloroketone is a compact molecule with a molecular weight of 351.5 which falls within the range of threshold molecular weight recorded by Hirom et al.,[69] although it exceeds the average value (cf 9-hydroxy dieldrin glucuronide).

With endrin too, a ketone (M.Wt. 395) is the main metabolite in male rat urine, but 9-hydroxy endrin is the main faecal metabolite.[88] In this case the urinary metabolite has a molecular weight that exceeds the range of threshold molecular weights found for the rat. However it should be noted that (1) these highly chlorinated molecules tend to be small in size for a given molecular weight in comparison with the compounds studied by Hirom et al.;[69] (2) the keto metabolite in contrast to 9-hydroxy endrin lacks a suitable group for glucuronide conjugation.

In contrast with dieldrin, photodieldrin and its metabolites seem to be excreted mainly via the urine in the rat.[89] One metabolite of photodieldrin is known to be the pentachloroketone, and this may partially explain this observation.

Interspecific differences have also been found in the metabolism of DDT and related compounds. pp'DDT (henceforward termed DDT) is the main insecticidal ingredient of technical DDT. Although its metabolism has been widely investigated, progress has been slow, partly because of the difficulty of determining very low concentrations of its metabolites in tissues, urine and faeces. The main degradative pathways known at the present time are given in Fig. 7.

The dehydrochlorination of DDT to form pp'DDE (henceforward termed DDE) has been found to occur in all organisms so far investigated with the possible exception of the monkey.[90] The enzyme DDT dehydrochlorinase has been isolated from DDT resistant house-flies and is glutathione dependent. Although the reaction is glutathione dependent, the production of DDE is not accompanied by any net consumption of glutathione. This does not exclude the possibility of the formation of a glutathione conjugate — it could be that such a conjugate is formed as an intermediate which then breaks down to release DDE.[11] DDT dehydrochlorination is a somewhat unusual reaction in that it does not lead to an increase in water solubility. DDE is highly liposoluble, is

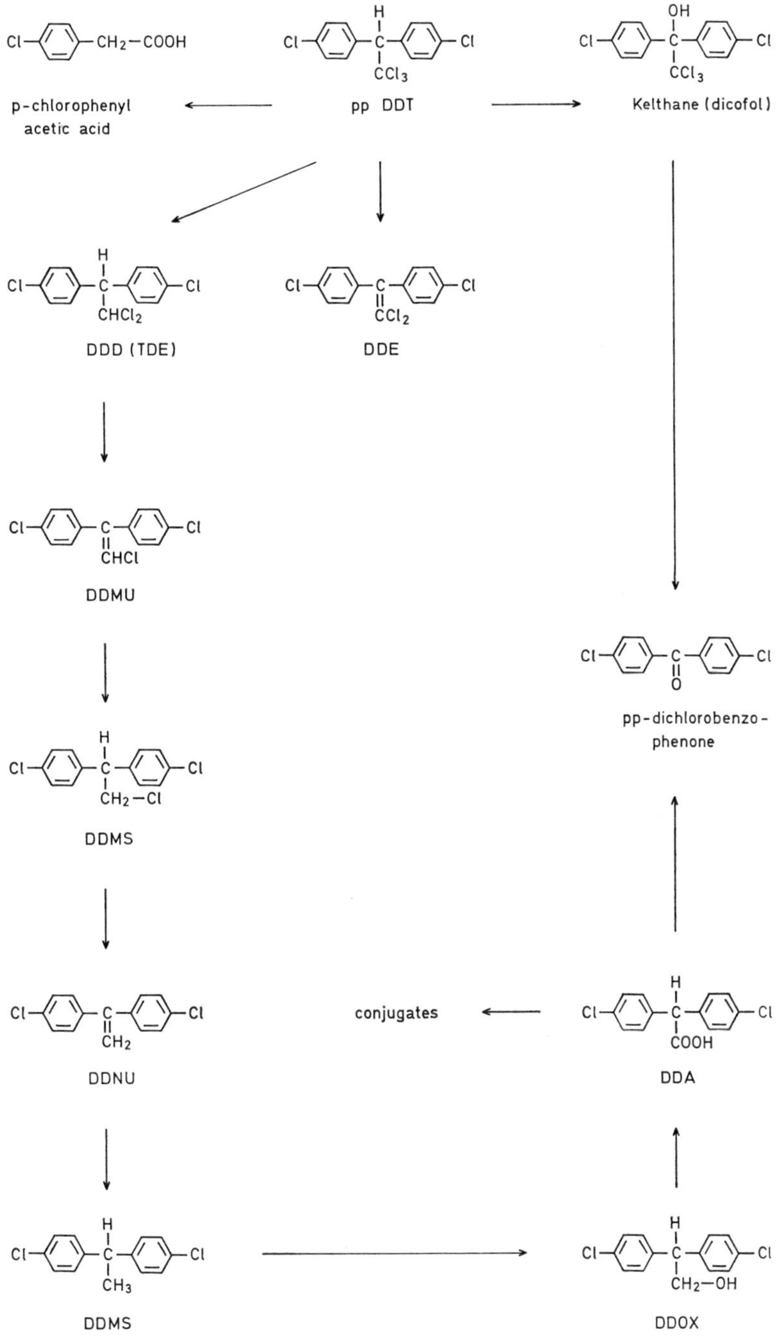

Fig. 7   *The degradation of pp DDT*

stored in fatty tissues, and shows very little tendency to be excreted by vertebrates. DDE evidently behaves in the same way in insects but nevertheless DDT dehydrochlorinase can have a detoxifying function here, suggesting that DDE has less intrinsic toxicity than DDT itself. DDT resistance in certain strains of house-fly is associated with an elevation of DDT dehydrochlorinase activity.[91] In culicine mosquitoes, anophelines, and the beetle *Tribolium castaneum* it is evidently the only metabolite of DDT formed (cf other insect species).[91]

DDE is not always the main metabolite of DDT in insects. Kelthane is the principal metabolite in the fruit fly (*Drosophilia melanogaster*)[92] and is also formed by *Triatoma infestans*[93] and probably by the house-fly. This metabolite of DDT can be produced by mixed function oxidation.[91] There is good evidence that resistance in a strain of *Sitophilus granarius* is associated with an increased capacity for oxidising DDT to kelthane.[94] Kelthane is less toxic to most insects than DDT, but this is not so with mites — kelthane is quite a potent acaricide. Kelthane is likely to be more readily excreted than DDT because it is more water soluble.

Other evidence suggesting that the versatile mixed function oxidase systems may be important in the elimination of DDT by insects comes from studies with synergists. Methylenedioxyphenyl compounds which inhibit mixed function oxidation can counteract the resistance shown by certain strains of house-fly to DDT.[95] Abdominal microsomes from resistant flies are able to degrade DDT to a number of water soluble products.[96] These metabolites appear to be produced by mixed function oxidation. The involvement of this system would be in keeping with the discovery that detoxication in these resistant strains is controlled by a single gene on the 5th chromosome. It would also explain the cross resistance found between DDT and certain organophosphates and carbamates, for which mixed function oxidation is a common detoxication system.[96, 97]

Another polar metabolite of DDT is pp'DDA (henceforward termed DDA) — see Fig. 6. A metabolic pathway has been proposed for DDA production involving pp'DDD (pp'TDE, henceforward termed DDD) as an intermediate. There are some uncertainties about this which will be discussed later. A conjugate of DDA is the principal excreted metabolite of DDT in the rat and is found mainly in the faeces.[98, 99] DDA is also excreted by humans, monkeys[90] and possibly by leghorn chicks,[100] and its formation has been demonstrated in the rabbit,[101] the body louse (*Pediculus humanus*)[102] and the tobacco budworm (*Heliothis virescens*).[103] The body louse can convert DDA into dichlorobenzophenone. On the other hand DDA does not seem to be produced at all by the pigeon (*Columba livia*), the quail (*Coturnix coturnix*) or the blackbird (*Turdus nerula*), suggesting that this metabolite is unimportant in birds.[104]

There are still some serious doubts about the circumstances under which DDT can be transformed into DDD. This reaction, which can be carried out by reduced porphyrins[105] readily proceeds under anaerobic conditions in micro-organisms, liver slices and microsomes,[107, 108] and post mortem in vertebrate tissues (even below −10° C).[109] However, it does not proceed in pigeon liver slices homogenates and microsomes in the presence of oxygen.[107, 108, 110] In pigeon liver microsomes the process is NADPH dependent, and is inhibited by carbon monoxide, suggesting an ivolvement of cytochrome P_{450} as has been argued for microsomal nitro reductase. Since the presence of oxygen is normally required for the microsomal enzyme to operate *in vivo* the extent to which this system operates in the live pigeon must be in doubt. At the same time, significant quantities of DDD did not appear in the livers of pigeons and Bengalese finches fed pp'DDT during life.[108, 109] After death DDD was rapidly produced (15% conversion in 1 hr at 20° C in the pigeon), suggesting that the conversion was only important after the establishment of anaerobic conditions following death, and not during life. This calls into question the proposal that a major metabolic pathway for pp'DDT operates through DDD. In their investigations upon rat liver Peterson and Robison [111] propose the formation of DDA via DDD but do not exclude the possibility that some or all of the DDD they find is produced post mortem. The results of Bailey *et al.*[112] for the pigeon are also in doubt, for although DDD was found in tissues such as muscle and liver which can form it post mortem, significant quantities were not found in the fat which cannot so form it. Experience with organochlorine insecticides including DDD [112] shows that they are partitioned between the different tissue of the body, reaching particularly high levels in the fat.[1, 3] Since the half life for DDD in the pigeon is 24 days,[112] it seems unlikely that it represents an important intermediate in DDT metabolism in this species when the quantities in the liver immediately after death can be so small in birds dosed with DDT.[109]

It should be emphasised that these comments refer to reductive dechlorination of DDT within vertebrates. The production of DDD in the gut is another matter. It has been shown that rumen flora can achieve this conversion, and DDD produced in this way may be absorbed into the bloodstream.[105]

Bearing these reservations in mind, it appears that the pigeon, the quail and the Bengalese finch form pp'DDE more rapidly than the blackbird, and that the blackbird produces greater quantities of DDD *in vivo* than the other two birds. The blackbird seems unusual in one other respect – it metabolises DDE more quickly than the pigeon and the quail.

Kapoor *et al*[113, 114] have used model aquatic ecosystems to investigate the fate of DDT and some of its more biodegradable insecticidal analogues such as methoxychlor, ethoxychlor, methylchlor and methiochlor. The analogues are usually degraded by attack upon the groups CH_3O-, CH_3- and CH_3S- which take the place of chlorine on the phenyl rings. In a system containing *Oedogonium* (alga), *Physa* (snail), *Culex* (mosquito) and *Gambusia* (fish) there were marked interspecific differences in the build up of these compounds and their metabolites. In the case of *Gambusia*, DDT was concentrated 85,000 fold over the concentration in water, but ethoxychlor and methylchlor were only concentrated 1500 fold and 1400 fold respectively. *Physa* on the other hand concentrated methoxychlor, ethoxychlor and methylchlor to a greater extent than pp'DDT and this may have been due to a limited capacity for microsomal o-dealkylation and side chain oxidation. Other studies by the same workers suggest that the salt marsh caterpillar also has difficulty in metabolising these DDT analogues.

Hydrogenomonas bacteria and body lice can eliminate one phenyl ring of DDT to produce *p*.chlorobenzoic acid. The enzymatic pathway for this conversion, and its occurrence in other species are as yet unknown.

γ BHC

Little is known of the comparative metabolism of γBHC and other isomers of hexachlorocyclohexane. Since glutathione conjugation is involved, however, there is reason to suspect significant interspecific variations. As we have already seen there is some evidence suggesting that γBHC may be conjugated directly by certain insects,[59, 64] but it appears that the rat and the rabbit can only carry out this conversion after dehydrochlorination to pentachlorocyclohexene has occurred. Bradbury and Standen[76] noted that γBHC was metabolised to water soluble products more rapidly in resistant than in normal house-flies and that this was associated with an increased rate of excretion. Subsequent studies indicate that the main water soluble metabolite was 2,4 dichlorophenyl-S glutathione.[115, 59]

The Organophosphorus Insecticides

The organophosphorus insecticides contrast in a number of ways with the organochlorine insecticides. They are powerful inhibitors of acetyl choline esterase and other esterases; they are in general more water soluble than the organochlorine insecticides although there is great variation within the group; they are readily biodegradable and are not very persistent within animals.

Organophosphorus insecticides are metabolised both oxidatively and hydrolytically. Oxidation of P = S to P = O or of

$$-S- \text{ to } -\overset{\overset{O}{\|}}{S}- \text{ and } -\overset{\overset{O}{\|}}{\underset{\underset{O}{\|}}{S}}- \text{ quite often yields meta-}$$

bolites of greater anticholinesterase activity and greater toxicity than the original insecticide. Hydrolysis of phosphate, carboxy ester or amide bonds nearly always lead to deactivation.

Malathion is an insecticide which shows pronounced selectivity between insects and mammals. The acute LD$_{50}$ values were found to be between 0.75 mg/kg

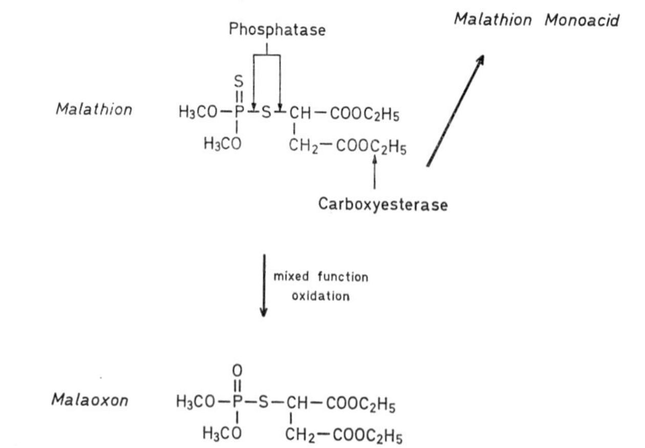

Fig. 8   *Malathion metabolism*

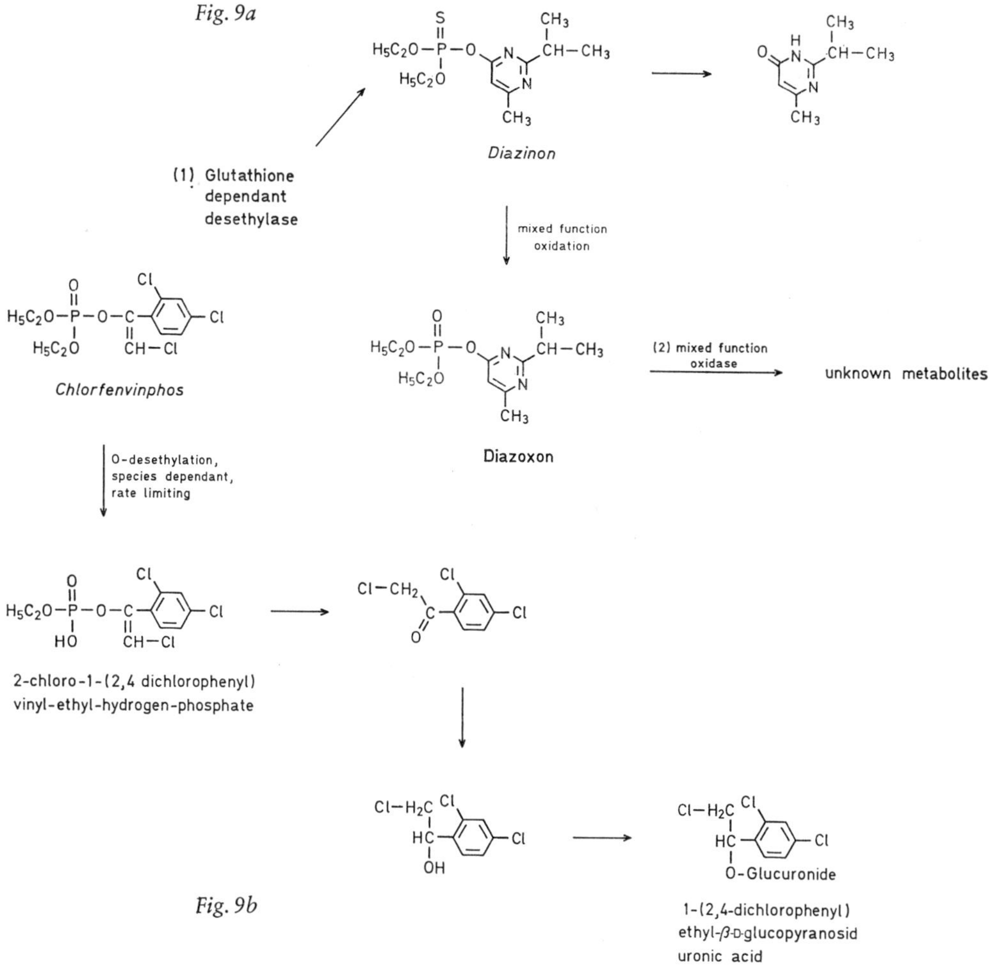

Fig. 9a

Fig. 9b

Fig. 9 *Metabolism of diazinon and chlorfenvinphos*

and 120 mg/kg in six insect species but between 275 mg/kg and 1609 mg/kg in five vertebrate species.[29] This discrimination seems to be due, at least in part, to differences in metabolism. Malathion may be activated by oxidation to malaoxon or deactivated by hydrolysis to a variety of products (*Fig. 8*). Malaoxon is a much more potent anticholinesterase than malathion and is deactivated by hydrolysis. In all of the species so far tested, two types of hydrolysis occur:– at the phosphate bonds and at the carboxy ester bonds. In a comparative *in vitro* study Krueger and O'Brien [116] showed that the pattern of hydrolytic attack upon malathion and metabolically derived malaoxon differed between the mouse on the one hand, and the American cockroach, the German cockroach and the housefly on the other. Hydrolytic degradation in the mouse was faster than in the three insect species, and this was associated with considerably greater carboxyesterase activity.

Whereas the three insect species showed a reasonable balance between the two forms of hydrolytic degradation, carboxy-esterase attack was predominant in the mouse. In an *in vivo* study, the cow, the rat and the dog hydrolysed malathion/malaoxon mainly by carboxyesterase attack.[117]

The relatively high carboxyesterase activity found in mammals appears to effectively limit the build up of malaoxon in the tissues. After injection with 30 mg/kg of malathion, malaoxon reached much higher levels and was more persistent in the American cockroach than in the mouse.[116] Furthermore mammals can show a similar order of sensitivity to malathion as is found in insects, when the insecticide is applied together with a carboxyesterase inhibitor (e.g. E.P.N.).[118]

The principle of incorporating a carboxy ester group into organophosphates possessing a thiono group has been followed in an attempt to make new insecticides of low mammalian toxicity. So far this has not led to the introduction of any new commercial insecticides, although one such compound, acethion, shows interesting selective toxicity. It is 136 times more toxic to the housefly than to the mouse.[29]

The metabolism of *diazinon* is relatively complex[11] (Fig. 9). In the first place, it is readily converted into its P=O analogue diazoxon by mixed function oxidation. Apart from this Lewis and Lord have demonstrated that there are four distinct enzymic degradative routes in resistant houseflies and that two of these appear to be acquired resistance mechanisms since they are not present in normal houseflies (they are also absent from rat liver).[119] The two systems in question are (1) a glutathione-dependent enzyme in the soluble fraction which is inhibited by S,S,S tributyl-phosphoro-trithioate, and removes an ethyl group from diazinon, (2) a microsomal oxidase which is dependent upon NADPH and O_2, is inhibited by sesamex and transforms diazoxon into unknown metabolites. Both of the inhibitors increase the toxicity of diazinon to the housefly. It is worth noting that a DDT resistant strain with enhanced microsomal oxidase activity is also resistant to diazinon.[97]

Interspecific differences have been noted with *chlorfenvinphos*[120] [2 chloro-(2'4'-dichlorophenyl) vinyl diethyl phosphate]. Fig. 9 Elimination was rapid and mainly via the urine in both the rat and the dog. The two principal excreted metabolites in the rat were (1) a product of oxidative desethylation, 2-chloro-1-(2'4'dichloro phenyl) vinyl ethyl hydrogen phosphate and (2) a conjugate [1-(2'4'dichloro phenyl) ethyl β D glucopyranosid] uronic acid, and these appeared in approximately equal amounts in the urine. In the dog, however, the first metabolite was dominant, accounting for approximately 70% of the total dose, whilst the glucuronide accounted for only 4%. No sex differences were found in either species. The preference of the rat for urinary excretion (cf dieldrin) is interesting. The desethylation product is very near the average threshold molecular weight; the glucuronide is considerably above it but falls within the range of threshold values quoted by Hirom *et al.*[69]

Other insecticides

Some interesting examples of interspecific differences in microsomal mixed function oxidase activity are found with the insecticidal carbamates. The subject has been well reviewed[121, 11] and will not be discussed in any detail here. The development of resistance to them by insects is frequently associated with increased oxidase activity.[122] For example, one housefly strain selected for resistance to 3-isopropyl phenyl-N-methyl carbamate shows cross resistance to 2-isopropoxy-phenyl N-methyl carbamate (Baygon), and this can be explained on the grounds of increased oxidase activity. So too can the high toxicity shown by baygon, carbaryl and other carbamates towards the honey bee, in contrast with the house-fly and the German cockroach which are not sensitive to them. The honey bee appears to be much poorer at oxidising these compounds than the other two species.

Carbaryl is not very toxic to either the mouse or (as we have seen) the housefly, and in both cases this is related to rapid detoxication. On the other hand carbaryl is powerfully synergised by 2,3 methylene-dioxy napthalene in the housefly but not in the mouse. The synergist yielded similar metabolites *in vivo* for both species.[123] Cleavage of the methylenedioxy ring produced a diol; oxidative attack upon the ring gave several products including 1 hydroxy 2,3 methylene dioxy-naphthalene. Both of the named metabolites were conjugated to glucosides in the housefly, but to glucuronides in the mouse. The striking difference between the species was in the rate of metabolism. Whereas the mouse achieved almost complete degradation in 12 hrs, very little breakdown occurred in the housefly after 24 hrs. This provided a satisfactory explanation of this remarkable example of synergism.

The insecticide *rotenone* is highly toxic to insects and fish but only weakly toxic to mammals. This seems to be connected with the operation of mixed function oxidases which detoxify rotenone by converting it to hydroxylated products. Fukami *et al.*[124] have found that the soluble fraction of rat liver homogenates remaining after separation of microsomes promotes hydroxylation of rotenone. By contrast, the corresponding fraction from the fat body and hind gut of the cockroach inhibits such metabolic attack. It appears that the rate of breakdown *in vivo* is controlled by endogenous cofactors and inhibitors, an important point that is discussed by the authors. They also argue that the relatively weak mixed function oxidase activity in fish accounts, at least in part, for their susceptibility to rotenone.

Discussion: The Practical Significance of Comparative Metabolism

The metabolic fate of insecticides influences their selective toxicity and environmental persistence, the effects of synergists upon them, and the resistance of species and strains to them. These are all matters of considerable practical importance and it would be very useful to be able to make predictions about the behaviour of insecticides based upon their comparative metabolism. Unfortunately this is only possible in a limited way at the present time, for too little is known about the subject. Indeed things have tended to happen the other way round. The discovery of some of the most interesting cases of comparative metabolism of insecticides has arisen out of the investigation of selective toxicity and resistance. In this concluding section some of the practical aspects of comparative metabolism will be considered.

As we have seen liposoluble compounds such as dieldrin and DDE, which are not readily biodegradable, tend to persist strongly in animal tissues, and the persistence of such compounds in different species can be assessed as biological half lives.[1, 3, 4] Some examples for dieldrin were referred to earlier. The rate of metabolism of these compounds to water soluble and readily excretable products in different species can be a very important factor in determining their persistence and may go a long way towards explaining the very pronounced interspecific differences in biological half life. The same principle applies in some cases of resistance to DDT and BHC. The principal dieldrin metabolite in the rat is produced by microsomal oxidation,[82] and the male rat shows considerably greater hepatic microsomal oxidative activity than the female.[25, 15] Dieldrin is considerably less persistent in the male and this may be because it has greater microsomal oxidase activity. Similarly the rate of hydroxylation of tolbutamide by liver microsomes is some 6 times greater in the male rat than in the male human, indicating weak microsomal oxidase activity in the human.[125] This suggests that slow oxidative metabolism may contribute to the relatively long persistence of dieldrin in man. It should be added that other factors such as the tendency of dieldrin to be stored, bound, or excreted in different species are also factors influencing half lives.

Other comparative studies with dieldrin have been concerned with its build up in the body tissues of vertebrates when included at low levels in the feed. It has been found, for example, that 0–4 ppm of dieldrin in the feed over 84 days produces 0.5 ppm and 10.0 ppm in the body fat of lambs and hens respectively.[126] It would be interesting to know the contribution of comparative metabolism towards this striking interspecific difference.

Half lives are of limited usefulness in assessing persistence, since they do not take into account the persistence of metabolites. Some metabolites e.g. DDE are more persistent than the parent compounds.[127] The excretion of conjugates in the bile usually leads to enterohepatic circulation. As discussed earlier there are marked interspecific differences with regard to the tendency for metabolites to be excreted in the bile. Ideally the persistence of both original compounds and their metabolites should be taken into account, and this can be achieved by carrying out suitably designed radiotracer-aided studies upon whole animals.

The metabolic basis for the development of resistance to DDT and BHC in certain strains of housefly has already been discussed.[90] Another example of such resistance is the enhanced carboxy esterase activity in a malathion-resistant strain of Culex tarsalis.[128] Some of the enzymes which provide the basis for resistance are very specialised in character and show little or no tendency to be involved in cross resistance phenomena, e.g. DDT dehydrochlorinase, and the carboxyesterase which attacks malathion in C. tarsalis. The involvement of mixed function oxidation in resistance is however quite a different matter. Because mixed function oxidases are rather nonspecific, their development tends to be accompanied by the appearance of cross resistance. It has been shown that certain strains of housefly possess DDT resistance which is reversible by sesamex, and that these strains are also resistant to diazinon.[94, 96] Studies with microsomes prepared from these strains showed that DDT is degraded to hydrophilic metabolites by a system that is dependent upon NADPH and O_2 indicating that it is a mixed function oxidase.[95, 128]

It also appears that resistance to certain organophosphates and certain carbamates and pyrethroids is attributable to the same or a similar system which is controlled by a factor on the 5th chromosome. The development of such a generalised detoxication system in insects raises practical problems in pest control. There is one encouraging feature, however. As with other types of resistance based upon metabolic systems, it can be counteracted by the use of synergists which inhibit detoxication.

A further aspect of mixed function oxidation requires consideration. Mixed function oxidases in insects can be induced by various liposoluble substances as they can in mammals. Therefore it is possible in theory for sub-lethal quantities of persistent liposoluble compounds to cause induction of these enzymes and thereby increase resistance to a wide range of insecticides. The possibility that the inducibility of this system may vary between strains does not appear to have been investigated, although interspecific differences in inducibility have been shown to exist in vertebrates.[129] The question of inducibility in different species, strains, sexes and age groups clearly deserves more attention.

Interspecific differences in metabolism can provide the basis of selective toxic action of an insecticide – malathion is one example of this and the related compound acethion appears to be another.[29] The possibility exists of incorporating certain groups in insecticidal molecules which confer selective toxicity upon them. The epoxide group, which is found in such familiar insecticides as dieldrin and endrin, shows promise in this respect. Chlorinated cyclodiene epoxides can be degraded in two distinct ways – by mixed function oxidation and by hydration – and both pathways yield water soluble metabolites that are readily excreted (q.v.). The hydration process is a particularly interesting one in the case of dieldrin for as we have seen it can have the effect of either activating or detoxifying depending upon where it takes place. There are great differences between species with regard to microsomal epoxide hydrase activities towards HCE and HEOM, two readily degradable dieldrin analogues.[11, 39, 47, 48] In contrast to the liver microsomes of rabbit, pig and rat, whole housefly microsomos do not carry out any measurable transformation of HCE into its trans dihydrodiol. Thus, the housefly is very largely dependent upon mixed function oxidation for metabolising of HCE. Consequently HCE is powerfully synergised by sesamex (a mixed function oxidase inhibitor) in the housefly, nearly reaching the toxicity of dieldrin.[11, 130] Both HCE and HEOM are very toxic to the tsetse fly G. austeni, and both are synergised by sesamex to a relatively small extent to give levels of toxicity comparable to that of dieldrin.[11] It appears that neither oxidative nor hydrative metabolism is very strong in either of these species.

Since the mammals tested show appreciable hydrative ability towards these compounds (especially HEOM) they may prove to be useful selective insecticides against species deficient in epoxide hydrase when applied with a suitable synergist. One uncertainty remains – certain birds e.g. the pigeon, show low hepatic microsomal epoxide hydrase activity. However it should be stressed that blockade upon mixed function oxidation will be removed as soon as the synergist itself has been metabolised – and methylene dioxyphenyl compounds are themselves broken down by mixed function oxidation.

HCE is metabolised very much more rapidly than dieldrin by liver microsomes of the rat and the rabbit. Studies with C^{14} HCE have shown that more than 50% of an injected dose is cleared within 2 days by the rabbit and within about 5 days by the male rat,[131] (dieldrin half life in adipose tissue = $10 \cdot 3$ days). Relatively rapid metabolism of dieldrin in vitro is matched by rapid excretion in vivo. It therefore seems that microsomal studies such as these are of value in predicting rate of excretion in vivo, a point we shall return to.

One of the problems in comparative metabolism of insecticides is obtaining valid information about experimental animals and then extrapolating this to man. As somebody recently observed – toxicology is advancing so rapidly as a subject the world will soon be a safe place for rats and mice to live in. The problem is particularly difficult with insecticides of high mammalian toxicity. Occasionally metabolic studies have been done on man e.g. a group of volunteers took regular small doses of dieldrin and blood samples were subsequently analysed for metabolites.[4] There are, however, serious limitations to what can be done.

A better knowledge of interspecific differences in metabolism should make it easier to compare experimental animals with man. The process should be aided by limited studies upon man e.g. *in vitro* studies with human liver samples obtained by biopsy, and metabolic studies of certain compounds at low concentrations. Regarding the techniques used for studying comparative metabolism it is generally much easier to carry out enzymic studies *in vitro* than to do *in vivo* balance experiments. This is particularly true of wild species that are hard to maintain in captivity.

It is therefore desirable to use *in vitro* techniques as far as possible and some of the work reported here holds out promise for this approach. Although there are many difficulties it is to be hoped that careful comparison of results from *in vivo* and *in vitro* investigations upon the same compounds will help to clarify to what extent the results from suitable designed enzymic studies can be used to predict events in the whole animal.

Acknowledgements

I am grateful to Dr. G. T. Brooks and Dr. J. Robinson for helpful discussion and advice, also to the Science Research Council for a grant (B/SR/4747) which supported some of the work mentioned here.

References

1 Robinson, J., M. Roberts, M. Baldwin, A. I. T. Walker: Fd Cosmet Toxicol 7, 317, 1969

2 Gilbert, D., L. Golberg: Fd Cosmet Toxicol 3, 417, 1965

3 Robinson, J., A. Richardson, V. K. H. Brown: Nature 213, 734, 1967

4 Hunter, C., J. Robinson, M. Roberts: Arch Env Health 18, 12, 1969

5 Matsumura, F.: Pesticide Chemistry Vol. II. Proc. 2nd Int. IUPAC Congress of Pesticide Chemistry. Gordon and Breach, 95, 1971

6 Wang, C. M., T. Narahashi, M. Yamada: Pestic. Biochem Physiol, 1, 84, 1972

7 Williams, R. T.: Detoxication Mechanism. Chapman and Hall. London 2nd Edition. 1954

8 Mason, H. S.: Science 125, 1185, 1957

9 Lake, B. G., D. V. Parke: Proc. Biochem. Soc. 530th meeting, Guildford, p. 40, 1972

10 Omura, T., R. Sato, D. Y. Cooper, O. Rosenthal, R. W. Estabrook. Fed. Proc. 24, 1181, 1965

11 Brooks, G. T.: Env. Quality Safety, 1, 106, 1972

12 Chakraborty, J., C. H. Sissons, J. N. Smith: Biochem. J. 102, 492, 1967

13 Gemrich, E. G.: J. Agric Fd Chem 15, 617, 1967

14 Price, G. M., R. J. Kuhr: Biochem. J. 112, 133 1969

15 Krieger, R. I., C. F. Wilkinson. Biochem. Pharmac. 18, 1403, 1969

16 Benke, G. M., J. F. Wilkinson. J. econ Ent 64, 1032, 1971

17 Sato, R., T. Omura, H. Nishibayashi: Intern. Symp. on Oxidases and Related Redox Systems. Amherst, Mass. 1969. Ed. T. E. King, H. S. Mason, M. Morrison. New York. Wiley. 861, 1969

18 Estabrook, R. W., J. Baron, J. Peterson, Y. Ishimura: Proc. Biochem. Soc. 517 th meeting, Edinburgh. p. 3, 1971

19 Casida, J. E., J. L. Engel, E. G. Esaac, F. Kamienski, S. Kuwatsuku. Science 153, 1130, 1966

20 Hutson, D. M. 'Mechanisms of Biotransformation' in Foreign Compound Metabolism in Mammals Vol. 1. The Chemical Society, London, 314, 1970

21 Remmer, H., R. W. Estabrook, J. B. Schenkmann, H. Greim: Enzymatic Oxidation of Toxicants. Ed. E. Hodgson. North Carolina State University and Raleigh, 65, 1968

22 Brodie, B. B., R. P. Maickel: Proc. 1st Int Pharmacol. Meeting 6, 299, 1961

[23] Williams, R. T.: Fundamentals of Drug Metabolism and Drug Disposition. Williams and Wilkins, 187, 1971

[24] Creaven, P. J., D. V. Parke, R. T. Williams: Biochem. J. 96, 390, 1965

[25] Terriere, L. C.: Enzymatic Oxidation of Toxicants. Ed. E. Hodgson. North Carolina State University Raleigh, 175, 1968

[26] Potter, J. L., R. D. O'Brien: Science 144, 55, 1964

[27] Parke, D. V.: Biochem. J. 77, 493, 1960

[28] La Du, B. N., H. Snady: Handbook of Experimental Pharmacology XXVIII/2. Springer Verlag 477, 1971

[29] O'Brien, R. D.: Pesticides: Action and Metabolism. Academic Press, 1967

[30] Augustinsson, K. B., K. Myrback: The Enzymes, 2nd Ed. Vol. 4. New York and London, Academic Press, 1961

[31] Main, A. R., P. E. Braid. Biochem. J. 84, 255, 1962

[32] Augustinsson, K. B.: Ann N. Y. Acad Sci 94, 844, 1961

[33] Augustinsson, K. B.: J. Histochem. Cytochem 12, 744, 1964

[34] Aldridge, W. N.: Biochem. J. 53, 117, 1953

[35] Brooks, G. T.: Wld Rev. Pest Control 5, 62, 1966

[36] Watabe, T., E. W. Maynert: Pharmacologist 10, 203, 1968

[37] Jerina, D. M.: Arch Biochem 128, 176, 1968

[38] Sims, P.: Biochem Pharmac. 19, 299, 1970

[39] Brooks, G. T.: Proc. 5th Br Insectic Fungic Conf. 472, 1969

[40] Brooks, G. T., A. Harrison, S. E. Lewis: Biochem. Pharmac 19, 255, 1970

[41] Matthews, H. B., F. Matsumura: J. Agr Fd Chem. 17, 845, 1969

[42] Oesch, F., C. R. Creveling, D. M. Jerina, J. Daly: Fed. Proc. 29, 473, 1970

[43] Oesch, F., D. M. Jerina, J. Daly: Arch. Biochem Biophys 144, 253, 1971

[44] Oesch, F., N. Kaubisch, D. M. Jerina, J. W. Daly: Biochem. 10, 4858, 1971

[45] Jerina, D. M., J. W. Daly, B. Witkop, P. Zaltmann-Nirenberg, S. Udenfriend: Biochem. 9, 147, 1970

[46] Sims, P., A. Haver, P. L. Grover: Proc. Biochem. Soc. 527th meeting, Edinburgh, p. 26, 1971

[47] El Zorgani, G. A., C. H. Walker, K. A. Hassall. Life Sci 9, 415, 1970

[48] Walker, C. H., G. A. El Zorgani: Env. Quality and Safety 1, 248, 1972

[49] Parke, D. V.: The Biochemistry of Foreign Compounds. Pergamon Press, 1968

[50] Dutton, G. J.: Handbook of Experimental Pharmacology. XXVIII/2, 378, 1971

[51] Arias, I. M.: Biochem. Biophys Res Commun 6, 81, 1961

[52] Adamson, R. H., J. W. Bridges, R. T. Williams. Biochem J 100, 71, 1966

[53] Mehendale, H. H., H. W. Dorough: Pesticide Chemistry Vol. 1. Proc. 2nd IUPAC Congress of Pesticide Chemistry. Gordon and Breach, 15, 1971

[54] Dutton, G. J.: in Glucuronic Acid. New York, Academic Press, 1966

[55] Boyland, E.: Handbook of Experimental Pharmacology. XXVIII/2, 584, 1971

[56] Booth, J., E. Boyland, P. Sims. Biochem. J. 74, 117, 1960

[57] Cohen, A. J., J. N. Smith: Biochem. J. 90, 449, 1964

[58] Boyland, E., P. Sims: Biochem. J. 97, 7, 1965

[59] Clark, A. G., F. J. Darby, J. N. Smith: Biochem. J. 103, 49, 1967

[60] Wit, J. G., P. Leeuwangh: Biochim. Biophys Acta 177, 329, 1969

[61] Boyland, E., L. F. Chasseaud: Biochem. J. 115, 985, 1969

[62] Clark, A. G., S. Murphy, J. N. Smith.: Biochem. J. 113, 89, 1969

[63] Grover, P. L., P. Sims. Biochem. J. 96, 521, 1965

[64] Smith, J. N.: Comparative Biochemistry of Detoxication. Comparative Biochemistry 6. Ed. M. Florkin, M. S. Mason. New York, Academic Press., 403, 1964

[65] Smith, J. N.: The comparative metabolism of xenobiotics. Adv. Comp. Physiol. Biochem. 3, 173, 1968

[66] Scoppa, P.: Aggiornamenti di Radiobiologia 1, VIII Congresso Nazionale della Associazione Italiana di Radiobiologia Medica, 1966, 255

[67] Smith, R. L.: Handbook of Experimental Pharmacology. XXVIII/1, 354, 1971

[68] Thompson, R., M. Sturtevant, O. D. Bird, A. J. Glazko: Endocrinology 55, 665, 1954

[69] Hirom, P. C., P. Millburn, R. L. Smith, R. T. Williams. Biochem. J. 129, 1071, 1972

[70] Abou-El-Makarem, H. M., P. Millburn, R. L. Smith, R. T. Williams: Biochem. J. 105, 1289, 1967

[71] Hirom, P. C., P. Millburn, R. L. Smith, R. T. Williams: Xenobiotica, 2, 205, 1972

[72] Clark, A. G., P. C. Hirom, P. Millburn, R. T. Williams: J. Pharm. Pharmac. 23, 150, 1971

[73] Maddrell, S. H. P.: 'Mechanisms of Insect Excretory Systems' in Advances in Insect Physiology. Academic Press 8, 200, 1971

[74] Lison, L.: Z. Zellforsch. Mikrostk. Anat 28, 179, 1938

152   Comparative Aspects of the Metabolism of Pesticides

[75] Clark, A. G., M. Hitchcock, J. N. Smith: Nature 209, 103, 1966
[76] Bradbury, F. R., H. Standen: J. Sci Fd Agric 7, 389, 1956
[77] Moore, N. W., C. H. Walker: Nature 201, 1072, 1964
[78] Walker, C. H., G. A. Hamilton, R. B. Harrison: J. Sci Fd Agric 18, 123, 1967
[79] Baldwin, M. K., J. Robinson, D. V. Parke: Fd Cosmet Toxicol. 10, 333, 1972
[80] Korte, F., H. Arent, Life Sci. 4, 2017, 1965
[81] Korte, F.: Nuclear Techniques for Studying Pesticide Residue Problems. International Atomic Energy Agency, Wien, 23, 1970
[82] Baldwin, M. K.: Ph. D. Thesis Univ. of Surrey 1971
[83] El Zorgani, G. A.: Unpublished results
[84] Oda, J., W. Muller: Env. Quality and Safety 1, 248, 1972
[85] Klein, W.: Env. Quality and Safety 1, 164, 1972
[86] Ludwig, G., H. Arent, W. Kochen, N. Poonawalla, G. Rechneier, M. Stiasni, J. Vogel, F. Korte: Paper presented at Scientific Plant Protection Conference, Budapest, Hungary Feb. 22nd–25th 1966
[87] Klein, W.: 'Metabolism of Chlorinated Insecticides' Radioisotopes in the Detection of Pesticide Residues. FAO/IAEA Div. of Atomic Energy in Agriculture, Wien 1965
[88] Baldwin, M. S., J. Robinson, D. V. Parke: J. Agric Fd Chem. 18, 1117, 1970
[89] Dailey, R. E., H. S. Walton, V. Beck, C. L. Leavens, S. K. Klein: J. Agric Fd Chem. 18, 443, 1970
[90] Durham, W. T., P. Ortega, J. W. Hayes jr.: Archives Internationales de Pharmacodynamic et de Therapie 141, 1963
[91] Busvine, J. R.: P.A.N.S. 17 Nr 2, 135, 1971
[92] Tsukamoto, M.: Botyu Kagaku 26, 74, 1961
[93] Agosin, M. N., N. Scaramelli, L. Gil, M. E. Letelier: Comp. Biochem Physiol 29, 785, 1969
[94] Rowlands, D. G., G. J. Lloyd: J. Stored Prod Res 5, 413, 1969
[95] Oppenoorth, F. J.: Med Landbouwk. Opzoek st Gent. 30, 1390, 1965
[96] Oppenoorth, F. J., N. W. H. Houx: Entomol. Exp. Appl. 11, 81, 1968
[97] Gil, L., B. C. Fine, M. L. Dinamarca, I. Balogs, J. R. Busvine, M. Argosin: Entomol Exp. Appl 11, 15, 1968
[98] Jensen, J. A., C. Cueto, W. E. Dale, C. F. Rothe, G. W. Pearce, A. M. Mattson: J. Agric Fd Chem 5, 919, 1957
[99] Pinto, J. D., M. N. Camien, M. S. Dunn: J. Biol Chem 240, 2148, 1965
[100] Abou Donia, M. B., D. B. Menzel: Biochem Pharmac 17, 2143, 1968
[101] Judah, J. D.: J. Pharmac. 4, 120, 1949
[102] Perry, A. S., A. M. Mattson, A. J. Buchner: J. Agric Fd Chem 11, 457, 1963
[103] Vinson, S. B., J. R. Brazzell: J. Econ Entomol 59, 600, 1966
[104] Bailey, S., P. J. Bunyan, A. Taylor: Env. Quality and Safety 1, 244, 1971
[105] Miskus, R. P., P. P. Blair, J. E. Casida: J. Agric Fd Chem 13, 481, 1965
[106] Johnson, B. T., R. N. Goodman, H. S. Goldberg: Science 157, 560, 1967
[107] Walker, C. H.: J. Appl. Ecol 3 (Suppl) 213, 1966
[108] Jefferies, D. J., C. H. Walker: Nature 212, 533, 1966
[109] Walker, C. H.: VII Int. Plant Protection Congress, Wien. Abstracts 602, 1967
[110] Walker, C. H.: Life Sci 8, 1111, 1969
[111] Peterson, J. E., W. H. Robison: Toxicol. Appl. Pharmacol. 6, 321, 1964
[112] Bailey, S., P. J. Bunyan, B. D. Rennison, A. Taylor: Toxic Appl Pharmac 14, 13, 1969
[113] Kapoor, I. P., R. L. Metcalf, R. F. Nystrom, G. K. Sangha: J. Agric Fd Chem. 18, 1145, 1970
[114] Kapoor, I. P., R. L. Metcalf, A. S. Hirwe, P-Y Lu, J. R. Coats, R. F. Nystrom: J. Agric Fd Chem 20, 1, 1972
[115] Bradbury, F. R., H. Standen: Nature Lond 183, 983, 1959
[116] Krieger, H. R., R. D. O'Brien: J. Econ Entomol 52, 1063, 1959
[117] O'Brien, R. D., W. C. Dauterman, R. P. Niedermeier: J. Agric Fd Chem 9, 39, 1961
[118] Plapp, F. W., G. W. Eddy: Science 134, 2043, 1961
[119] Lewis, J. B., K. A. Lord: Proc Fifth Brit Insectic Fungic Conf 465, 1969
[120] Hutson, D. H., D. A. A. Akintonwa, D. E. Hathway: Biochem J. 102, 133, 1967
[121] Metcalf, R. L.: Enzymatic Oxidation of Toxicants. Ed. F. Hodgson. p. 151, 1968
[122] Hewlett, P. S., C. F. Wilkinson: J Sci Fd Agric 18, 279, 1967
[123] Sacher, R. M., R. L. Metcalf, T. R. Fukuto: J. Agric Fd Chem 17, 551, 1969
[124] Fukami, J. I., T. Shishido, K. Fukunaga, J. E. Casida: J Agric Fd Chem 17, 1217, 1969
[125] Darby, F. J., D. A. Price-Evans.: Proc. Biochem Soc. 517th meeting, Edinburgh p. 45, 1971
[126] Gannon, N., R. P. Link, G. C. Decker: J Agric Fd Chem 7, 826, 1959
[127] Bailey, S., P. J. Bunyan, B. D. Rennison, A. Taylor: Toxicol. Appl. Pharmac. 14, 13, 1969

[128] Matsumura, F., A. W. A. Brown: J. Econ Entomol 54, 1176, 1961

[129] Bunyan, P. J., M. E. Townsend, A. Taylor: Chem. Biol. Inter. 5, 13, 1972

[130] Debanné, E. G., M. Sc. Dissertation, Reading University, 1971

[131] Walker, C. H., G. A. El Zorgani, J. A. Kenny: Paper given at Joint FAO/IAEA Research Coordination Meeting on Isotope-Tracer Aided Studies of the Fate and Significance of Foreign Substances in Food. Euratom Centre, Ispra, Italy November 1972

Blood Levels of DDT in Nonoccupationally Exposed Mothers and Newborn Infants in a City in Brazil

Samuel Schvartsman
Professor-Docente of Pediatrics. Chief of the Pediatric Clinic Poison Control Center.

Waldemar F. Almeida
Director of the Division of Biology of the Instituto Biológico, São Paulo.

Flavio A. Costa Vaz
Assistant of the Pediatric Clinic Nursery.

Helcio B. Corradini
Chief of the Pediatric Clinic Nursery.

Pedro Pigati
Chief of the Section of Pesticide Residue Analyses, Instituto Biológico, São Paulo.

Rosa Gaeta
Maria Tereza Ungaro
Assistants of the Instituto Biológico, São Paulo.

Pediatric Clinic of Hospital das Clínicas of São Paulo's Medical School and Instituto Biológico of São Paulo, Brasil

Summary Blood serum levels of p,p'-DDE and p,p'-DDT in nonoccupational exposed mothers (23.7 ± 9.5 ppb of DDE and 18.9 ± 4.0 ppb of DDT) and in their newborn infants (10.4 ± 7.5 ppb of DDE and 11.9 ± 3.5 ppb of DDT) living in Sao Paulo, Brazil, are presented. There were significant differences between maternal and newborn blood levels for DDE and DDT.

Zusammenfassung Die Arbeit enthält die Ergebnisse von Messungen der Blutserumkonzentrationen an p,p'-DDE und p,p'-DDT in Müttern aus Sao Paulo, Brasilien, die nicht am Arbeitsplatz diesen Substanzen ausgesetzt waren, und ihren Neugeborenen. Es wurden signifikante Unterschiede der Blutkonzentrationen von Müttern (23,7 ± 9,5 ppb DDE und 18,9 ± 4,0 ppb DDT) und der Neugeborenen (10,4 ± 7,5 ppb DDE und 11,9 ± 3,5 ppb DDT) gefunden.

In recent years a great and universal concern about the possible health hazards that may ensue from excessive pesticide exposure has arisen. With the development of highly sensitive techniques for the residue analysis of chlorinated hydrocarbon pesticides many studies have been carried out in the United States [3, 6] and in some European, South American and Asiatic countries. [2, 4, 5]

This paper presents the results of an investigation on DDT blood levels in mothers and their newborn infants in Sao Paulo, Brazil. The peculiar socio-economic and climatic conditions, and the less rigid and less effective regulatory controls in Brazil are interesting for comparison with the levels referred to in other countries.

Methods

Fifteen pregnant women living in Sao Paulo's urban area, with non-occupational exposure to pesticides but only common domestic use of insecticides who were admitted at Hospital das Clínicas for delivery, were selected. The ages ranged from 19 to 35 years, and the racial distribution was 12 Whites and 3 Negroes.
The newborn infants, all of them from normal deliveries, were 12 Whites and 3 Negroes, their weights ranging from 2500 to 3900 g.
Maternal blood samples were drawn during the expulsive period of labour and newborn blood samples, immediately after birth, were obtained from umbilical cord. The analyses were carried out in the blood serum by the Dale et al. method,[1] in which the blood is pre-treated with formic acid which permits the release of protein-bound DDT. GLC equipment, Beckman-model GC4 – with electron capture detector, was used.

Results

The serum levels are shown in Table I. The levels of p,p'-DDE ranged from 10 to 43 ppb (micrograms per liter), with a

Table I p,p'-DDE and p,p'-DDT levels in parts per billion (μg/l) in maternal blood and umbilical cord blood

Case n°	Maternal blood	Umbilical cord blood	Maternal blood	Umbilical cord blood
	p,p'-DDE	p,p'-DDE	p,p'-DDT	p,p'-DDT
1	20	10	15	15
2	25	10	15	15
3	20	10	25	10
4	25	10	25	10
5	10	10	20	10
6	20	10	20	10
7	30	10	20	10
8	20	10	20	20
9	20	10	20	10
10	40	10	20	15
11	10	0	10	10
12	15	0	20	10
13	30	10	20	15
14	43	34	20	12
15	28	12	14	6
	$\bar{x} = 23.733$ $s+ = 9.482$	$\bar{x}' = 10.400$ $s+ = 7,452$	$\bar{x} = 18.933$ $s+ = 3.954$	$\bar{x}' = 11.866$ $s+ = 3.461$
	$\bar{x} - \bar{x}' = 13.333$ $t = 4.281$		$\bar{x} - \bar{x}' = 7.066$ $t = 5.207$	

mean of 23.733 ± 9.482 in the mothers and from 0 to 34 ppb, with a mean of 10.400 ± 7.452 in the newborn infants. The levels of p,p'-DDT ranged from 10 to 25 ppb, with a mean of 18.933 ± 3.954 in the mothers and from 6 to 20 ppb with a mean of 11.866 ± 3.461 in the newborns.

Comments

The blood serum samples from pregnant women non-occupationally exposed to chlorinated hydrocarbon insecticides living in Sao Paulo urban area and the ones from their newborn infants have shown levels of DDT and DDE similar or even greater than those referred for other countries. For instance, O'Leary et al.[3], in Florida, referred 10.8 ± 6.2 ppb of DDE and a maximum of 17 ppb of DDT in Caucasian pregnant women, and 4.8 ± 3.4 ppb of DDE and a maximum of 5 ppb of DDT in the umbilical cord blood of their newborn infants. Radomsky et al.[4] observed in Argentina 13.43 ± 7.69 ppb of DDE and 6.85 ± 2.07 ppb of DDT in maternal blood and 4.72 ± 2.54 ppb of DDE and 2.54 ± 1.46 ppb of DDT in the corresponding infant blood.

The higher levels obtained in Sao Paulo city are probably due to the less effective and less rigid regulatory controls and perhaps to the method of extraction used for DDT and related compounds which permitted the release of the protein bound DDT and DDT metabolites, giving consistently higher results than those obtained with simple hexane extraction method.[1]

Insecticide levels, p,p'-DDT as well as p,p'-DDE, in mothers and their newborn infants were statistically different, suggesting the presence of some kind of barrier in the transplacental passage.

References

1 Dale, W. E., Miles, J. W. & Gaines, T. B.: Quantitative method for determination of DDT and DDT metabolites in blood serum. J. A. O. A. C., 53: 1287–1292, 1970
2 Hayes, W. J., Jr., Dale, W. E. & Le Breton, R.: Storage of insecticides in French people. Nature, 199: 1189–1191, 1963
3 O'Leary, J. A., Davies, J. E., Edmundson, W. F. & Reich, G. A.: Transplacental passage of pesticides. Amer. J. Obst. Gynec. 107: 65–68, 1970
4 Radomsky, J. L., Astolfi, E., Deichmann, W. B. & Rey, A. A.: Blood levels of organochlorine pesticides in Argentina: occupationally and nonoccupationally exposed adults, children and newborn infants. Toxic. Appl. Pharmac. 20: 186–193, 1971
5 Wassermann, M., Gon, M., Wassermann, D. & Zellermayer, L.: DDT and DDE in the body fat of people in Israel. Arch. Environ. Health (Chicago), 11: 375–379, 1965
6 Zavon, M. R., Tye, R. & Latorre, L.: Chlorinated hydrocarbon insecticide content of the neonate. Ann. N. Y. Acad. Sci. 160: 196–200, 1969

The Impact of FDA Publicity Releases on Industry, Consumers and Taxpayers*

Esther O. Kegan
Kegan, Kegan & Berkman, Chicago, Illinois, USA

Immediate nationwide publicity is assured when an HEW or FDA release mentions any one of the following four words:

Botulism
Cancer
Salmonella
Filth

The mental images conjured up by any one of these accusations in a 60 second TV news report and newspaper headlines condemn the alleged offending company for years – and sometimes forever.

Let me say at the outset, I am completely in accord with *any* action necessary to protect the public health. But study of some of the notorious instances in recent years leads me to question seriously whether FDA scare tactics by publicity is in the public good. There appears to be an FDA syndrome. First FDA calls a crisis press conference with nationwide publicity, and immediate widespread recalls. Then there is investigation with a limitation of first warnings, which announcement gets little publicity. Then, because the economic damage to the affected company or industry is tremendous, financial relief is frequently sought from some government agency and sometimes is obtained. Under such circumstances, we *all* suffer, the industry involved, each consumer and each taxpayer. And who benefits? I don't know the answer.

I am sure you would not go along with the myth that FDA or any governmental agency can guarantee us health and safety.[1] Probably the most dangerous

instrumentality we all face is the automobile. The direct cigarette hazard is well known but the sale of cigarettes is not restricted.[2] For only a 1 year period, the Public Health Service of FDA reported over 97,000 poisonings and 202 fatalities due to ingestion of products in the home; over 10,000 children under 5 suffered from serious aspirin poisoning.[3] With this perspective in mind, although recognizing that the wellbeing and safety of *every* human being is important, let us examine the role of FDA in tainting a company or industry with one of the four dreaded words first mentioned.

In the brief time allotted here I cannot discuss fully the immediate destruction of the STARLAC brand of nonfat dry milk because of an FDA charge of salmonella.[4] This ubiquitous contaminant was discovered during an inspection of Borden's Dixon plant[5] but the news media made it seem people were seriously sick from STARLAC. Typical of the TV newscasters on November 2, 1966 was the announcement:[6]

"The Food & Drug Administration is recalling from distribution across the country all stock of the Borden Company's nonfat dry milk called STARLAC. The FDA says it is being withdrawn from distributors and stores because of the discovery in samples of an organism called salmonella which produces gastrointestinal infection."

In view of these announcements it is not surprising that Borden Company bore the brunt of about 1600 law suits whereas there had been no prior complaints of

---

* Paper presented at New York State Bar Association. Jan. 1973

salmonella injury from powdered skim milk. I am informed that there was no instance of proven salmonella injury but the litigation expense of defending these suits as well as reimbursement of all returns from 6700 retail stores and customers could bankrupt a small company. The Borden Company survived this salmonella onslaught but adverse public reaction as a result of the FDA accusation was so intense that Borden Co. got out of the nonfat dry milk consumer field and the popular STARLAC brand was killed in the United States.

Nor do I have time to discuss the famed case of Ocean Spray cranberries. Three weeks before Thanksgiving of 1959 FDA announced this seasonal fruit might subject consumers to cancer – because the herbicide aminotriazole had been used – a herbicide approved by the U. S. Department of Agriculture and on which feeding studies were still in progress on November 4, 1959.[7] This odious charge almost bankrupted the company and still is remembered by some.

Nor will I have time to review the full impact of the 1965 botulism charge against the smokefish industry. Three deaths from botulism were traced to one lot of smoked whitefish chubs which was unrefrigerated for four days before receipt by dealer.[8] Industry leaders and the U. S. Bureau of commercial fisheries compelled FDA to issue releases explaining that only smoked fish from the Great Lakes region was involved and not smoked fish from other areas nor any fresh, frozen, pickled or canned fish and seafood products.[9] You may be interested to know that the following year Congress provided for an appropriation of $ 400,000 to pay for destruction of affected frozen white fish chubs.[10] In addition, special loans were made available to "small business" smoked fish concerns because of the botulism episode.[11]

Most people do not realize the important part aesthetics plays in enforcement of our food laws. I refer to the horror engendered at the mention of the word "filth". Dirt or even rodent hairs may be repulsive to the sensitive but they are not in themselves dangerous to health. I am not condoning insanitary conditions and FDA should, by its inspection powers, raise the level of good manufacturing practices in this regard. But the public should not be needlessly scared – and faith in the food industry needlessly impaired, by headlines as to insects, rat hairs or other filth in foods.[12]

Periodically FDA brands a company president as a criminal for holding a food under conditions where it may become "contaminated with filth". Usually, the offending food is immediately destroyed and there is no charge that any insanitary food was in fact shipped. But when FDA and the District Attorney announce to the press that Company A and its President held foods for sale which contained rodent hairs or dead insects, the newspaper may headline *"selling* contaminated filthy ———" – with the further assertion that the officer faces a maximum fine of $ 1000 and one year in prison for each count if convicted. Experienced food manufacturing executives, who were criminally judged with holding a food under conditions of "filth" either leave the food industry or live under constant threat of a prison sentence if a rat is found in his plant even while he is on his summer vacation.[13] From the viewpoint of consumers, I question whether FDA should assign its top priorities to brand a corporate officer a criminal for not maintaining as sanitary a plant as is possible.

Two recent FDA releases warrant more complete exposure – namely, the Bon Vivant and cyclamate incidents. The Bon Vivant Company went into bankruptcy after a charge that a Westchester man died from botulism. The cyclamate sweetened food industry was worth about a billion dollars in October, 1969 and it went virtually to zero immediately because of the FDA release "Cancer". These situations emphasize the tremendous impact of FDA public releases.

What recourse does a small food processor have when the FDA might is unleashed against it? The dread plague "botulism" understandably puts fear into everyone's mind and heart. When FDA announced a can of Bon Vivant vichysoisse soup was the cause of a botulism death on July 1, 1971, the whole country was alarmed. This well established canned soup company went down the drain because the name Bon Vivant became synonymous with the plague. It seems potential harm could have been averted by zeroing in on the offending product rather than a broadside attack on the entire company. Investigation disclosed that one retort crate of 1 lot totalling 460 tins had been underprocessed and 5 cans were contaminated.[14] Thus, immediate recall of the offending lot of 460 cans of soup which had been undercooked was essential. But was it necessary to compel immediately so-called "voluntary" recall of all 91 different products of the Bon Vivant Company – totalling two million cans – before any investigation was undertaken?[15] Recalls involve financial reimbursement and there appears to be an ongoing controversy between FDA and the Company concerning the completeness of the recall, with about 100 seizures actions in process.

It is particularly significant that FDA pressured Bon Vivant to agree to "voluntary recalls" of products not claimed to be harmful and the Company succumbed to this pressure. Yet, the U. S. Comptroller General reported to Congress[16] that FDA does not presently have power to compel recalls of products "known or suspected of being harmful"; FDA power being restricted to removal of known "harmful products".

Contrasted with the FDA crisis-approach in the Bon Vivant soup case was its low key reaction when Campbell Soup Co. produced a batch of botulism toxin-contaminated soup in July, 1971. The Director of FDA's Bureau of Foods testified:

> "There is something to be said for not alarming people too much for what is a rare occurrence".[17]

I concur heartily with this approach. In fact, the record on some of these national "emergency" releases indicates many suffer – the "fingered" company or industry, consumers and taxpayers.

We are not here as either judge or jury to determine whether FDA or Bon Vivant's story is true. We do know that the Bon Vivant situation dramatized FDA request for more funds for inspections – a total of $ 154.1 million for fiscal 1973.[18] We can, however, also be sensitive to the tremendous "life or death" power which FDA has by virtue of its press releases and question whether the public could have been safeguarded by direct action against the involved product and not against this 108 year old company. Moreover in the case of condemnation by publicity the damage in the public mind is done immediately and frequently is irreversible.

Let us examine what impact does the charge "Cancer" have. The most recent use of the "cancer" scare was by the FDA ban against cyclamates, a product consumed by millions for over 25 years. The cyclamate non-nutritive sweetener was patented in 1942[19] and marketed by Abbott Laboratories, as Sucaryl Sweetener, as a new drug in the early fifties. When the Food Additives Amendment requiring proof of safety was passed in 1958, several hundred substances then in use, including cyclamates (and the other popular non-nutritive sweetener saccharine) were exempt from the provisions of the Additives Amendment being "generally recognized as safe" – and placed on the GRAS list. All would admit that in the 20 years of use cyclamates amounting to millions of pounds per year, there were no complaints of injury due to its ingestion.

Then on Saturday, October 18, 1969 [20] a press conference called by then HEW Secretary Robert H. Finch started with these ominous words:

"Ladies & Gentlemen: I am today ordering that the artificial sweetener cyclamate be removed from the list of substances generally recognized as safe for use in foods. The recent experiments conducted on laboratory animals disclose the presence of malignant bladder tumors after these animals had been subjected to strong dose levels of cyclamates for long periods."[21]

At the crucial press conference in 1969, notwithstanding disclaimers by FDA Dr. Jesse Steinfeld that "there is absolutely no evidence to demonstrate in any way that the use of cyclamates has caused cancer in man",[22] page 1 newspaper headlines read:

"Cancer fear – U. S. Bans Diet-Drink Sweetener" . . . . Secretary HEW Finch ordered all foods and drinks containing the artificial sweetener cyclamate be removed from grocery shelves by Feb. 1 because of new evidence the substance causes cancer in animals."[23]

This press conference was called promptly after Abbott Laboratories, an important manufacturer of cyclamates, reported to FDA that experiments conducted on its behalf showed that 8 rats developed bladder tumors after having eaten large doses of cyclamates in various forms. It is significant that the level of cyclamates required to produce these tumors in these 8 rats was 2500 milligrams per kilogram of body weight per day for every day of the entire life of the rat [24] or almost two years.

To compare these doses with levels for human consumption, a person would have to drink about 400 bottles of cyclamate-containing soda every day throughout his life.[25] A Dr. Roger Egeberg at the same press conference tried to give some perspective and stated:

"that cyclamates or non-caloric sweetener have probably saved and prolonged a tremendous number of lives the last few years by helping people keep their weight down and, from what some dentists say, maybe they saved a lot of teeth, too."[26]

All FDA officials admitted there was not a single known case of hazard to man from millions of people who used cyclmataes for years except 8 cases of a skin sensitivity to sunlight.[27]

Secretary Finch justified his emergency ban on the use of cyclamate in the production of general purpose foods and beverages on the Delaney Amendment, saying "I have no choice".[28] But is discretion permitted? There is one view that the Delaney clause prohibits the setting of tolerances for any food additive found to induce cancer when ingested by man or animal. The Food & Drug Committee of the Section on Corporation Banking and Business Law of the American Bar Association recommends amendment of this Delaney clause (§ 409) to clarify this point. It appears to me that the legislative history and language of the Delaney clause obligates the Secretary of HEW to base his decisions on "a fair evaluation of the data before him.[29] But was the evidence before the Secretary on October 18, 1969 fairly evaluated? On the basis of one study of 8 rats FDA deprived the 70 per cent of all adults, who believe they are overweight,[30] the choice of cylamate sweetened products.

Moreover at least one court does not agree with Secretary Finch that the Delaney clause was applicable to cyclamate inasmuch as cyclamate was on the GRAS list at the time of the ban. In the case of *Rossi v. Finck,* the California District Court refused to review the FDA cyclamate order and held that the Delaney clause applies only to *new* food additives or to those not exempted at the time of its enactment in 1958, and that the Delaney clause was inapplicable to the cyclamate ban because cyclamate were exempted at the time by inclusion in the GRAS list.[31]

Contrast the precipitous action on cyclamates with FDA action on saccharine-sweetened products, saccharine being the only artificial sweetener known to FDA to be in use at the present time.[32] Studies of potential cancer link of saccharine similar to the cyclamate studies were presented to FDA, but the answer appeared to be – let's study the matter further. In fact, a Chicago paper headlined "Cancer link found – No restriction yet on saccharin". The lead sentence was "No panic buttons will be pushed to restrict use of saccharin, the artificial sweetener newly implicated as a cancer producer in experimental animals".[33]

I am not privy to the behind-the-scenes pressures underlying the cyclamate episode but I can report that the same Robert Finch whose announcement destroyed the cyclamate industry in October, 1969, testified in 1971 as White House aide, to present Administration endorsement[34] to the Cyclamate Compensation bill.[35] The cyclamate compensation would give all who suffered losses from the government ban on cyclamates, the right to sue the Federal government to recover out-of-pocket costs, after tax offsets, such as destroyed inventories of canned fruits and soft drinks. Awards in excess of $ 100,000 would have to be ratified by Congress but it is estimated that taxpayers may have been subjected to claims of more than $ 100 million to half a billion dollars.[36] One arm of the government, FDA, prohibits the sale of cyclamate containing food which we all have been consuming for years – this causes a multi-million dollar injury to industry. Then another arm of the government, the Commerce Department,[37] supports the cyclamate claim bill even though it may cost taxpayers millions. Who benefitted from the half-billion dollar loss? The consumer might well ask – was my health really in a crisis on October 18, 1969? Was the situation significantly different on that date from prior years 1968–1967 and earlier, when we ate the same cyclamate foods? Should further studies have been undertaken? Could canners and others in the industry have been alerted to proposed FDA objections and thus avoid these tremendous losses? The taxpayer might well ask – couldn't the phase-out have been gradual to avoid industry damage and not increase any hazard to health? It seems we all lost by the precipitous action of FDA.

The real purpose of Food, Drug & Cosmetic Act is remedial – namely, to assure the manufacture and distribution of safe and wholesome foods. FDA has discretion by statute to determine, even in cases of technical violation of the Act, when the public interest necessitates any action whether by publicity, seizure, recalls or criminal prosecution. It would appear that FDA monies and personnel should be given priorities based on these factors in best interests of the public health.

The food industry is just as concerned as FDA with the public health but it is hoped that FDA, USDA and other governmental agencies would make the *regulatory hazard* of operating a food establishment more consistent with the *health hazard.*[38] In the final analysis, regulation by sensational publicity can only be detrimental to the best interests of the food and drug industry, the consuming public and all taxpayers.

Footnotes

1 "You don't live in a cocoon of safety established by the FDA and you never will": John
   Neary, "A Consumer Looks at FDA as it
   tries to look out for him." LIFE, Oct. 20,
   1972, p. 73. A new FDA approach is exemplified by its current television ads – "Without
   proper supervision any toy can be hazardous
   and FDA needs your help."
2 HEW Secretary Finch was asked how he
   could move so fast on cyclamates and not on
   cigarettes. He responded by reporting HEW
   has no power over cigarettes. "That would be
   higher legislation." (Transcript of HEW cyclamate Press Conference on October 18, 1969,
   p. 20.)
3 Letter to author dated August 24, 1970 from
   Division of Poison Control – for year 1968
   P C Table 1C. See also U. S. Census Report
   of Death and Death Rates for each cause for
   1966 – Table 1–22 p. 1–84
4 FDA Release Nov. 2, 1966 (66–24). "There
   were 85 recalls of Salmonella – contaminated
   foods and drugs from the market in 1967
   reported by Kenneth R. Lennington, "Status
   & Review of the Salmonella Program" before
   FDL 1-FDA Conference, Nov. 27, 1967
5 FDA enforced a zero tolerance rule on salmonella – no salmonella organism can be
   present in the final product: "How Food
   Manufacturers Can Control Salmonella,"
   published by Grocery Manufacturer
6 Julian Barber on Station WTOP-TV, Washington, D. C. at 6:00 P. M. newscast Nov. 2,
   1966
7 Special labeling was announced for cranberries from 1958 and 1959 crops due to possible
   contamination with herbicide aminotriazole:
   24 F. R. 9543, reported in Kleinfeld and Kap-
   lan Food Drug & Cosmetic Act 1958–60,
   p. 237
8 FDA release dated October 25, 1963. GMP
   regulations for smoked fish were promulgated
   on Nov. 6, 1969, CCH FD & C Reg. § 58020
   A–G
9 FDA release of October 29, 1963, HEW p. 95
10 Pub. Law 88–309 approved May 20, 1964,
   Sec. 4 (b) payments for fishery failure due to
   resource disaster, as reported by National
   Fisheries Institute, Inc. on August 4, 1964
11 Amendment to Small Business Act, 15 USC
   636, Sec. 7b, House Report No. 1097, as
   reported in CCH FDC Rep. § 50, 075.64
12 FDA has not yet established standards for
   foreign material in intravenous injections. Wm.

B. Mead, "Particles in Intravenous Fluids",
   287 The New England Journal of Medicine
   1152 (Nov. 30, 1972)
13 Sec. 303 (a) of FDC Act makes the second
   offense of violating the Act a felony subject
   to imprisonment for not more than 3 years or
   a fine of not more than $ 10,000 or both for
   each "count": (21 USC § 333 a). The Courts
   have held executives criminally responsible
   for unsanitary conditions: Golden Grain Mac-
   aroni Co. Inc. v. U. S. 209 F. 2 d 166 (9th
   Cir. 1953)
14 Statement of Andrew Paretti for the Over-
   sight Hearings on Federal Food Inspection
   Sub-Committee on Public Health and Environment, House Committee on Interstate and
   Foreign Commerce 1971
15 The company claims that on July 6, 1971,
   FDA gave President Andrew Paretti a few
   hours to decide to "voluntarily" recall all of
   91 products made by Bon Vivant; it appeared
   that resistance of such voluntary act would be
   more adverse publicity, Statement of Andrew
   Paretti, President of Bon Vivant, submitted to
   the Sub-Committee on Public Health and
   Environment, House committee on Interstate
   and Foreign Commerce, 92nd Cong. Sept.
   1971 (p. 13) p. 471
16 Report B–164031 (2), CCH Food Drug Cosmetic Law Reports No. 504, October 10, 1972
17 Testimony of Dr. Virgil Wodicka on September 10, 1971 before the House Subcommittee
   on Public Health and Environment, Committee on Interstate & Foreign Commerce
18 Judy Gardner, "To Confront Members of
   93rd Congress, National Journal Dec. 2, 1972,
   p. 1856, 1861
19 U. S. Patent 2,275,125 issued to E. I. du Pont
   de Nemours & Co. on an invention by Mi-
   chael Sveda
20 TV and News releases by FDA officials on
   October 1st and October 3, 1969 started the
   cyclamate scare with scenes of deformed chick
   embryos from cyclamate injections in chicken
   eggs. Dr. Jacqueline Verrett appeared on
   WRC-TV, Washington, D. C. on October 1,
   1969 dramatizing deprived chick embryos
   claimed to result from cyclamate injections.
   On October 3, 1969, FDA Administrator Dr.
   Herbert Ley was reported on CBS-TV Morn-
   ing News to have said "If the Academy Experts consider these new items of information
   to be highly significant, I think the appropriate response on the part of this agency
   would be a banning of this material (cyclamate)." On October 8, 1969, HEW Secretary
   criticized these FDA officials as being over-

zealous. (Washington Post, October 8, 1969, p. 6)

21 Transcript of Press Conference held at HEW North Building Room 5051 Saturday, October 18, 1959 et 9:30 a. m. by the Honorable Robert H. Finch, Sectretary HEW, p. 2

22 P. 5 of transcript of Press Conf. op. cit.

23 Chicago Daily News, Oct. 18, 1969

24 Statement of Dr. Jesse Steinfeld at HEW Press Conference of October 18, 1969, p. 9, 16 of Transcript

25 Estimate of the Abbott Co. Public Relations Dept. employee familiar with Abbott studies

26 Press Conference, op. cit. Transcript p. 14

27 Transcript of Press Conference p. 34

28 P. 35 of Press Conference transcript

29 Delaney clause – § 409 (c) (3) (A), CCH Food Drug & Cosmetic Reporter § 55, 113

30 Estimate by John Pope of General Mills, Inc., Chicago Daily News, Dec. 21, 1972, p. 61

31 Rossi v. Finch, CCH § 40, 391 (N. C. Cal. 1970)

32 21 CFR Pts. 1,3,5, published in 38 Fed. Reg. 2141 (Jan. 19, 1973)

33 Chicago Daily News, May 18, 1970, p. 56, Dr. Geo. T. Bryan of U. of Wis. reported his implantation experiments of cyclamate with mice showed 78 and 61% more developing bladder cancer in 2 experiments whereas bladder cancer was produced in 47% and 52% of mice implanted with saccharin. See "Saccharin: Future Uncertain" Science 971, Sept. 15, 1972

34 Chicago Daily News, Sept. 23, 1971

35 H. R. 13366, 92nd Cong. Act to provide for payment of losses incurred by domestic grocers, manufacturers, packers and distributors as a result of the barring of the use of cyclamates, etc. – passed in the House, died in the Senate Judiciary Committee. The Consumers' Federation protested "the cyclamate industry should not be rewarded for adding a substance with these serious risks to our food." (Rep. Sidney Yates, July 31, 1972, Newsletter No. 318)

36 „Cyclamate Bill, A Sleeper" by Edward Cowan, New York Times, May 7, 1972, p. 3

37 Wm. N. Letson, Commerce Dept.'s General Counsel testified in support of H. R. 13367 as reported in New York Times May 7, 1972

38 Lawrence Atkin, "Changing Concepts in Sanitation," Food, Drug, Cosmetic Law Journal, p. 24, 68, 72 (1969)

Environmental Factors in the Etiology of Human Malformations: Perspectives and Problems of Evaluation

T.V.N. Persaud
The University of Manitoba, Winnipeg, Manitoba, Canada

Summary   Teratogenic compounds are discussed, i.e. active products which probably have teratogenic effects in man. For environmental chemicals, the general principles for the causation of deformities are enumerated and evaluated. The difficulties of predicting possible teratogenic effects of any chemical from animal experiments are pointed out, especially as there are no standardized methods.

Zusammenfassung   Zunächst werden Wirkstoffe vorgestellt, die mit Sicherheit teratogen sind bzw. die mit einer gewissen Wahrscheinlichkeit im Menschen teratogene Effekte haben. Für Umweltchemikalien werden die allgemeinen Prinzipien zur Entwicklung von Mißbildungen aufgezählt und bewertet. Es wird auf die Schwierigkeit der Voraussage möglicher teratogener Effekte irgendeiner Chemikalie aus Tierexperimenten hingewiesen, besonders da keine standardisierten Methoden vorhanden sind.

Congenital malformations have assumed great importance in recent years, due not only to the thalidomide tragedy, but also to improved antenatal care and better management of traditional infectious and nutritional diseases. The mortality rate from birth defects has risen proportionally as the mortality rate from infection and malnutrition has decreased.

The severe damage done to unborn children by the use of thalidomide during pregnancy has helped to focus attention on the potential hazards of adverse environmental agents to the pregnant woman and her offspring. It is now established that most birth defects have an environmental component in their multifactorial etiology.[10, 11, 15, 34, 75] Some measure of control will only become possible with the identification of potential environmental hazards and an understanding of their envolvement in the production of developmental defects. The increasing contamination of the human environment with harmful substances[3, 12, 20, 21, 25, 29, 42, 67] makes this an urgent problem.

Human Teratogens

In 1942 the first environmental factor recognized as causing human malformations was described. Cataract, microcephaly, deaf-mutism and heart lesions were observed in infants of mothers who had contracted German measles during early pregnancy.[26] Since then numerous reports have been published implicating other viruses and infectious agents in the etiology of human malformations. Apart from rubella, cytomegalic inclusion virus,[33] syphilis[5] and toxoplasmosis,[30, 55] the evidence is not conclusive that other *maternal infections* can lead to fetal damage and fetal abnormalities.[4, 18, 19, 45, 60, 61]

Particular attention should be directed to the increasing contamination of the human environment with various ionizing and non-ionizing *radiations* and their potential harmful effect on the human conceptus. The teratogenic hazards of ionizing radiations during early pregnancy are well established.[28, 29, 53] Microcephaly, spina bifida, cleft palate, visceral malformations and limb defects have been observed following irradiation of the abdomen and pelvis in early pregnancy. There is some relationship between the dose level and time of irradiation and the adverse effects produced.

Aminopterin, an antagonist of folic acid, produced malformed fetuses when administered during early pregnancy to tuberculous women for the purpose of inducing therapeutic abortion[70] and in cases of illegal abortion.[43, 63, 76] Intrauterine growth retardation, anencephaly, hydrocephaly, meningocele, cleft palate, and skull anomalies were observed on the fetuses recovered.

Progestational compounds are used clinically for the prevention of threatened abortion, but maternal treatment with synthetic progestins in early pregnancy has caused masculinization of female infants.[57, 59, 74, 79]

Thalidomide provided an almost perfect example of a causal relationship between a specific teratogen and human congenital malformations. The teratogenicity of this substance in man was demonstrated during its use as a sedative which resulted in the birth of thousands of severely malformed infants.[14, 35, 40, 77] A wide spectrum of congenital malformations, including limb defects (Figure 1), absence of the

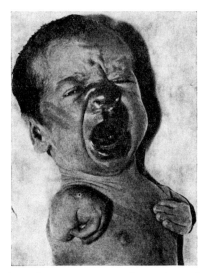

Fig. 1 *Infant showing severe malformations of the upper limbs and ears induced by thalidomide. (Courtesy of Professor W. Lenz)*

internal and external ears, deafness, haemangioma on the forehead, and malformations of the cardiovascular, digestive and urogenital systems were detected in the offspring of mothers who ingested thalidomide during early pregnancy.

The use of *psychotropic substances,* in particular marihuana and LSD (lysergic acid diethylamide), has increased considerably in the past few years.[7, 8, 39, 73] It is not surprising that there is wide-spread concern that these substances may prove to be harmful to the pregnant woman and her offspring,[46] particularly since two cases of multiple malformations in infants of mothers, who used cannabis in combination with other psychotropic drugs, have been reported.[9, 27] The results of animal experimental studies lend support to these observations.[22, 23, 50, 51]

Of 161 infants born to parents who took LSD before or during pregnancy, 5 showed gross malformations. The incidence rate of abortion is apparently increased following the use of LSD during pregnancy. However, the results of animal studies with LSD have been conflicting and do not support the view that LSD is teratogenic in man.[36]

There have been isolated reports relating other environmental agents to the occurrence of congenital abnormalities in pregnant women.[2, 24, 38, 62, 64, 65, 66, 75] Many of these observations must be interpreted with caution, since they are invariably based on fragmentary and inconclusive evidence.[17, 38, 47, 71]

Experimental Studies

Numerous reports have appeared on the teratogenic effects of a wide spectrum of environmental agents in laboratory animals [12, 20, 47, 58, 69, 71, 81, 82] and it has been suggested that almost any environmental agent is capable of inducing developmental defects under appropriate condi-

tions. Investigations of this nature are neither ethical nor justifiable in man. On this account, the data derived from experimental studies in animals will remain an important source, not only for predicting possible harmful effects of environmental agents on the human fetus, but also in determining the underlying mechanisms operating at various phases of intrauterine existence.

Although the exact *mechanisms* by which the majority of environmental teratogens may interfere with embryonic development and so produce abnormalities remain obscure, certain general principles and guidelines relating to the occurrence of abnormalities have emerged. These are presented in summary as follows:

1. The site of primary action of teratogens may be either the embryo itself, the mother, the placenta or hormonal and other regulatory mechanisms involved in pregnancy.

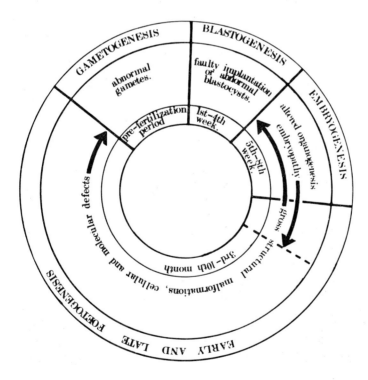

Fig. 2 Gestational periods and the timing of teratogenicity

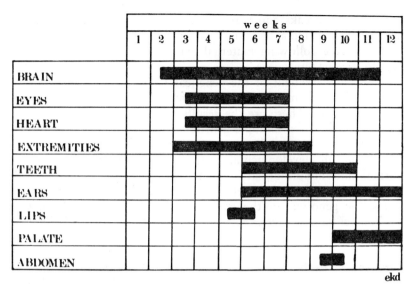

Fig. 3   Critical periods during organogenesis

2. The period of gestation during which the teratogen is administered influences the teratogenic responses (Figure 2). These "critical phases" during embryonic and fetal development are related to the degree of differentiation of specific organs; as differentiation proceeds susceptibility to teratogenesis decreases (Figure 3). For this reason gross structural defects hardly ever occur after organogenesis is completed.

The concept that congenital abnormalities cannot be induced during the pre-implantation period of the blastocyst is invalid. The early conceptus is highly susceptible to teratogenesis, particularly during implantation and placentation.

3. Teratogenic activity of the noxious agent is often dependent on the species and strain of animals involved. Our studies on the teratogenicity of hypoglycin and diethyl barbituric acid demonstrate the significance of species differences in *susceptibility to teratogenesis.*[48, 52]

4. Congenital malformations are generally induced by a dosage of the teratogenic agent which is slightly higher than that which has no effect on the embryo, but much smaller than that which will kill the mother. If small doses of the teratogen are administered, the embryos will not be affected and will appear quite normal at birth. Large doses of the teratogen will invariably kill the conceptus. The *teratogenic zone* is a relatively small range of dosage. Within this range the mortality and malformation rates tend to follow a parallel course and vary with both the dosage and period of treatment.

5. *Hereditary influences* are of considerable importance in determining the occurrence of congenital abnormalities. In particular the following genetic conditions should be taken into consideration in the evaluation of teratological data:

(a) Mutant genes which are the source of a wide variety of malformations probably influence the structure or rate of synthesis of polypeptides during embryonic development. The resulting biochemical errors may induce abnormal morphological changes.

(b) Chromosomal aberrations invariably produce major congenital abnormalities;

chromosomal breaks and rearrangements and abnormal metaphase figures have been observed following maternal exposure to various teratogens.

(c) The most frequent of the genetically influenced malformations are multifactorial in nature. These are the results of interactions between multiple genetic and environmental factors. It is now recognized that all developmental processes, normal and abnormal, are due to the complex interplay between maternal genes, the genotype of the embryo and environmental influences.

Teratological Evaluation

Animal studies, designed to uncover teratogenic side-effects of environmental agents, have a poor predictive value for the human fetus. The validity and some of the limitations of these tests have been discussed in previous reports.[1, 6, 13, 16, 32, 37, 41, 49, 54, 58, 72, 78]

There is some agreement that mammals, in particular rodents and primates,[69, 72, 81, 82] are best suited for teratological evaluation studies. However, the high cost of maintenance, the lengthy period of gestation and the small numer of offspring produced by primates would limit their extensive use in teratological investigations.

Any recommended *experimental procedure* in these species involves production and verification of pregnancy in the selected animals under controlled laboratory conditions. The test animal is exposed to a suitable and measured dose of the suspected environmental factor, on one or more days during pregnancy, which should include the period of organogenesis. Fetuses are recovered by Caesarean-section immediately before or at term in order to prevent the mothers from devouring damaged fetuses. Fetuses of both the control and treated groups of animals are weighed, measured and subjected to the same detailed and systematic examination for abnormalities.

A small number of fetuses are usually fixed in Bouin's solution and sectioned by the Wilson's technique[80] for the identification of gross visceral malformations. Other fetuses are subjected to histological examination of selected tissues, and selected fetuses are fixed in 95% ethyl alcohol in order to examine the skeletal system after clearing and staining by the Alizarin S technique. It is desirable also that the fetuses be studied further for cellular and metabolic changes.

The occurrence of congenital abnormalities in the offspring of treated animals can only suggest *possible* teratogenicity for the human conceptus, and with this a substantial risk that if the child was born it may suffer from such physical or mental abnormalities as to be seriously handicapped. On the contrary, negative results give no positive clearance for safety in man.

In the design and interpretation of these laboratory evaluation, consideration must be given to factors such as age, nutritional requirements, general health and maintenance of the animals, and the number and size of the litters. During gestation, the pregnant animals should regularly be weighed and subjected to frequent physical examinations for the presence of obvious signs of harm.

The teratological evaluation of chemicals, drugs and natural products represents a complex type of toxicological problem, where multiple factors involving the mother, fetus, placenta and the suspected noxious agent itself influence the response of the developing conceptus. Because of species and strain variation in susceptibility to teratogenesis, these environmental agents must be tested in several species and possibly of different strains. As a rule, screening should be carried out in two or more species for a preliminary evaluation of possible teratogenic activity.

Surprisingly, very few teratological studies, involving a specific environmental agent in several animal species, have been reported from the same laboratory. This would facilitate the evaluation of data obtained since individual investigators have worked out their own screening procedures. Invariably these are carried out under different methodological, laboratory and environmental conditions.

Because of the varying conditions under which teratological testing of suspected environmental agents is carried out, every effort should be made to standardize methods and define clearly the objective of these investigations. Taking this into consideration, teratological evaluation in laboratory animals would continue to provide useful information on the ability of exogenous agents to induce developmental deviations and also in determining the underlying mechanisms operating at various stages of prenatal development.

It is unlikely that laboratory evaluation of any environmental factor can provide conclusive evidence of possible harmful effects for the human conceptus. This data can only be derived from detailed clinical observations of pregnant women and their abnormal offsprings. The application of *epidemiological techniques* is contributing significantly to the recognition of environmental teratogens and in increasing our understanding of the nature of birth defects.[31, 38, 44, 56, 62, 68, 75] For this reason, the systematic collection and analysis of reports of adverse effects produced on the human conceptus should also be considered important for the early recognition of deleterious environmental teratogens.

References

1 Baker, S. B., and Davey, D. G. (1970): The predictive value for man of toxicological tests of drugs in laboratory animals. Br. med. Bull. 26, 208–211

2 Batstone, G. F., Blair, A. W., and Slater, J. M. (1972): A handbook of prenatal paediatrics for obstetricians and paediatricians. J. B. Lippincott Company, Philadelphia and Toronto

3 Brent, R. L. (1972): Protecting the public from teratogenic and mutagenic hazards. J. Clin. Pharmacol. 12, 61–70

4 Brown, G. C. (1970): Maternal virus infection and congenital anomalies. Arch. Environ. Health 21, 362–365

5 Bulova, S., Schwartz, E., and Harrer, W. V. (1972): Hydrops fetalis and congenital syphilis. Pediatrics 49, 285–287

6 Cahen, R. L. (1964): Evaluation of the teratogenicity of drugs. Clin. Pharmacol. Ther. 5, 480–514

7 Cannabis – Report by the Advisory Committee on Drug Dependence. Her Majesty's Stationery Office, Lond., 1968

8 Cannabis – A report of the commission of inquiry into the non-medical use of drugs. Ottawa, 1972

9 Carakushansky, G., Neu, R. L., and Gardner, L. I. (1969). Lysergide and cannabis as possible teratogens in man. Lancet 1, 150–151

10 Carter, C. O. (1967): Congenital malformations. WHO Chronicle 21, 287–292

11 Carter, C. (1970): The genetics of congenital malformations. In Scientific Foundations of Obstetrics and Gynaecology (Eds. E. E. Philipp, J. Barnes, and M. Newton), William Heinemann Medical Books Ltd., London. pp. 655–660

12 Clegg, D. J. (1971): Embryotoxicity of chemical contaminants of foods. Fd. Cosmet. Toxicol. 9, 195–205

13 Cook, M. J., Fairweather, F. A., and Hardwick, M. (1969): Further thoughts on teratogenic testing. In Teratology (Eds. A. Bertelli and L. Donati), Excerpta Medica Foundation, Amsterdam. pp. 34–42

14 Curran, W. J. (1971): The thalidomide tragedy in Germany. The end of a historic medicolegal trial. N. Eng. J. Med. 284, 481–482

15 de la Cruz, M. V., mu Noz-Castellanos, L., and Nadal-Ginard, B. (1971): Extrinsic factors in the genesis of congenital heart disease. Brit. Heart J. 33, 203–213

16 Delahunt, C. S. (1970): Detection of teratogenic action. In Methods in Toxicology (Ed.

G. E. Paget), Blackwell Scientific Publ. pp. 132–157

[17] Döring, G. K., and Hossfeld, C. (1964): Uber die Gefahren einer übertriebenen Medikamentenfurcht in der Schwangerschaft. Dtsch. med. Wschr. 89, 1069–1072

[18] Dudgeon, J. A. (1968): Fetal infections. J. Obstet. Gynaec. Br. Commonw. 75, 1229–1233

[19] Dudgeon, J. A. (1968): Breakdown in maternal protection: infections. Proc. roy. Soc. Med. 61, 1236–1243

[20] Durham, W. F., and Williams, C. H. (1972): Mutagenic, teratogenic, and carcinogenic properties of pesticides. Annual Rev. Entomol. 17, 123–148

[21] Epstein, S. (1972): Environmental Pathology. Am. J. Pathol. 66, 252–374

[22] Geber, W. F., and Schramm, L. C. (1969a): Effects of marihuana extract on fetal hamsters and rabbits. Toxicol. Appl. Pharmacol. 14, 276–282

[23] Geber, W. F., and Schramm, L. C. (1969b): Teratogenicity of marihuana extract as influenced by plant origin and seasonal variation. Arch. Int. Pharmacodyn. Ther. 177, 224–230

[24] Gerfeldt, E. (1964): Frequenz, Aetiologie und Prophylaxe von angeborenen Entwicklungsstörungen. Med. Klin. 59, 1287–1292

[25] Goldberg, L. (1971): Trace chemical contaminants in food: Potential for harm. Fd. Cosmet. Toxicol. 9, 65–80

[26] Gregg, N. M. (1942): Congenital cataract following German measles in the mother. Trans. Ophthal. Soc. Aust. 3, 35–46

[27] Hecht, F., Beals, R. K., Lees, M. H., Jolly, H., and Roberts, P. (1968): Lysergic-acid-diethylamide and cannabis as possible teratogens in man. Lancet 2, 1087

[28] Hicks, S. P., and D'Amato, C. J. (1966): Effects of ionizing radiations on mammalian development. In Advances in Teratology (Ed. D. H. M. Woollam) Logos and Academic Press, New York. Vol. 1, pp. 195–259

[29] Hueper, W. C. (1971): Public health hazards from environmental chemical carcinogens, mutagens and teratogens. Health Phys. 21, 689–707

[30] Hume, O. S. (1972): Toxoplasmosis and pregnancy. Am. J. Obstet. Gynecol. 114, 703–715

[31] Kennedy, W. P. (1967): Epidemiologic aspects of the problem of congenital malformations. Birth Defects Original Article Series 3, 1–18

[32] Keplinger, M. L. (1971): Assessment of toxicity of substances. J. Occup. Med. 13, 2–7

[33] Krech, U., Jung, M., and Jung, F. (1971): Cytomegalovirus infections of man. S. Karger A. G., Basel

[34] Leck, I. (1972): The etiology of human malformations: Insights from epidemiology. Teratology 5, 303–314

[35] Lenz, W., and Knapp, K. (1962): Die Thalidomid-Embryopathie. Dtsch. med. Wschr. 87, 1232–1242

[36] Long, S. Y. (1972): Does LSD induce chromosomal damage and malformations? A review of the literature. Teratology 6, 75–90

[37] Lorke, O. (1963): Zur Methodik der Untersuchungen embryotoxischer und teratogener Wirkungen an der Ratte. Arch. exp. Path. Pharmak. 246, 147–151

[38] Lowe, R. (1972): Congenital malformations and the problem of their control. Brit. med. J. 3, 515–520

[39] Marihuana and health – A report to Congress from the Secretary, U. S. Department of Health, Education and Welfare. Washington, 1971

[40] McBride, A. (1961): Thalidomide and congenital abnormalities. Lancet 2, 1358

[41] McKenzie, J. (1969): The chick embryo grown in vitro. In Teratology (Eds. A. Bertelli and L. Donati). Excerpta Medica Foundation. Amsterdam. pp. 43–54

[42] McLeod, H. A., Grant, D. L., and Phillips, W. E. (1971): Pesticide residues and metabolites in placentas. Can. J. Publ. Hlth. 62, 341–433.

[43] Meltzer, H. J. (1955): Congenital anomalies due to attempted abortion with 4-aminopteroglutamic acid. J. Am. med. Ass. 161, 1253

[44] Miller, J. R. (1964): The use of registries and vital statistics in the study of congenital malformations. In: Second International Conference on Congenital Malformations (Ed. M. Fishbein) International Medical Congress, New York. pp. 334–340

[45] Monif, G. R. G. (1969). Viral infections of the human fetus. The Collier-MacMillan Company, Toronto, Canada

[46] Neuberg, R. (1972): Drug addiction in pregnancy: Review of the problem. Proc. roy. Soc. Med. 65, 867

[47] Persaud, T. V. N. (1968): Aspects of teratology. W. I. Med. J. 17, 74–82

[48] Persaud, T. V. N. (1972a): Teratogenic activity of hypoglycin-A. In Advances in Teratology (Ed. D. H. M. Woollam), Logos and Academic Press. Vol. 5, pp. 77–95

[49] Persaud, T. V. N. (1972b): Effect of intra-amniotic administration of hypoglycin B on foetal development in the rat. Exp. Pathol. 6, 55–58

[50] Persaud, T. V. N., and Ellington, A. C. (1968a): Teratogenic activity of cannabis resin. Lancet 2, 406–407

[51] **Persaud, T. V. N.**, and Ellington, A. C. (1968b): The effects of cannabis sativa L. (Ganja) on developing rat embryos-preliminary observations. W. I. Med. J. 17, 232–234

[52] Persaud, T. V. N., and Henderson, W. M. (1969): The teratogenicity of barbital sodium in mice. Arzneim.-Forsch. (Drug. Res.) 19, 1309–1310

[53] Plummer, G. (1952): Anomalies occurring in children exposed *in utero* to the atomic bomb in Hiroshima. Pediatrics 10, 687–693

[54] Poswillo, D. E., Hamilton, W. J., and Sopher, D. (1972): The marmoset as an animal model for teratological research. Nature (Lond.) 239, 460–462

[55] Remington, J. S. (1968): Toxoplasmosis and congenital infection. Birth Defects Original Article Series 4, 47–56

[56] Renwick, J. H. (1972): Anencephaly and spina bifida are usually preventable by evidence of a specific but unidentified substance present in certain potato tubers. Brit. J. prev. soc. Med. 26, 67–88

[57] Rice-Wray, E., Cervantes, A., Gutierrez, J., and Marquez-Monter, H. (1971). Pregnancy and progeny after hormonal contraceptive studies. J. Reprod. Med. 6, 101–104

[58] Robson, J. M. (1970): Testing drugs for teratogenicity and their effects on fertility. The present position. Br. Med. Bull. 26, 212–216

[59] Schreiner, W. E. (1971): Nebenwirkungen der medikamentösen Antikonzeption. Schweiz. Med. Wochenschr. 100, 778–784

[60] Sever, J. L. (1970): Viruses and embryos. In Congenital Malformations (Ed. F. C. Fraser and V. A. McJusick), pp. 180–186. Excerpta Medica Foundation, Amsterdam

[61] Sever, J. L. (1971): Virus infections and malformations. Fed. Proc. 30, 114–117

[62] Shapiro, S., Ross, L. J., and Levine, H. S. (1965): Relationship of selected prenatal factors to pregnancy outcome and congenital anomalies. Am. J. Publ. Hlth. 55, 268–282

[63] Shaw, E. B., and Steinbach, H. L. (1968): Aminopterin-induced fetal malformation, survival of infant after attempted abortion. Am. J. Dis. Child. 115, 477–482

[64] Skoupý, M., Skoupá, M., and Saxl, O. (1967): Angeborene Mißbildungen und Arzneimittel. Dtsch. Ges. Wesen. 22, 1267–1273

[65] Smithells, R. W. (1966): Drugs and human malformations. In Advances in Teratology (Ed. D. H. M. Woollam), Logos Press Ltd., London. Vol. 1, pp. 251–278

[66] Sutherland, J. M., and Light, I. J. (1965): The effect of drugs upon the developing fetus. Pediat Clin. North America 12, 781–806

[67] Sutton, H. E. (1971): Workshop on monitoring of human mutagenesis, Teratology 4, 103–107

[68] Stevenson, A. C., Johnston, H. A., Stewart, M. I. P., and Golding, D. R. (1966): Congenital malformations. A report of a series of consecutive births in 24 centres. Bull. Wld. Hlth. Org. 34, Suppl. 1–127

[69] Tanimura, T. (1972): Effects on macaque embryos of drugs reported or suspected to be teratogenic to humans. Acta endocrin. (suppl. Number) 166, 293–308

[70] Thiersch, J. B. (1952): Therapeutic abortions with folic acid antagonist, 4-aminopteroylglutamic acid (4-amino-P. G. A.) administered by oral route. Am. J. Obstet. Gynec. 63, 1298–1325

[71] Tuchmann-Duplessis, H. (1970): The effects of teratogenic drugs. In Scientific Foundations of Obstetrics and Gynaecology (Eds. E. E. Phillip, J. Barnes, and M. Newton), William Heinemann Medical Books Ltd., London. pp. 636–648

[72] Tuchmann-Duplessis, H. (1972): Teratogenic drug screening. Present procedures and requirements. Teratology 5, 271–286

[73] United Nations Commission on Narcotic Drugs. Document E/3648, E/CN 7/432. W. H. O., Geneva, 1962

[74] Venning, G. R. (1965): The problem of human foetal abnormalities with special reference to sex hormones. In Embryopathic Activity of Drugs (Eds. J. M. Robson, F. M. Sullivan, and R. L. Smith), Little, Brown and Company, Boston

[75] Villumsen, A. L. (1970): Environmental factors in congenital malformations. A prospective study of 9006 human pregnancies. F. A. D. L. S. Forlag, Copenhagen, Aarhus, Odense

[76] Warkany, J., Beaudry, P. H., and Hornstein, S. (1959): Attempted abortion with aminopterin, malformations of the child. Am. J. Dis. Child. 97, 274–281

[77] **Weicker, H.**, and Hungerland, H. (1962): Thalidomid-Embryopathie. I. Vorkommen inner- und ausserhalb Deutschlands. Dtsch. med. Wschr. 87, 992–994

[78] WHO (1967): Principles for the testing of drugs for teratogenicity. WHO Tech. Rep. Ser. No. 364, Geneva

[79] Wilkins, L. (1960): Masculinization of female fetus due to use of orally given progestins. J. Am. med. Ass. 172, 1028–1033

[80] Wilson, J. G. (1965): Methods for administering agents and detecting malformations in experimental animals. In Teratology, Principles and Techniques (Eds. J. G. Wilson and J. Warkany). University of Chicago Press, pp. 262–277

[81] Wilson, J. G. (1969): Teratological and reproductive studies in non-human primates. In methods for teratological studies in experimental animals and man (Eds. H. Nishimura and J. R. Miller) Igaku Shoin, Tokyo, pp. 16–31

[82] Wilson, J. G. (1972): Abnormalities of intrauternie development in non-human primates. Acta endocrin. (Suppl. Number) 166, 261–272

[83] Herbst, A. L., Ulfelder, H., and Poskanzer, D. C. (1971) Adenocarcinoma of the vagina. Association of maternal stilbestrol therapy with tumor appearance in young women. New Engl. J. Med. 284, 878–881

[84] Moore, K. L. (1973) The developing human. W. B. Saunders Co., Philadelphia. pp. 108–124

Addendum

Recently, Herbst et al.[83] made the important observation that vaginal adenocarcinoma developed in some young women many years after administration of stilboestrol to their mothers during pregnancy. This is the first report drawing attention to the possible carcinogenic action of drugs on the human fetus and to the prenatal origins of certain cancers. For a discussion on the embryological basis of congenital malformations and a comprehensive survey of known and suspected human teratogens, see Moore.[84]

Delayed Neurotoxicity of Organophosphorus Compounds and Copper Concentration in the Serum of Hens

G. Kimmerle and E. Löser

Institut für Toxikologie der BAYER AG, 56 Wuppertal, West Germany

Summary Azinphos-methyl, dichlorvos, ediphensoph, fenthion, oxydemeton-methyl, parathion, trichlorfon, TOCP, and 5 additional compounds chemically closely related to dichlorvos were tested for delayed neurotoxicity in hens after single and repeated oral administration. Delayed neurotoxicity was found only with TOCP and the experimental compounds I, II, III, IV and V. A strong relationship between delayed neurotoxicity and the increase of copper and ceruloplasmin levels was evident in hens. In this respect compound V showed a dose-relationship. In testing organophosphorus compounds for delayed neurotoxicity in hens the determination of the copper concentration in serum can be recommended.

Zusammenfassung An Hühnern wurden Azinphos-methyl, Dichlorvos, Ediphensoph, Fenthion, Oxydemeton-methyl, Parathion, Trichlorfon, TOCP und fünf dem Dichlorvos chemisch verwandte Verbindungen nach einmaligen und zum Teil mehrmaligen oralen Gaben auf neurotoxische Wirkungen untersucht. Neurotoxizität ergab sich nur mit den experimentellen Verbindungen I bis V. In akuten Versuchen bestand eine gute Beziehung zwischen der Erhöhung der Kupferkonzentration und auch der Caeruloplasminaktivität im Serum und der Neurotoxizität bei den Hühnern. Bei der Verbindung V konnte eine Dosisabhängigkeit dieser Beziehung festgestellt werden. Die Bestimmung der Kupferkonzentration im Serum von Hühnern bei Prüfung von organischen Phosphorsäureverbindungen auf Neurotoxizität kann zusätzlich empfohlen werden.

Introduction

The symptoms after poisoning by some organophosphorus compounds are well known. For more than 40 years it has been common knowledge that tri-o-cresyl phosphate causes symptoms of delayed neurotoxicity (ataxia, weakness and paralysis of the limbs) after a latent period of 10 to 14 days.[1] This effect was also experimentally demonstrated with other triaryl phosphates. Poisoning of a different nature was caused by an insecticidal organophosphorus compound in England. Two persons were accidentally poisoned with Mipafox. In contrast to triaryl phosphate poisoning, typical symptoms of cholinesterase-inhibiting organophosphate poisoning first developed shortly after uptake, then followed an interval free from symptoms after which neurotoxic injuries developed.[2]

In testing organophosphorus compounds for delayed neurotoxicity, hens older than 1 year are used. Delayed neurotoxic effects have been observed in 12 animal species [3] (mammals, birds), but only the adult hen closely resembles man in its sensitivity to a single toxic dose of TOCP.[4] In primates TOCP produces neurotoxic effects with difficulty and does not closely resemble the response seen in man.[5]

The mode of action of delayed neurotoxicity caused by organophosphorus compounds is not known. Recently Johnson [6-10] and Aldridge and Johnson [11] found a relationship between delayed neurotoxicity of organophosphorus compounds and the phosphorylation of a brain protein in hens which was characterized as an esterase. The current knowledge on delayed neurotoxicity of organophosphorus compounds was summarized by Barnes,[4] Johnson,[9] and Aldridge, Barnes and Johnson.[3]

The symptoms of organophosphorus compound-neurotoxicity show some similarities to Wilson's disease. Patients with this disease have elevated copper concentrations in serum. It was found [12] that a copper deficiency in the diet does not change the sensitivity of sheep against the neurotoxic effect of Haloxon. The repeated administration of the chelating agent sodium diethyldithio-carbamate caused similar damage of neurones and nerve fibers in hens as has been demonstrated with TOCP.[13]

These observations were the reason to test copper concentrations and ceruloplasmin activities in serum after administration of neurotoxic and non-neurotoxic organophosphorus compounds to hens.

Methods

1. Compounds

Active ingredients of pesticides: Azinphos-methyl (®GUSATHION), dichlorvos (DDVP), ediphensoph (®HINOSAN), fenthion (®BAYTEX, ®LEBAYCID), oxydemetonmethyl (®META-SYSTOX-R), parathion, trichlorfon (®DIPTEREX)*

Experimental compounds (related to DDVP)

Compound No.	R_1 \ ‖O / P–O–CH=CCl$_2$ R_2		Rat Approximate LD$_{50}$ Oral mg/kg
	R_1	R_2	
I	C$_2$H$_5$O	C$_2$H$_5$O	2, 5
II	ClC$_2$H$_4$O	C$_2$H$_5$O	5 – 10
III	ClC$_2$H$_4$O	ClC$_2$H$_4$O	25
IV	ClC$_2$H$_4$O	CH$_2$=CH–CH$_2$–NH	25
V	⬡– O	CH$_2$=CH–CH$_2$–NH	100

Tri-o-cresyl phosphate (TOCP)

2. Animals

White leghorn hens age 16 to 18 months and 1.5 to 2.0 kg body weight were used. The hens were housed individually but could move freely.

3. Experimental Procedure

Hens were dosed orally or intraperitoneally. In some cases atropine (50 mg/kg) or atropine (50 mg/kg) plus 2-PAM (100 mg/kg) were predosed by intraperitoneal injection. The time of observation was 42 days or more. In subacute tests the compounds were administered in the food for 30 days and the observation period was 28 days.

In some tests anesthesized hens were per-

---

* GUSATHION, HINOSAN, BAYTEX, LEBAYCID, META-SYSTOX-R and DIPTEREX are trade marks of BAYER AG, Leverkusen

Table 1 Testing for Neurotoxicity in Hens After Single Application

Compound	Application	Antidote	Approximate LD$_{50}$ mg/kg	Dose Without Neurotoxic Effect mg/kg	Neurotoxic Dose mg/kg	Histology
Azinphos-methyl	Oral	None	250—500	1—250		
	Oral	None	30	5—30		
Ediphensoph	Oral	None	550	500—750		No Injury
	Oral	Atropine	—	550		No Injury
Fenthion	Oral	None	20	10—25		
	Intraperitoneal	None	20	10—25		
	Oral	Atropine + PAM	—	20—25		
Oxydemeton	Oral	None	100	65—130		
	Oral	Atropine + PAM	—	65—130		
Parathion	Oral	None	10	2.5—15		
	Intraperitoneal	None	2.5—5.0	1.0—7.5		
	Oral	Atropine + PAM	—	20—50		
	Intraperitoneal	Atropine + PAM	—	20—50		
Trichlorfon	Oral	None	75	25—100		
	Intraperitoneal	None	75	25—100		
I	Oral	None	10—25	0.1—0.5	1.0—2.5	
II	Oral	None	2.5	0.1—0.5	1.0—2.5	
III	Oral	None	5.0	0.1—0.5	1.0—5.0	
IV	Oral	None	10—25	1—25	5—10	
V	Oral	None	500—750	0.5—1.0	2.0—500	
TOCP	Oral	None	500	10—25	50—750	Demyelination
	Intraperitoneal	None	500	10—25	50—750	

fused with formalin. Brain, spinal cord and N. ischiadicus were then investigated histologically.

The copper concentrations and ceruloplasmin activities were determined 1, 2, 3, 4, 7, 10 and 14 days after a single oral dose. Copper was analyzed photometrically with bathocuproin,[14] ceruloplasmin with p-phenylendiamine.[15]

Results

A. Testing for Delayed Neurotoxicity

The results after single application are shown in Table 1.

Azinphos-methyl, dichlorvos, ediphensoph, fenthion, oxydemeton-methyl, parathion and trichlorfon failed to produce neurotoxic symptoms after application of highly toxic doses, but such effects have been observed with the compounds I, II, III, IV, V and TOCP.

The results of feeding some compounds in the diet for one month are given in Table 2.

The repeated application of azinphos-methyl, fenthion and trichlorfon did not cause any neurotoxic effect. In contrast TOCP produced delayed neurotoxicity after feeding the low dose of 10 ppm.

B. Influence of Neurotoxic and Non-neurotoxic Compounds on the Copper Concentration and Ceruloplasmin Activity in Serum of Hens

After single oral doses of compounds I, II, III, IV, V, dichlorvos and TOCP the copper levels and ceruloplasmin activities were determined at intervals for 14 days (Figures 1 and 2).

After 1 to 2 days the copper concentration was increased almost twice by the neurotoxic compounds I, II, III, IV, V and TOCP (Figure 1). The maximum increase was in 7 to 10 days. Then the concentration decreased. In accordance with this

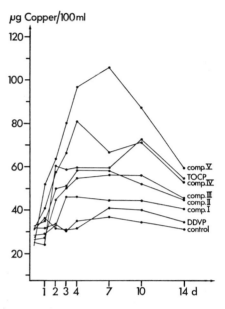

Fig. 1   Copper concentration in serum of hens after single oral doses of organophosphorus compounds

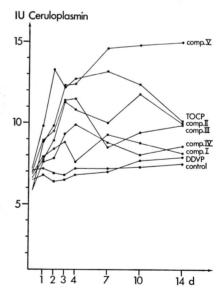

Fig. 2   Ceruloplasmin-activities in serum of hens after single oral doses of organophosphorus compounds

Table 2   Testing for Neurotoxicity in Hens After Feeding for 30 Days

Compound	Concentration in the Diet (ppm)		Histology
	Doses Tested	Neurotoxicity	
Azinphos-methyl	900; 1200; 1500; 1800	None	No Injury
Fenthion	10; 25; 50; 100	None	No Injury
Trichlorfon	500; 1000; 2000; 5000	None	No Injury
TOCP	5; 10; 25; 50; 100; 200	10 and Higher	Demyelination

we found the same alterations in the activities of ceruloplasmin (Figure 2).
Dichlorvos, which is not neurotoxic, but chemically closely related to compounds I, II, III, IV, and V, did not change the copper and ceruloplasmin levels significantly. The application of azinphos-methyl, ediphensoph, fenthion, oxydemetonmethyl, parathion and trichlorfon tested by the same procedure also did not result in an increase of these levels.

C. Dose-Relationship in Copper Concentrations and Ceruloplasmin Activities

Compound V showed a large range between the lowest neurotoxic dose (2.5 mg/kg) and the lethal dose (500–750 mg/kg). Therefore this compound was used for studying the dose-relationship. The influence of different oral doses of compound V on copper concentrations and ceruloplasmin activities are demonstrated in Figures 3 and 4.

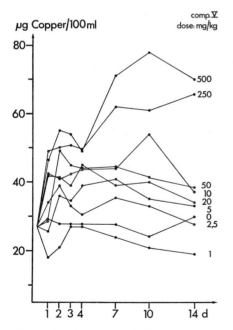

Fig. 3   Dose-related increase of the copper concentration in the serum of hens after single oral neurotoxic and non-neurotoxic doses of compound V

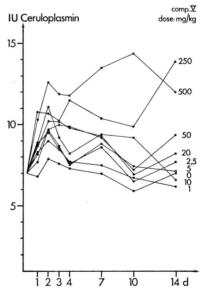

Fig. 4   Dose-related increase of the ceruloplasmin-activity in the serum of hens after single oral neurotoxic and non-neurotoxic doses of compound V

The dose of 1 mg of compound V/kg, which is not neurotoxic, did not cause any alterations, but after application of the higher neurotoxic doses (2.5–500.0 mg/kg), a dose-related increase of the copper and ceruloplasmin levels could be observed.

Discussion

Our test results of studies of delayed neurotoxic effects on hens are in accordance with some other authors. Tests with parathion,[16, 17] oxydemetonmethyl,[18] dichlorvos,[11, 19–22] and trichlorfon [11, 18] produced no neurotoxic effects, but such effects were shown with compound I,[11] and with compounds II and III.[22]

In spite of the small number of organophosphorus compounds tested, a good relationship between increased copper concentrations in serum and neurotoxic effects in hens was found. Compounds not producing delayed neurotoxicity did not alter the copper levels. According to preliminary tests, penicillamine was of no therapeutic value after application of neurotoxic organophosphorus compounds.

At this time an explanation for the biochemical mechanism of altering copper levels in cases of delayed neurotoxicity cannot be given, but in testing organophosphorus compounds for neurotoxicity in hens the determination of copper levels may give an indication of this effect in a short time.

Literature

1 Smith, M. J., R. D. Sillie: Arch. Neurol. Psychiat. 26, 976, 1931
2 Bidstrup, P. L., J. A. Bonnell, A. G. Beckett: Brit. Med. J. 1–53, I, 1068
3 Aldridge, W. N., J. M. Barnes, M. K. Johnson: Ann. N. Y. Acad. Sci. 160, 314, 1969
4 Barnes, J. M.: Proc. Roy. Soc. Med. 62, 205, 1969
5 Hern, J. E. C.: Nature 215, 963, 1967
6 Johnson, M. K.: Biochem. J. 110, 13 P, 1968
7 Johnson, M. K.: Biochem. J. 111, 487, 1969
8 Johnson, M. K.: Biochem. J. 114, 711, 1969
9 Johnson, M. K.: Brit. Med. Bull. 25, 231, 1969
10 Johnson, M. K.: Biochem. J. 120, 523, 1970
11 Aldridge, W. N., M. K. Johnson: Bull. Wld. Hlth. Org. 44, 259, 1971
12 Malone, J. C.: Res. Vet. Sci. 5, 17, 1964
13 Howell, J. M., N. Edington: J. Neuropath. Exptl. Neurol. 27, 464, 1968
14 Zack, B.: Clin. Chim. Acta 3, 328, 1958
15 Weber, H., T. Wegmann: Atlas der klinischen Enzymologie. Thieme, Stuttgart 1968
16 Barnes, J. M., F. A. Denz: J. Path. Bact. 65, 597, 1953
17 Frawley, J. P., R. E. Zwickey, H. N. Fuyat: Fed. Proc. 15, 424, 1957
18 Gaines, T. B.: Toxicol. Appl. Pharmacol. 14, 515, 1969
19 Durham, W. F., T. B. Gaines, W. J. Hayes: Arch. Ind. Health 13, 326, 1956
20 Durham, W. F., T. B. Gaines, R. H. McCauley: V. A. Sedlak. Arch. Ind. Health 15, 340, 1957
21 Witter, R. F., T. B. Gaines. Biochem. Pharmacol 12, 1377, 1963
22 Aldridge, W. N., J. M. Barnes: Biochem. Pharmacol. 15, 541, 1966

No-Effect Level and Extrapolation as Applied to Pesticide Residues and Radioactive Substances

Frederick Coulston and J. H. Wills

Institute of Comparative and Human Toxicology Albany Medical College of Union University, Albany, New York, 12208 U.S.A.

The question of prediction from animal data to man is one of the serious problems of modern toxicology. Can a mouse predict correctly whether a man will get cancer after receiving various amounts of chemicals, drugs, natural products, or physical agents such as radiation or radio chemicals? Species variation in biochemistry, pharmacology and toxicology is well known. If a chemical produces a tumor in a mouse but not in any other species, can we assume that the mouse is predictive of cancer risk in man? The recent dilemma with DDT and dieldrin indicates clearly the problem. In the case of these chemicals, only the mouse has proven to be a factor in the production of hepatomas which may become carcinomas; rats, dogs, monkeys and even men do not develop hepatomas. And yet, based upon this evidence, there are many who would contend that DDT and dieldrin should be banned from further use.

In 1969, a WHO/FAO Expert Committee on Pesticide Residues clearly indicated that DDT should be phased out of use but should not be banned until an adequate substitute can be found. The feeling of this group of experts still maintains this position. The question at issue is whether the benefits derived from the use of DDT are sufficiently important to mankind that they far outweigh any small risk to man and his environment.

A recent Ad-Hoc Expert Committee of WHO considered the drug hycanthone. Hycanthone is a chemotherapeutic agent that is extremely useful in the treatment of schistosomiasis, a severe worm infestation of man. In spite of the fact that it can be shown under certain conditions to be a teratogen, a mutagen, and even perhaps a carcinogen, the benefits to be derived from the use of this compound far outweighed any risk that might be considered. Therefore, the Expert Committee decided that Hycanthone should be used in a mass chemotherapeutic field trial, in Africa, South America and other parts of the world where this disease is endemic.

Benefit versus risk relationships therefore must be considered for each type of toxic agent. To treat a simple headache, aspirin must be so safe that it can be used without prescription anywhere. In other words, the individual will diagnose and prescribe for himself a readily obtainable therapeutic agent. Yet aspirin is a well known teratogen in mice and rats but not in monkeys and man. On the other hand, one would *not* propose the use of nitrogen mustards for the treatment of a simple headache, and yet, nitrogen mustards, in their own right chemical carcinogens in many species of animals including man, are used in the treatment of cancer. The risk for the use of this compound is very great and the side effects

* Presented at: Symposium on Nuclear Techniques in Comparative Studies of Food & Environmental Contamination, Otaniemi, Finland. August 27–31, 1973

arc most undesirable. However, since there is little else that one can do, the nitrogen mustards and their analogs have been widely used for the treatment of cancer.

The benefit-risk relationship applies also to the topic that I am going to talk about at the present time. Toxicologists for years have been able to establish tolerances for toxic chemicals, such as parathion and other pesticides, with great safety to man.

In addition, many other chemicals found in our food, either put there deliberately by man or occurring inadvertantly, such as pesticide residues, can be used safely, based upon animal and human research. If truly toxic chemicals can be used for the benefit of mankind, then why can we not use radiochemicals and even foodstuffs contaminated with background radiation? Why is it that tolerances cannot be easily set for radiation health effects? The answer is that in some instances one must do so. Just as the presence of nitrosamines or aflatoxin in our food supply can be tolerated, we must also use foodstuffs in which radiation is used for sterilization or in which small amounts of background radionuclides and chemicals have entered into the food source.

In 1972, Weil published[1] a consensus by 58 toxicologists on guidelines believed to be pertinent to studies in which the objective is to predict from observations on experimental animals the safety of some particular material for use by man. Among these guidelines is the following: " ... for any material and adverse effect, some dose level exists for man or animal below which this adverse effect will not appear." This principle of the existence of a no-effect level is recognized generally to be applicable to various kinds of toxic actions; the only type of toxic action to which its applicability is questioned by some is the alteration of normal cells into those capable of forming malignant tumors. The purpose of this talk is to examine this apparently exceptional situation and to try to arrive at some conclusion about the truth of its claimed unusual nature.

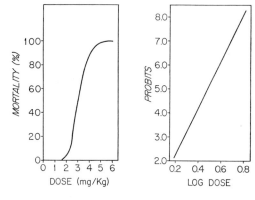

Fig. 1

Let us look first at a standard toxicologic study: an estimation of the lethal oral dose of parathion for the female white rat, taken from some work of Frawley et al.[2] The left-hand section of Figure One shows a plot of the percents of the rats killed by the various doses against the doses. The regression line is a sigmoid curve, with initial and terminal curvilinear sections of comparatively low slopes and a central linear portion of high slope. Such relationships are difficult to extrapolate to values within the curvilinear sections of the curves from measurements made only within the linear ranges, and vice versa. A great deal of thought and effort has gone into attempts to find transformations of such data that will yield straight, or nearly straight, lines for easy extrapolation to extreme values.

One such transformation used widely by toxicologists is expression of the dose of an agent administered in logarithms and of the mortality or other effect in probits (right-hand side of *Figure One*). In case there are people here who are not acquainted with probits. I shall try to explain this type of unit briefly. The basis of the probit system is that an effect upon one-half the organisms in a group is given arbitrarily the value of 5. Successive whole numbers above and below 5 are attached to percents of effects displaced from the 50 percent one by successive multiples of the standard deviation of a normally distributed population of responses to an agent.

Although the usual table of probit values ranges from 1.2810, corresponding to a percent affected of 0.01, to 8.7190, corresponding to a 99.99 percent effect, even larger multiples of the standard deviation below probit 5 do not reach a zero probability of occurrence within a normally distributed population, nor do larger multiples above probit 5 reach a probability of occurrence of 100 percent. Thus, there is a finite probality (2.6×10^{-10}) that a dose of an agent even 7 standard deviations smaller than the mean dose producing effects in 50 percent (ED 50) of the subjects will produce an effect in one subject of an appropriately sized population. Conversely, a dose greater than the ED 50 by 7 standard deviations will not affect all the members of the same population.

The population sudied in the example just above would need to number at least 3.9×10^{9} individuals – an impossible number to handle experimentally. Even to demonstrate the occurrence of an effect at probit values of zero or 10, a population of 1.8×10^{4} individuals would need to be studied. This is within the realm of possibility, at least for epidemiologic studies.

The probit transformation makes clear the fact that absolute certainty of hazard or safety can never be guaranteed. The best

that one can do is to say that on the basis of the available information the chance of an individual's receiving an adverse effect from a certain amount of an agent is 1/1000 or 1/10,000 or greater. This indeterminateness of effect, reminiscent of the uncertainty principle in physics, raises the necessity of using risk-benefit considerations in deciding, for example, whether parathion should be permitted for use as a pesticide.

On one hand, we have the definite toxicity of parathion shown in *Figure One*. On the other hand, we have its effectiveness in killing a variety of insects. Some of these insects destroy materials desired by man for his own use whereas others prey upon some of the destructive insects. Thus, we have at least two negative values to be weighed against one positive value in this insecticide. So long as parathion could be said to have an effectiveness as an insecticide for use in agriculture that was not reproduced in any other available compound or combination of compounds, its hazards could be accepted. Now that substances with more selective actions on destructive species of insects have become available, parathion is being phased out of agricultural use. Radiation and sources of radiation, both internal and external, should be considered in a similar manner.

We wish to look now at the effects of radiations on the animal body. *Figure Two*, made with data from a paper by L. H. Smith,[3] shows plots of mortality, expressed both as percents and as probits, against the logarithms of the quantities of X-radiation received by male mice. A single exposure to X-radiation was followed by an observation period of 30 days. This figure shows that the log dose-probit transformation does not yield a straight line for these data, suggesting that the population of mice used in the experiment did not have a normal distri-

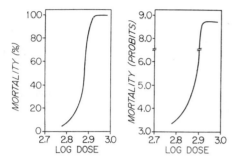

Fig. 2

bution of sensitivities to X-radiation. Because the probit is based on the properties of a normal population, any deviation from a normal distribution within the experimental population disturbs the standard relationship between dose and probit. Although expressing the dose in logarithms tends to minimise deviation from a straight line, it has not been able to do a good job in this case.

Figure Three, made from data of Beach and Dolphin[4] on the incidence of malignant tumors of the thyroid as a result of irradiation of the thymus during childhood, shows that the log dose-probit transformation can produce a straitht line of regression when a particular sensitivity to X-radiation is distributed normally within a population. Burch,[5] examining the same data with a log-log plot, con-

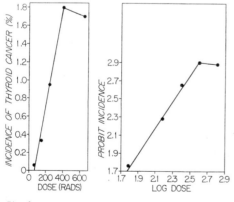

Fig. 3

cluded also that this particular sensitivity to X-radiation was distributed normally within the population studied.

Extrapolation of our line yields the conclusion that a dose of about 2.4 rads to a child's chest and neck has a probability of only 1:17,422 of producing a malignant tumor of the thyroid. The usual dose of X-radiation to the thymus of an adolescent with a persistent or enlarged gland seems to be at least 100 roentgens, however, and may be as much as 1100 or 1200 roentgens. The incidence of malignant tumors of the thyroid following such irradiation has been somewhat below 1.0 percent;[6] children treated in this way may develop also malignancies of other tissues in addition to benign tumors of both the thyroid gland and other parts of the body.[6,7]

We are faced then with the question whether the benefit to some 97.5 percent of the patients treated with X-radiation is sufficiently valuable to society to make acceptable the risk of production of neoplasms in the others treated. The most common physical disability leading to irradiation of the thymus is muscular weakness, so that the irradiation may be assumed to have enabled a substantial number of those treated to become productive workers of one sort or another, at the cost of inducing neoplasms in about 2.5 percent of the children. This last figure has been corrected to take account of the occurrence of spontaneous neoplasms within a group of untreated siblings of the children whose thymus glands were irradiated.

Fetuses seem to be particularly sensitive to induction of cancer by X-radiation.[8] *Figure Four,* taken from Dr. Stewart's paper, shows that she has chosen to draw her line in such a way as to indicate that there is no threshold dose of radiation in this regard. *Figure Five,* using the same data, shows two extrapolations made by

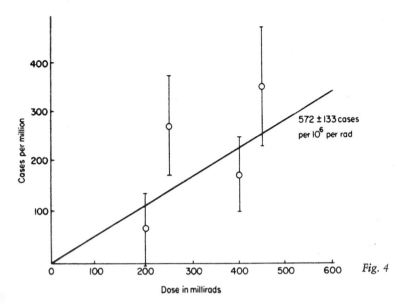

Fig. 4

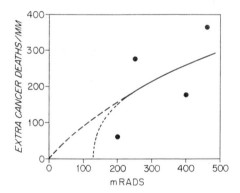

Fig. 5

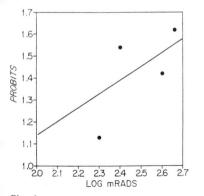

Fig. 6

us that fit the data even better than the straight line drawn by Dr. Stewart. One of these indicates a threshold dose of radiation that must be exceeded to produce cancers.

Figure Six also made by us, gives a log dose-probit transformation of the same data. This transformation cannot indicate a no-effect dose, of course, but does suggest, by extrapolation, that a dose of X-radiation of 10 milli rads would have a probability of inducing malignant change in a human fetus of only about 1:14,300. If an X-ray film capable of making a picture by an exposure to only 10 milli rads could be made, then the benefit from making routine radiographs of pregnant women might be judged to be worth the risk of increased production of neoplasia and possible malignancy.

Although we are unable to make a case for an absolutely safe dose of radiation, neither can we do this for chemical substances. From fundamental considerations, the existence of a small, absolutely safe dose of radiation seems likely from the fact that an amount of energy variously estimated to lie between 34 and 83 electron volts[9] is needed to produce an ion in preparations of nucleoprotein or in mammalian cells.

The further estimate that about 9 atoms are excited for each one ionized,[10] means that something like 440 electron volts may be required for each ionization produced. Although this is a very small amount of energy, the actual requirement for the practical induction of transformations of cells leading to the production of cancers may well be considerably larger because of the recovery processes that are now known to take place within damaged nucleic acid.[11, 12] Such information as that of Costolow et al.[13] on the relative efficacies of various total doses of radiation applied during varying periods of time in treating cancer of the corpus uteri, showing an increasing requirement for summated radiation as the period of application increases (Figure Seven), supports the idea of reduction by reparative processes of the impact upon biological systems of ionizing radiations. Such reparative processes are likely to be particularly important in determining the effect of a subacute or chronic exposure to ionizing radiation, in a manner analogous to that in which the rates of regeneration of cholinesterases determine the severity of the effects of subacute or chronic exposures to such organophosphorus compounds as parathion.

In summary, we have shown a number of parallelisms between the actions of toxic chemicals and ionizing radiation on the animal body. In both cases, the identification of a completely safe dose is impossible. Acceptable or allowable doses must be established through careful consideration of the risk-benefit relation and with the realization that some hazard from exposure of the body to extraneous agents, whether chemical or physical in

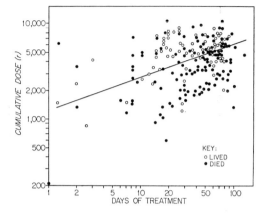

Fig. 7

nature, is unavoidable and not predictable toxicologically in any specific instance. Only through previous experience of the same subject with the same agent can prediction be made with any degree of certainty. Animals may serve to indicate the comparative safeties of various agents for man, but not the quantitative safeties. The fact that a fairly well established LD 50 for gamma-radiation for man is available gives a reference point for judging the quantitative safeties of other radiations for man from their comparative safeties for animal species.

The hazard of incurring a malignancy from ionizing radiation seems to us no more abhorrent than that of incurring some other slowly fatal lesion, such as, chronic nephrosis from mercuric mercury, from an exposure to a chemical either as such in industry or other occupation or as a drug or food additive. In all cases, it seems to us, the value or benefit to be derived from exposure to an agent must be weighed against the possible hazard or risk of such exposure.

The realization that complete safety cannot be guaranteed for any agent that may act upon the human body emphasizes the importance of assessing as realistically as possible the probability that any partic-ular dose of an agent will be harmful. To this end, the best animal models used in toxicology for extrapolation to man should be employed for preliminary esti-mates of the likelihood of damage; these estimates should then be checked, at least at the lower ends of their ranges, in hu-man subjects whenever possible, either by direct observations or by epidemiologic surveys.

We cannot accept as a basic principle that no radioelements or by-products can be tolerated in the food supply. If this ban were to be carried out to its extreme, much of our current food and water could not be used and the consequences of this are obvious. The great need for foodstuffs in this world is one of the great issues of the day. If populations cannot be controlled, then more and more food is needed. The result is ob-vious: the answer is not too difficult to give. We must learn how to use safely what we have and to improve our know-ledge and methodologies so that we can make food ever safer and safer for ani-mal and man. We must clarify and seek terms of reference so that tolerances can be set for all food additives and con-taminants, whether they are pesticides, colors, or radioactive substances.

The question of zero tolerances, detect-able levels of hazardous substances, per-missible levels, and threshold effects, goes on and on. There are those who still fol-low the doctrine of one-molecule inter-action with DNA and those who believe that permissible levels are possible be-cause of the now well established repair mechanisms.

A quotation is pertinent from the paper by C. L. Comar commenting on the Re-port of the Advisory Committee on the Biological Effects of Ionizing Radiations (BEIR), to the National Academy of Sciences, U. S. A., 1972:

"It is a misuse of resources and a dis-service to society to add costs for the purpose of decreasing the risks of any one system greatly below acceptable lev-els, when other societal activities with unacceptable risks are not being attended. Some examples of choices that could be made are: a national program to persuade people to use seat belts is estimated to cost less than $ 100 for each death avert-ed; a program of early cancer detection and treatment is estimated to cost up to about $ 40,000 for each death averted. At the height of fallout it was calculated that the removal of ^{90}Sr from milk at a cost of 2 to 3 cents per quart would cost about 20 million dollars for each case of cancer averted. It has been estimated that money spent on improved collimation of X-ray machines would be 1000 to 10,000 times more effective in reducing radiation dosages than money spent on improving present reactor waste systems."

Risk is with us every day, whether we drive a car, breathe polluted air, or eat food containing indirect or direct addi-tives. In our environment and in our world as it exists today, residues of all kinds are present. Defining these residues and risks in terms of benefit to man is the question of today and the future. We are confident that man can answer the questions without destroying the social and economic base of civilization.

References

[1] Weil, C. S., Tox. Appl. Pharmacol. 21: 194–199, 1972. Guidelines for experiments to predict the degree of safety of a material for man

[2] Frawley, J. P., E. C. Hagan, and O. G. Fitz-hugh, J. Pharmacol. Exp. Therap. 105: 156–165, 1952. A comparative pharmacologi-cal and toxicological study of organic phos-phate anticholinesterase compounds

[3] Smith, L. H., Trans. N. Y. Acad. Sci. 32: 448–452, 1970. Hemopoietic stem-cell number

and radiosensitivity – radioprotection with phenylhydrazine

[4] Beach, S. A., and G. W. Dolphin, Phys. Med. Biol. *6*: 583–598, 1962. A study of the relationship between x-ray dose delivered to the thyroids of children and the subsequent development of malignant tumours

[5] Burch, P. R., J. Proc. Roy, Soc. Lond. B *162*: 263–287, 1965. Natural and radiation carcinogenesis in man. III. Radiation carcinogenesis

[6] Toyooka, E. T., J. W. Pifer, S. L. Crump, A. M. Dulton, and L. H. Hempelmann, J. Nat. Canc. Inst. *31*: 1357–1378, 1963. Neoplasms in children treated with x-rays for thymic enlargement. II. Tumor incidence as a function of radiation factors

[7] Pifer, J. W., and L. H. Hempelmann, Prog. Clin. Canc. *1*: 394–403, 1965. Radiation-induced thyroid carcinoma

[8] Stewart, A., Adv. Canc. Res. *14*: 359–390, 1971. Low dose radiation cancers in man

[9] Setlow, R. B., and J. K. Setlow, Ann. Rev. Biophys. Bioeng. *1*: 293–346, 1972. Effects of radiation on polynucleotides

[10] Cember, H., Introduction to Health Physics, Pergamon Press, Oxford-Elmsford Rushcutters Bay, 1969

[11] Moseley, B. E. B., and H. Laser, Proc. Roy. Soc. Lond. B *162*: 210–222, 1965. Repair of x-ray damage in micrococcus radiodurans.

[12] Glickman, B. W., K. J. Walker, and A. Rörsch, Mutat, Res. *14*: 265–270, 1972. The repair of ^{32}P decay-damaged phage λ in various radiation-sensitive strains of E. coli K_{12}

[13] Costolow, W. E., J. F. Nolan, G. C. Budenz, and L. DuSault, Am. J. Roentgenol. *71*: 669–675, 1954. Radiation treatment of carcinoma of the corpus uteri

[14] Comar, Cyril C., Presentation to the International Radiation Protection Association, for the National Academy of Sciences (U.S.A.), of a general review of the report of its Advisory Committee on the Biological Effects of Ionizing Radiations on The Effects on Populations of Exposure to how hevels of Ionizing Radiation (BEIR Report), August 1973

How Safe is Safe? A Regulator's Viewpoint*

Peter Barton Hutt

Assistant General Counsel for Food and Drugs, Department of Health, Education, and Welfare

Safety Regulation in the Real World

Regulation of the safety of food and drugs should be an extremely simple and perfunctory task. After all, one need only hold up the indisputable scientific facts, and compare them with equally explicit statutory requirements. The regulatory result will then ineluctably follow, with the full concurrence and acclaim of the Congress, the regulated industry, the consumer advocates, the academic community, and the public at large.

Unfortunately, however, this does not occur in the real world. In the twenty months that I have held my current position, I cannot recall one major safety decision by the Food and Drug Administration – regardless which way it was resolved – that has failed to provoke prolonged, and at times bitter, public dispute. Moreover, even if we had reached exactly the opposite conclusion on any of those decisions, it is unlikely that there would have been any greater or lesser amount of dispute.

In short, public policy design and execution with respect to the safety of food and drugs is highly, and perhaps irretrievably, controversial. It raises up a welter of subjective and emotional views that often obscure rational analysis and that can severely hinder regulation by scientific decision-making.

My remarks today will initially outline the statutory mandate for safe food and drugs. I will then discuss what I discern to be the principal obstacles to decision-making on safety matters. Finally, I will describe the action that is being undertaken to improve the situation.

I

Any discussion of decision-making on the safety of food and drugs must begin with an understanding of the broad statutory mandate Congress has given to the Food and Drug Administration.

As early as the Food and Drugs Act of 1906, Congress demanded protection of the public from unsafe food and drugs. That law prohibited the use in food of "any added poisonous or other added deleterious ingredient which may render such article injurious to health." It similarly prohibited the use in drugs of any "ingredient deleterious or detrimental to health."

When Congress modernized this law in 1938, it was unable to improve upon those general statutory admonitions. The Federal Food, Drug, and Cosmetic Act states that a food may not contain any "poisonous or deleterious substance which may render it injurious to health," and that a drug may not be recommended for any use for which it is "dangerous to health". Even the Food Additives Amendments of 1958 and the Drug Amendments of 1962, which were enacted specifically to provide more stringent protection against unsafe food and drugs, again are couched in very broad and general terms. The food additive provisions of

* Presented at the first Academy Forum, "How Safe is Safe? The Design of Policy on Drugs and Food Additives," May 15, 1973, in Washington, D.C.

the law require the Food and Drug Administration to consider "safety factors which in the opinion of experts qualified by scientific training and experience to evaluate the safety of food additives are generally recognized as appropriate for the use of animal experimentation data". The new drug provisions of the law state that safety must be shown by "adequate tests by all methods reasonably applicable to show whether or not such drug is safe for use".

The only detailed safety criteria contained in the statute are contained in the famous anti-cancer clauses. In contrast to the public attention they have received, however, those clauses are actually an issue in very few safety decisions made by the Food and Drug Administration – certainly, far less than one-tenth of one percent of those decisions. And in most of the instances where they have been an issue, the matter has been resolved using sound scientific judgment, based upon general principles of food safety, before it was necessary even to consider invoking them. As a practical matter, therefore, the anti-cancer clauses are a relatively insignificant factor in the daily administration of the safety provisions of the law, although they unquestionably present a fascinating subject for discussion at a forum such as this one.

In giving the Food and Drug Administration sweeping authority to require that all food and drugs be safe, therefore, Congress has relied upon a very broad and general mandate rather than upon narrow and specific rules. Not one of the critical statutory terms or phrases which controls the numerous safety decisions made daily by the Food and Drug Administration is defined in the Act. Nor, indeed, do I believe that they can or should be defined at this point in time. Safety evaluation is today an imprecise and uncertain task. Until the ambiguities

and imponderables that now inhere in that task are clarified and elucidated, rigid safety definitions seem unlikely to lead to sound public policy.

Perhaps the best example of the thicket into which any legislative body wanders in attempting to enact any rigid safety criteria may be found in the various anti-cancer clauses now contained in the Act. Regardless whether one supports or opposes inclusion of a specific anti-cancer provision in the law – and I take no position whatever on that issue – I think we can all agree that the present versions are indefensible from any viewpoint.

In 1958, when it first included an anti-cancer clause in the law, Congress applied it only to food ingredients that are not generally recognized as safe or were not previously approved for use in food by the Food and Drug Administration or the United States Department of Agriculture. From this, one might deduce that Congress favored use of old and familiar carcinogens over newly discovered ones.

In 1960, a second anti-cancer clause was enacted as part of the Color Additive Amendments. This time Congress applied the clause to colors that are permanently approved for use in food and drugs after adequate safety testing, but not to colors that are only temporarily allowed for such use because of a lack of adequate safety testing. From this, one might deduce that Congress thought that the American public was entitled to at least a few more colorful years of some of its favorite carcinogens before it must face the prospect of a supply of drab food and drugs.

Then in 1962, faced with the inconsistency of its destinction between pre-1958 and post-1958 carcinogens, Congress amended the two clauses to solve the problem. The principal issue was diethylstilbestrol, which had been approved for use by some manufacturers as an animal growth promotant prior to 1958. Those manufacturers who had a pre-1958 approval could make it, and all others could not. Instead of eliminating this distinction, however, Congress added yet another in order to require the Food and Drug Administration to allow production of DES by all manufacturers. Under the Drug Amendments of 1962 – and under a third anti-cancer clause added to the law in the Animal Drug Amendments of 1968 – the Food and Drug Administration must now approve a known carcinogen for use in food-producing animals as long as available analytical methodology is unable to detect that carcinogen in the food obtained from the animal. From this, one might deduce that Congress simply wanted to inject a little excitement into an otherwise rather stodgy law, and reverted to that favorite old childhood game of hide-and-go-seek.

Nor is that the last chapter. In 1972, when scientists finally did find DES in animal livers using radioactive tracers, and the Food and Drug Administration banned it from animal feed with a five-month phase-out period, the Senate promptly passed a bill to ban use of DES immediately. The House did not act on that bill. From this, one might deduce that half of Congress sincerely regretted that it had ever wandered into this thicket, and the other half was simply immobilized by the total incongruity of the matter.

This rather incredible chronicle of legislative groping for political and scientific truth holds important lessons for all of us. Congress, in attempting to deal in detail with just one of many thousands of safety issues, has clearly floundered. The rule it has erected is so riddled with exemptions and exceptions as to make it indefensible in its present form. It presently serves more as a barrier to removing unsafe animal drugs from the market than as a measure for public protection. Indeed, that is the very reason why it is so seldom invoked. Its underlying purpose is and properly should be served by the general safety provisions of the law.

In the last analysis, regulation of the safety of food and drugs must depend upon informed scientific judgment. The scientific uncertainty that exists at this moment in history simply requires that safety determinations be made more on the basis of subjective evaluation than objective standards. And so long as this remains the situation, it must be expected that reasonable men can, and frequently will, differ on the judgment made by the Food and Drug Administration in any given situation, and thus on whether the statutory requirement of safety is properly being implemented.

II

The Food and Drug Administration's decision-making process on safety issues, and the public perception of it, are hampered by five basic obstacles. No one of these obstacles is critical, but their combined impact can at times be severe. And while each of these obstacles may be present to a greater or lesser degree in any particular safety decision, there is probably no major safety issue involving the Food and Drug Administration to which all do not contribute.

First, the scientific data base is seldom adequate to make a definitive safety judgment on any food or drug.

With every passing year, scientists develop new, more sophisticated safety testing methodology. Just one adverse finding, from whatever test method employed, seems sufficient today to call into public question the safety of virtually any ingredient used in food or drugs. If the product has been on the market for many years, as is true with much of our food supply, it is unlikely that it would have been subjected to many, if indeed any, of the scientific tests that are considered commonplace today. It simply is not feasible every year to go back and retest, using the newest methods, all the components of food and drugs that have previously been placed on the market. And even with the most recent additions to the marketplace, it is doubtful that any substance has been, or can be, so thoroughly tested as to preclude further scientific question.

It has long been recognized that no amount of human or animal testing can ever demonstrate the absolute absence of harm. All that one can ever show with certainty is the existence of harm. The marketing of any product therefore carries with it an inescapable but undeterminable risk. With the recent association of vaginal cancer in the female offspring of mothers with the use of diethylstilbestrol during pregnancy, moreover, this point has become a matter of immediate and serious policy concern to the Food and Drug Administration. We presently have no way whatever to predict this type of future harm for products about to be marketed, and our ability to monitor the safety of already-marketed products is limited. Even centuries of use of natural substances in the diet, without noticeable adverse effects, cannot be regarded as proof of safety, since it is based only upon uncontrolled observations.

Thus, proof of complete safety appears at this moment to be an illusory goal. Both those who challenge and those who defend the safety of any particular substance can do so with the assurance that information adequate either to support or to refute their contentions is not now available, and may never be. And today's decisions on the safety of food and drugs will therefore inevitably be made on the basis of incomplete scientific information. Second, even when substantial safety data are available on a particular substance, there is seldom scientific agreement on the meaning or significance of that information.

Scientists have been far more successful in inventing new methods of safety testing than they have been in determining the significance of the results obtained. This is particularly true with the still-evolving animal tests for carcinogenicity, teratogenicity, and mutagenicity. The meaning of adverse results obtained from these experiments, and especially their relevance to human use, is usually open to severe scientific disagreement. And of course the likelihood of obtaining at least one adverse or questionable finding increases with every test that is conducted.

Even those animal tests which have become widely accepted by scientists frequently produce results that are variable and inconclusive. Every scientist knows that quite different results can be obtained from a standard test protocol using different animal species, different strains of the same species, different animal rations, different routes of administration, and a host of far more subtle variables. Different laboratories not infrequently obtain diverse results even trying to replicate the identical testing procedures.

In short, the significance of much of the animal safety testing conducted today is poorly understood, and the widely variable results obtained are subject to differing interpretations. Its usefulness in the design and execution of sound public policy under these circumstances is unfortunately limited. As a matter of practical necessity, therefore, we often regulate more out of fear of the unknown than out of respect and appreciation of the known. And until science begins to bring greater understanding to safety testing, regulation of the safety of food and drugs must be accomplished in the midst of un-resolvable scientific disagreement.

Third, even assuming that an adequate scientific data base were available, to-gether with scientific agreement on the meaning and significance of the data, there appears to be no public or scientific consensus today on the risk or uncer-tainty acceptable to justify the marketing of any substance as a food or drug.

To some, who favor a return to more simple days, no risk or uncertainty what-ever is justified for any addition of a chemical to food. They would, indeed, re-quire a showing of some greater benefit to society before any ingredient is per-mitted. To others, who see enormous progress in food technology and nutrition from the use of food additives, the usual risks associated with technological inno-vation are regarded as entirely reason-able. Even in the area of therapeutic drugs, there is intense public dispute about whether, for example, the risks of an abortion outweigh the risks that are raised by the use of diethylstilbestrol as a post-coital contraceptive.

We must recognize that this type of issue presents fundamental differences in phil-osophical principles, not simply a nar-row dispute on technical details. It raises the most basic questions of personal be-liefs and human values – the degree of risk or uncertainty that any individual is willing to accept in his daily life. At-tempts to resolve it on the basis of rig-orous scientific testing or analytical dis-course therefore simply miss the point. A mathematical benefit/risk formula or computer program may eventually be able to quantitate the risk or uncertainty that inheres in a given product, but it is not even relevant to the moral and ethi-cal issues involved in deciding whether that risk or uncertainty is acceptable.

This problem arises whenever new doubts or suspicions are cast upon the safety of an already-marketed substance. Those who favor a very low public risk demand that the product immediately be removed from the market. Those who advocate a higher risk demand that it remain on the market until it is shown to be unsafe. If, as I suspect will happen, we eventually prove that many of our basic foods and drugs contain at least trace amounts of highly toxic substances – including carcinogens, teratogens, and mutagens – the public will simply have to face these issues in a more fortright way than it has up to now.

One does not need a degree in science to hold and express deeply-felt beliefs on the degree of risk or uncertainty society should accept from food and drugs. Nor, indeed, does a scientific background equip one with any greater insight into the intricacies of this type of policy issue or any more impressive credentials or greater authority to act as an arbiter in resolving these matters. As long as we remain a free society, these basic philo-sophical principles will, and properly should, remain the subject of intense public scrutiny and debate.

Fourth, there is enormous and continu-ing public pressure for the Food and Drug Administration to resolve whatever may be the latest current safety issue promptly and decisively.

Delay and indecision weaken public con-fidence and intensify fear and concern. Industrial representatives, faced with po-tential harm to their economic interests, demand reassurance that the public need fear no danger. Consumer activists, sens-ing a further victory in their war against unsafe products, intensify the public cam-paign to discredit the suspect product. Con-gress, reacting to the legitimate concern of their constituencies, demand a prompt resolution. The media, recognizing a story of interest to the entire public, does not fail to give it ample prominence.

Thus, regardless of the uncertainties and imponderables, a decision must frequently be reached immediately, on the basis of whatever meager information may exist.

On economic issues, a government agency may be able to take its time, to sift the facts, to make further investigations, and to act calmly and deliberately. Certainly, scientists in the academic world have ample opportunity to conduct further studies, obtain additional information, and engage in reflective thought, before reaching difficult judgments on complex scientific issues. In the emotion-charged atmosphere of a botulism or cancer scare, however, that process is necessarily foreshortened. It is simply unrealistic to believe that the Food and Drug Administration can ignore or even long resist the need to act promptly and decisively under those cirmcumstances.

Fifth, regardless of the outcome of the decision, those who disagree with it will continue to pursue the matter through all available channels, while those who agree with it will inevitably remain silent, preparing themselves for the next issue.

Graceful acceptance, or even grudging acquiescence, by those who have lost any important safety decision is a rare exception. And praise or even mild support from those who have prevailed is equally rare.

The price of virtually any major safety decision is at least one Congressional hearing, and perhaps more – regardless which way the decision goes. At least one Congressman will be persuaded, sooner or later, that important facts were not adequately considered, or appropriate weight was not given to particular viewpoints, and therefore that the entire matter should be subjected to further public scrutiny. This is obviously an important and appropriate Congressional function.

For those in industry or consumer organizations whose views were not accepted by the Agency, moreover, there is ready access to the courts. This is not only their right, but indeed their duty when they believe we have made an incorrect decision or acted unlawfully. Quite frequently, the economic stakes are extremely high. I have framed a law that, while not immutable, certainly has general application today: industry is likely to challenge in the courts any Food and Drug Administration action where the net adverse economic impact exceeds the legal fees involved.

Thus, no matter how promptly and decisively the matter is resolved, it usually does not end there. It continues to reverberate in the media, in Congress, in the courts, and in public debate, for months or years to come. Invariably, new scientific evidence will come to light on which one side of the issue or the other will find new sustenance. It is not at all surprising that the 1959 cranberry episode, the 1962 thalidomide tragedy, and the 1968 cyclamate ban, are still discussed as though they happened yesterday. And I am confident that our current ban of DES as an animal growth promotant, and whatever decision is ultimately reached on saccharin, will still be debated in lively terms twenty years hence. Nor is there any greater likelihood that a scientific or policy consensus on these issues will ultimately be reached then than there is that one could be reached at this moment.

As a lawyer, I am not only accustomed to the adversary process, but also a strong advocate of it. Nevertheless, we must be careful to prevent trial by combat from replacing reasoned decision-making on important safety issues.

III

In the midst of all this disarray and confusion stands the Food and Drug Administration, bearing its heavy statutory responsibility of assuring the safety of all food and drugs marketed in this country. With inadequate scientific data, with fundamental scientific disagreement on technical issues and public disagreement on policy issues, with the necessity to act decisively and promptly, and with the assurance of widespread dispute about whatever action emerges, the Agency daily makes some of the most important public policy decisions that directly affect all of our lives. I say this with neither exaggeration nor rancor, but simply with candor, based upon the insight gained from active participation in this process. Nor do I believe hat it is reasonable to expect that these very real obstacles will change dramatically, much less disappear, in the near future.

These obstacles have clearly taken their toll. Public and Congressional confidence in the ability of the Food and Drug Administration to carry out its statutory responsibilities has unquestionably been undermined. It has thus become apparent that the Agency must meet this challenge of face potential destruction.

Instead of throwing up our hands in despair, however, we have already instituted major changes in the decision-making processes of the Food and Drug Administration to accommodate and even assimilate these obstacles. Faced with deeper public concern about the safety of food and drugs than ever before, we have begun to open up the Agency's deliberations to substantially greater public scrutiny and participation, and thus equally greater public accountability, than perhaps any government agency in history. These changes, which are still in progress and will undoubtedly not be completed for some time, involve three essential elements.

First, we are developing new procedural mechanisms to guarantee that all interested persons have access to the Food and Drug Administration before important decisions are made. These procedures cannot permit Agency decisions to be tied up forever in needless red tape that only delays the process. But they must provide all segments of the public – consumer activists, the regulated industry, the academic world, and the public at large – information about what the Agency is considering and a meaningful opportunity for their voices to be heard before a decision is reached.

We have, in the past 18 months, developed such procedures for review of over-the-counter drugs and biological products. Anyone may submit written information or may make oral presentations to the reviewing panel at its frequent meetings. Our new procedures which for the first time permit the Food and Drug Administration to impose additional safety testing for already-marketed food ingredients encourage petitions by any person who wishes to designate specific testing that should be required for a particular substance. We have just announced a public hearing to consider internal guidelines that will govern the formulation and labeling of a class of prescription drugs – the first such hearing in the Agency's history. These are just a few examples of the changes taking place. And we are now beginning to re-think all of the procedures by which the Food and Drug Administration promulgates its regulations and makes its decisions in order to assure that this new policy is in fact fully implemented.

Mr. Justice Frankfurter pointed out thirty years ago that "The history of liberty has largely been the history of observance of procedural safeguards". I am not so naive as to believe that, simply by improving our procedures, a scientific and lay consensus will be reached on difficult safety issues and our critics will be stilled. Greater public access and representation of divergent viewpoints will, however, inevitably bring with it the beneficial impact that results from any person feeling that he has, in fact, participated in the decision-making process.

Second, in addition to guaranteeing more direct and immediate access to the Agency's decision-making, we are broadening the base of many of our decisions. Since subjective judgment plays such a large role in safety decisions, we are attempting to make certain that the most informed and respected judgment the country has to offer on these matters is in fact brought to bear on them. During the past three years, the Food and Drug Administration has increasingly relied upon independent technical advisory committees, consisting of scientific experts, to provide advice on major regulatory issues. In the review of over-the-counter drugs and biological products, moreover, we have now gone one step further and have included non-voting consumer and industry members on the technical committees.

It seems clear that, in addition to placing even greater reliance on independent advisory committees in the future, we must begin to include a broader representation of interests on these technical committees, rather than adhering strictly to scientists with specific expertise in the issues immediately before the committee. For as I have already indicated, the difficulties we encounter in our decisions increasingly involve fundamental philosophical principles and basic questions about the quality of life that trouble our entire society, as well as detailed scientific judgments. Deliberation on these issues properly deserves representation from the entire public.

Third, we are more fully articulating our policy decisions and the reasoning behind them. The public cannot be expected to understand and accept decisions that are nowhere explained. Both the rationale for each decision and any underlying documentation must be laid bare to critical scrutiny.

The Food and Drug Administration has publicly committed itself to this goal, with results that have been seen daily in the Federal Register for over a year. The explanation of Agency actions, contained in lengthy preambles to new regulations, frequently takes up five to ten times as much space as the regulations themselves. And the procedures for the current review of OTC drugs, biologicals, and *in vitro* diagnostic products, provide for public release of virtually all data provided by industry – including volumes of heretofore unpublished scientific information – upon publication of the proposed regulation.

We have not yet fully solved the problem of making public all of the scientific information that has been accumulating in the Food and Drug Administration files since 1906. That is a problem of resources and logistics to do the job, however, and not any desire to retain it as secret. Nor have we fully settled the question of what data and information provided to the Food and Drug Administration by industry represents true trade secrets that deserve to be held by us in strict confidence. We are hopeful that both of these problems can successfully be resolved in the near future.

Opening up Food and Drug Administration deliberations in these three ways has already substantially improved both our ability to handle difficult safety issues and the public's appreciation of what we are doing. We are, in short, beginning to surmount the obstacles that I have described, and I anticipate enormous further progress in this endeavor in the next year.

IV

Thus, I am extremely proud of the Food and Drug Administration's recent achievements, and very optimistic indeed for its future, in spite of the very difficult obstacles it must overcome to achieve full and fair enforcement of the law. The fact remains that, if there were no Food and Drug Administration, one would have to be invented. Some government regulatory agency must be responsible for making the daily decisions as to whether a given food or drug is sufficiently safe to be permitted on the market. The tremendous success of the Food and Drug Administration in carrying out this difficult responsibility is shown by the fact that, in spite of the hundreds of thousands of foods and drugs marketed, the number of known instances of harm that could have been avoided by regulatory action has been extraordinarily small. We intend simply to continue making the most responsible judgments possible, on the basis of the best available information and advice, and we welcome the help of everyone who believes, as we do, in the vital importance of this mission to the public welfare.

The Chemistry of Environmentalism

Emil M. Mrak

University of California, University House, Davis, Cal. 95616, U.S.A.

When I was first asked to speak to this distinguished group, I accepted with some reluctane because I had a fear of not being able to deliver a message of interest to you. However, it was suggested that I talk about "The Chemistry of Environmentalism" and, too, that I might cover the rationale involved so much in the thinking of the environmental advocates – and finally what the intelligent and concerned businessman should do about it. Believe me, this is a big order, but I will try.

Before I do this, however, first I would like to present some of my thoughts regarding the rationale for the thinking of some of the environmental advocates. What I am about to say is entirely my own opinion and, to a considerable extent, is based on firsthand contact with a number of such people.

The ones I want to talk about most are those who are very vocal and speak at every opportunity. A chinese philosopher once said "Those who know, do not speak, and those who speak, do not know." I am therefore speaking, to a large extent, about those who speak.

To be certain of what I am doing, I looked up the word "rationale" in Webster's, and he says it means – explanation of some opinion or hypotheses or the like – or – the *underlying reason for such actions*. I would like to concentrate on the underlying reasons for such actions. I am not a psychologist, and I have great fears about venturing into this field. Nevertheless, as I have already indicated, I have had some firsthand contact with advocates and have arrived at certain conclusions, and here they are.

First of all, there are the idealists – the people who are truly sincere about changing things – about improving the environment – about making this world a better place to live in. Many in these groups are students. Generally speaking, I would say they are not well informed, though highly opinionated, and they are victims of what I would call a reductionist type of education. They have been victims of learning more and more about less and less, and unfortunately have not been exposed to the breadth of thinking we need today. Then again, they have been exposed to the communications media, which tend to dramatize and publish exaggerations, half truths, and as one of our distinguished leaders in agriculture once said, even dramatic lies because people seem to accept these more than dull truths.

Another group of activists, I have termed lay scientists who appear to want to be heard. They have made their mark in one field of science, even to the extent of receiving an award for their accomplishments. He may be a person of great expertise in a field such as physics, far from agriculture, or food safety, yet he is willing ot speak in an authoritative manner about it. These are people the news media respond to because of their reputations. Dr. Darby, the president of the Nutrition Foundation, has spoken on this and has pointed out that he believes these

* Sponsored by the International Academy of Environmental Safety.

people, in a way, do as much harm as do the news media, if not more, because the news media are inclined to listen to them and publish what they say. The average person, too, is inclined to listen to these people.

Another group of advocates appear to have ulterior motives – they want to change the system, they want to raise hell and, in fact, be as destructive as they can. Naturally, I cannot prove this, but seeing some in action, it is hard for me to believe otherwise.

While on the subject of advocates, I would certainly be inclined to include a group that I might call frustrated scientists. They haven't done very well in their field of expertise and they feel it. They want to be heard, they want to get their names before the public some way. They, therefore, speak out, and they are very often careless about the statements they make. Of course, they too can be and often are destructive. Only recently a person testified to a Congressional committee to the effect that there is some 30 billion dollars worth of harm being done as a result of poor foods and malnutrition in this country. Where did such a figure come from? Why make such a statement? Let's skip the scientists now and consider others.

Another group involves politicians who have learned that by speaking of the environment – becoming experts in this field and becoming which I would term molecular politicians – they can make headlines. Headlines, of course, are very valuable to them. As you well know, we have had instances in California where suggestions have been made that certain chemicals be outlawed. These people need scientific advice, but they seldom get it, and when they do, it is so often from irresponsible sources. I have known of a situation in Sacramento where the extremists of both ends of the spectrum

have only caused confusion and harm. Which one was the politician to believe the one who wished to ban everything, or the one who would permit anything to be used freely and without regulation. The result was, the legislators were inclined to use their own views and those of their close advisors in developing legislation. Unfortunately, more often than not, scientists with good judgment are not apt to speak – they so often yield to the irresponsible ones.

There are many people in administrative positions in the government who are subjected to tremendous pressures, emotional actions, and even court suits. These people have a terrible time defending themselves, even when they are well informed and have a terrible time using good judgment, acting logically and methodically, even when they are well informed. These are the people we must help, and I believe an organization concerned with the environment, such as the Nutrition Foundation is with foods, that would enable a reliable and open forum would help greatly – but more about this later.

While I am speaking of government people, I would categorize another group that doesn't want to be in a position of using judgment. They feel the law is written, and if they can enforce the law to its very word without using judgment at all, it is easier and finite. Many of these people are lawyers, and of course do not want to lose a case in which they may be involved. I have been impressed with the fact that scientists in government so often will call on peer groups of scientists to advise them and consider any judgments they may make. On the other hand, when it comes to the lawyers who are handling cases where judgment and only judgment is involved, I am not aware of a single case where they have called on peer groups to discuss a particular situation with them. This, to me, is indeed surprising. Let's go on.

There ist another group that is hard for me to classify. It is composed of individuals who would sponsor initiatives and change laws because they are motivated to do what they think is best for all — yet so often they are not well informed. I am certain you recall Proposition 9 which was on the ballot in California last June.

Finally, there are those in all groups who are truly sincere, but they suffer from the effects of reductionism — in other words, their background is narrow and they are not well informed, and their thinking, though sincere, is indeed narrow. Students often fall into this group.

Who is at fault for the situation of limited education? I believe it is a weakness in our system of education. Those institutions of higher learning usually enroll in a specific major. Those responsible for administration of the majors insist on a specific curriculum and burden the students with so many required courses, that they do not have an opportunity to broaden their views and understanding. This has been one of the great criticisms of engineering, even when students have been given an opportunity to take a few elective courses. This reductionism certainly applies, in general, to every area in institutions of higher learning.

But then there is another side to the coin. Suppose a student is permitted more time for courses of breadth, the courses needed are generally non existent. This is particularly true with respect to courses related to the environment. But before I go to this, I would like now to give you a few examples of the problems confronting us as an indication of where we are today.

Since you are a group of chemists and represent the chemical industry, I believe I am safe in saying that you have been concerned with constructive advances, and these indeed have contributed greatly to our quality of life, and I hope we will never give these up, although some say we should.

In any event, until recently the chances are that you haven't had an opportunity or an orientation that has encouraged you to think in terms of side effects, such as those related to the environment. Furthermore, as scientists, you have failed to speak out, and when you do, who listens? The news medium, as I have already indicated, is not interested in dull truths, but rather dramatic and perhaps half truths and mistruths. As responsible people, you find it difficult to speak dramatically. Let me give you a few examples of what has happened in the last few years.

Let's consider DDT. The people who developed this product saw the advantages, but failed to think in terms of the distant future and the possible disadvantages — but then who would have thought of environmental problems then.

When it was introduced, persistence was an advantage, and who would have thought that eventually this might be considered a disadvantage. In any event, it was and still is hard to define persistence, although some talk about it a great deal and with certainty. Yet the Finch Commission was not able to do so. This is the type of thing I hope the chemist will consider in the future. There is no question but what DDT has done tremendous things for man. The advantages, in my opinion, have far outweighed the disadvantages, yet it got into trouble. We were not prepared factually or emotionally to combat the pressures and onslaughts made on it by those who would have it outlawed.

When DDT was thought to be found in excessive amounts in the fish of Lake Michigan, there was a great deal of concern. The secretary of HEW appointed a commission to study the relation of DDT and other pesticides to health. There was then an FDA tolerance of 3 ppm of DDT in fish, but it was raised on an interim basis to 5 ppm. The question I have raised is why 5 ppm, why not 10 or 15, or even zero. There was no evidence that DDT was harmful to humans and there still isn't any. In any event, as time went on, it was shown that the analytical procedure used for determining the quantity of DDT in fish was unreliable. Furthermore the total fish, including the head, belly fat and tail, was analyzed. In other words, the parts not normally eaten were included in the sample analyzed as well as those that were eaten. Yet, most of the DDT was found in the belly fat and the head. This to me was an irresponsible procedure. Yet, these were scientists who had developed the procedure. But, more important than that, it finally became known that those making the analyses confused DDT with polychlorinated biphenyls (PCBs), if you please. The FDA banned interstate shipment of fish containing more than 5 ppm of DDT. Later it was found that a large part of what was thought to be DDT was actually PCB's. The analytical procedures used were unreliable. Unfortunately, there was no prestigious impartial body to study the situation and make a reliable study and factual statement. This confusion factor is well known now, but I haven't heard it called to the attention of any congressional committee, and if it were, it probably would not reach the newspapers. PCB's have been found to be quite widespread and occur even in carbonless carbon paper, plywood, packaging material made from recyled paper, and so on. As a result, it has been picked up in a breakfast food, which in turn picked it up from packaging material. It has also been found in poultry, fish, milk and other products. The government

agencies just moved too fast – but what else could they do.

Then again, there is the matter of 2, 4, 5-T which has almost gone to its demise as a result of emotions and irresponsibility. It would take up several hours to discuss in detail the 2, 4, 5-T story. I would merely like to point out that here again, responsible scientists failed to speak out, but not so the misinformed advocate scientists. As a result, politicians listened to those who presented a biased point of view and mobilized and directed their pressures toward those administering the law. Here again there was no impartial, prestigious body of offer a forum to clarify this confusion of views and opinions. So in the end, those who could mobilize emotions and pressures appear to be the ones who have succeeded.

Now, let's consider agricultural chemicals in general and some of the areas in which we have failed and some in which we have succeeded. Agricultural chemicals have contributed tremendously to our way and quality of life. They have enabled food production at a lower cost than any place in the world. Yet, we don't hear too much about these facts in the halls of Congress, or from the legislators or newspapers. On the other hand, we hear agricultural chemicals contaminating water, air and solid waste and endangering the health and welfare of humans and wildlife too.

It has been alarming and distressing to me to note what is taking place. Congress passes bills containing irresponsible sections, and these bills assigned to uninformed and even irresponsible people to implement and enforce. Congress has passed bills that overlap so there is, at times, confusion as to which department in government should enforce the law. Here again, this has taken place, in part, because there has been no single prestigious source of information to which

Congress or the enforcing agencies can go for information, or if you wish to put it another way, backbone stiffening that will enable them to use good judgment – call it the corset of good judgment, if you will.

So much for that. But, there is more that adds to our problems. We have failed to even consider satisfactory methods for monitoring, therefore, information in this area is meager or lacking so we often use information to promolgate regulations and enforce laws. I have already spoken of the tragic errors made in the analyses of fish for DDT. Believe it or not, it was a food company that called this analytical debacle to the attention of government agencies.

Then again, there is the case of mercury and the procedures used for analyses. The Food and Drug Administration was using the wet method of analysis, which I understand is highly inaccurate and gives about half of what is present. The Dow Chemical Company pointed this out to the FDA and indicated that the atomic absorption methods ist far more accurate and gives higher results. As a result, the FDA changed their procedures, but retained the tolerance at the same level – in other words, cut it in half.

Perhaps the greatest problems we have today is testing for safety, whether it be food additives, agricultural chemicals, or even any ordinary chemical to which a person may be exposed.

When it comes to food additives, there is the Delaney Clause which just cannot be enforced completely for if it were, we would outlaw many of the foods we are eating everyday. Yet, cyclamates were banned on the basis of the Delaney Clause. I know something about the background of this situation, and here again, if we had a responsible prestigious organization that the Secretary could have relied on, and one who could have been a "corset" for good judgment, I doubt if the tragic ban would have taken place.

As a result, some of us were able to induce the government to establish at Pine Bluff, Arkansas, a facility to develop protocols for testing for safety, satisfactory methods for analysis, and procedures for monitoring. This facility is barely off the ground but has started a few projects relating to safety. It has an advisory body involving government, universities, industry and civilian scientists.

While I am quite happy about certain aspects of what has taken place, I can't say I am highly elated. I think industry could support the Pine Bluff activity morally. Industry should speak about it, understand it and even work with it. In cases where industry scientists have spoken out, it has been more derogatory than good, but this has resulted from a failure of understanding and communications.

I have been involved in another area – the reorganization and recreation, so to speak, of the Nutrition Foundation. In one brief year, the new and reoriented organization has really done some tremendous things. I believe this is something that should be studied carefully by those concerned with the environment and agriculture, with the view of establishing a similar organization for these areas of activity.

Let me tell you a little about what the new Nutrition Foundation has done within a year. It has made known that its objectives are education at all levels, from grammar school through the universities and medical schools too. Beyond this, it has in mind the average citizen and especially politicians and government workers. This is indeed a big task, and one that will take time, but as I have already indicated, great progress has been made in one single year. The budget thus far is about a million dollars a year and the hopes are that it will eventually be increased to between three and five million per year.

Let's get back to some of the specific things that it has done.

Perhaps some of you have heard that saccharin might have been banned because of the formation of bladder tumors in mice when bladder implantations were made. Over a year has now passed and you have not heard anymore about this threat. There is a reason for this. The Nutrition Foundation, with some additional aid from industry, brought together all the scientists in the world working on the safety of saccharin. In addition, scientists from the Food and Drug Administrations of Canada and the U. S. were invited to attend. For several days, these scientists sat around a table and discussed their work, the details, the methods, the strengths and the weaknesses of each of the scientists' programs. Out of fourteen different scientists working on saccharin, it was found that only one observed positive carcinogenesis. As a result, it was concluded the scientists should continue their work until March 1973 when they will again meet in this country. In the meantime, samples of the saccharin from the laboratory obtaining positive results have been sent to the Canadian Food and Drug Administration for analysis to determine whether or not there are impurities. Other factors, procedures and details used by this laboratory are being studied. As a result of this action, our FDA and the Canadian agency too, have decided to withhold any judgment on saccharin until next March. This has given them sufficient strength, backing and information so they are able to withstand pressures and emotions insisting they take action, though it be an irresponsible action. In the end, they may ban saccharin, but it will be based on sound information gathered from the world over. Furthermore, industry has been amply informed and has plenty of time to make orderly adjustments. No one has psuhed a panic button.

The Nutrition Foundation, in collaboration with the Vanderbilt University, also held a four-day symposium in Nashville on the health aspects of sugar. I attended this meeting and certainly learned a great deal. Here again, scientists from all over the world, were present, from Japan, Israel, Finland, Sweden, Germany, England, Canada, U. S., and others.

Much has been said about the harm of eating sugar, empty calories, sugar causing heart disease, high blood pressure, gout, and heaven-knows-what. In the end, it became quite clear that normal amounts of sugar included in normal diets are desirable and not harmful. A scientific editor was present and he is preparing a series of articles for the public and the communications media. In addition, the total proceedings will appear in a book, and it is not only hopeful but really expected that this will lay to rest for once and all the irresponsible statements that are made by unilaterally thinking scientists about sugars.

The Foundation was also involved in a meeting at Williamsburg concerned with nutrition and food safety education in the medical schools. Believe it or not, an M. D. rarely, if ever, is required to take courses concerned with food safety and nutrition. Nevertheless an M. D. is considered an expert in the field and generally is the one who is willing to speak authoritatively on the subject. They, unfortunately, can say so much and yet know so little. I have known a few M. D. 's who are well informed on nutrition and food safety, but these have read a tremendous amount and this is a rarity. I have known many M. D.'s and have been involved in establishing a school of medicine, and I know very well that the average M. D. is not going to bother about nutrition unless he is compelled to do so.

In any event, forces are at work to require nutrition education in medical schools.

Only two weeks ago, the real impact of the new Nutrition Foundation really started to show its effects. Commissioner Edwards of the FDA called on Dr. Darby to discuss with him the possibility of having a world symposium on food safety. The formulation of plans are underway. This is something that Dr. Edwards desires because it will give him sound information, and especially a basis for taking strong stands when he needs to. I believe he is a logical and highly qualified man, but he is exposed to tremendous pressures, emotions, and abuses, and it is not easy to stand up against such forces without backing. In any event, Dr. Darby has been able to develop the interest of other foundations in the programm – namely, the Rockefeller, Ford and Macy Foundations in promoting such a plan. It will involve a substantial sum of money – perhaps several hundred thousand dollars a year and will be conducted on a continuing basis. The first symposium may very well be a general one, but after that, there will be specific sessions concerned with specific problems, such as nitrosamines, certain pesticides, and so on. This will be a body of world scientists, and believe me, it will have an impact, and positive influence. It will give those who are administering our laws the strength and backing that they need, for they can then take a strong stand on world opinion, and this has all come about through the new Nutrition Foundation.

Dr. Darby has gone one step further. He is now organizing a union of nutrition foundations throughout the world. These will give us added strength.

What I am leading up to is that I believe that something like this is needed for agriculture and the environment, and unless we do develop something of this type, I can only see for the future, chaos and costly chaos, if you please. I believe sincerely we must develop an organization that can dedicate itself to education and bringing together of facts and sound scientists so in the future regulations, judgments, and decisions, and even laws, can be based on sound and unbiased information. I would like to quote here a statement made – believe it or not – by a graduate student at a conference held in Sacramento about a year ago. He stated: "Lack of proper information manifests itself in many ways – for example, subjectivity, tunnel vision, haggling over semantics, emotionalism, nonsolution of problems and often the creation of new ones." In my opinion, he said it well, but he did not go on to point out that the present situation results in irresponsible and unenforceable laws and irresponsible actions by government officials and irresponsible activities by irresponsible people.

With this I close and sincerely hope we can do something that will avoid the frequent piecemeal expenditures such as those used to defeat Proposition 9 last June. I only hope we are not too late, for things of this type do take time for organization and their accomplishment.

Environmental Control Impact on Food Production*

Emil M. Mrak

University of California, University House, Davis, Cal. 95616, U.S.A.

I find myself in a unique position in that I have been exposed to some extent, to the problems of the people in Washington as well as to those on the farm and in the processing plant.

In the last few years I have had an opportunity to observe firsthand the tremendous changes that are taking place and what appears to be at its ever-accelerating rate. I have had an opportunity to observe the impact of these changes and the fears, concerns, misunderstandings, and so on that have arisen as a result.

Not so many years ago, the people in our country were genuinely interested in food production at lower costs, a greater variety of foods and better foods, especially for those in the cities. The need for improvement in the food situation became very apparent when people in great numbers moved from the farms to the cities. Farm production increased dramatically to the point where today it only requires about one worker to produce food for forty people, whereas not so many years ago one person produced for only five people.

It is indeed unfortunate that our people did not realize years ago how serious the environmental situation might become and how it would be related to food production, and particularly the cost of producing food and the cost to the consumer. We were so busy with our constructive advances that we just overlooked the possibility of being destructive. Now we find ourselves in a situation that is dangerously near getting out of hand as a result of the pressure of emotions, and the failure of some of our law makers and those implementing the laws to have the perspective and the broad outlook needed to give an understanding of just what the effects of the laws might be. We seem to be undergoing a process that Talbot termed "Reductionism", where each narrow group is so concerned with its own narrow area of interest, that it fails to consider the total or even partial impact of its actions on areas apart from its own interest such as the canning industry.

Until quite recently, agriculture and food preservation favored and revered industries to the people of our nation. I can recall very well during my period in college, the attitude of legislature, federal government and people as a whole was indeed favorable to agriculture and food processing.

But these are no longer favored industries, and in fact, many people consider them well-healed and abusive. This change is well manifested by the actions of Congress, legislators, court judgments and even the people who would take advantage of initiatives and referendums. Accordingly, research support is dwindling, likewise understanding and appreciation, though the problems are increasing at an accelerating rate.

Regulations with respect to pesticides, for example, are occurring so rapidly to correct the environmental situation that the average food producer just fails to

---

* Sponsored by the International Academy of Environmental Safety.

understand, and finds himself in a dilemma as to what to do and how to cope with the situation. In time I hope this will change, and especially as communications improve but, at present, the situation is indeed confusing and even chaotic. Beyond the matter of pesticides, there are many who are caught in the bureaucratic miles with respect to such a simple thing as the disposal of pesticide containers.

We have in California a rather unusual situation that seems almost unbelievable. There are laws that require the farmers to fence in empty pesticide containers. They would like to dispose of them, but then the bureaucracies concerned with water, air, health, wildlife, transportation on the highways, agriculture, landfills, and heaven-knows-what create roadblocks that make it impossible. There are eight such bureaucracies in California alone, but that is not all. I have heard it said that in Washington, there are as many as 36 agencies concerned with the movement of empty pesticide containers on the highways. How can an average farmer or processor understand all this bureaucratic confusion?

The processor, too, is exposed to all the pressures that the farmer has been experiencing, not only because of the raw materials he needs, but because of the possibility of contaminating water with sewage, air, noise and even odors. He deals with state agencies and then finds, at times, there are federal agencies that overrule the State agencies.

Right at present, we have a situation in the area where I live this is almost unbelievable. The problem relates to liquid waste disposal of a number of canneries, the construction of a new sewage treatment plant, and who will pay for it. But the real problem, as I see it, relates to the number of local, State, regional and federal agencies involved. Communications need to be changed and improved drastically between these agencies and between the agencies and industry. There needs to be clarification, when industry is involved as to how regulations are made – is industry permitted to have an input – are there to be hearings, is each industry treated differently, and within industry, is each plant forced into a common mold. I could go on and on, but I think I've said enough on this. In some way or another, all must work together to bring about constructive accomplishments rather than continued chaos as a product of reductionism.

All these things add to the cost of food production and, of course, must be passed on to the consumer, if our food pricing administration will permit it to be passed on. I am aware of at least one case where this has not occurred with the result that the value of the stock has tumbled, and the income of the company has really gone down, yet this is a very efficient company. I am aware, too, that some of the smaller ones may go out of business. These are some of the problems I see confronting both the grower and processor, but this is only one side of the story. Let's look at the other side of the story and the situation in Washington.

We are discussing the environment and, of course the EPA is a new agency created for this and which, in my opinion, has a superb leadership.

But that is not all. There are other agencies in Washington, the interests of which overlap with those of EPA and, in my opinion, some of the laws have been so poorly written, that they leave plenty of ground for confusion. This is where we are today. In my opinion, the law relating to OSHA definitely overlaps with the responsibilities given EPA. But there are also the interests of the Food and Drug Administration, Department of Transportation, and even the Federal Trade Commission that I believe overlaps at times. There are State agencies, and as you well know, there are 50 states. I don't know just how many total State agencies there are, but there are plenty.

At a recent meeting in New Orleans concerned with the disposal of used pesticide containers, it was pointed out that there are at least 36 agencies in the federal government concerned with this problem, and there are at least eight state agencies in California.

It is amazing to me, therefore, that this new agency – the Environmental Protection Agency – has done as well as it has. Once again, I would attribute it to good leadership.

There are problems of communication, not only between the agencies and industry, but also between departments in Washington, but also between federal and state governments. The latter one, to me, is indeed very important. As a matter of fact, I have called to the attention of the EPA administration on two occasions the need for better collaboration between the regional offices, state agencies and industry. It is essential that the regional leaders work closely with the state agencies and industry. If this is not done, we cannot expect to alleviate the chaotic situation in which we find ourselves today.

Only recently I attended two meetings concerned with OSHA relating to worker's safety.

In the past few years, I have been at times confused, but I came away from the OSHA[1] meetings an utterly confused person. Who is responsible for what – what is expected of OSHA, what is expected of EPA[2], HEW[3], NIOSH[4], and so on. Where does the CEO[5] and the Working Group fit into the picture – yet they are in it.

1. Occupational Safety & Health Act.
2. Environmental Protection Agency.
3. Health Education & Welfare.
4. National Institute of Occupational & Safety & Health.
5. Council of Environmental Quality.

What about state agencies? And so its goes.

We have a high level person in California assigned to this task, but in spite of this the various interests in California have not been brought together or congealed. The great universities in California have not been called upon for input with respect to safety, health and toxicology. Sometimes I think we have too much government; we have centralized power in the capitols and then we have diffused it among the various agencies to the point where it does not seem to work. I can't but wonder how this may be straightened out.

The chaotic situation was well manifested by a very well-known cattleman who not only operates a large cattle ranch, but a feedlot. He indicated that he felt, at best, he could not hold out as leader of this large operation for more than two years. He felt it was becoming so confusing from a technological standpoint and the multiplicity of government regulations that he just could not handle the situation beyond that time. Rather than panic and have a nervous breakdown, he felt it would be better to get someone else to handle it, if someone else would.

Another farmer said to me: "I am leasing out my six hundred acres, for, even though I am a college graduate, I cannot follow all these things and operate a farm." This is what is happening on the one hand, yet on the other, we talk about maintaining the small family farm. There is a bit of inconsistency here.

In conclusion, I would say there is a need for coordination between agencies at the federal level, agencies at the state level, and between agencies at the federal-state levels, and between the various government agencies and industry. This, to me, is a most urgent need.

Industry needs to know what is expected of it, what methods it must use in making changes, what is expected of it when it is told to clean up. How clean is clean in the plant or in the environment. I might add here, too, that industry is completely confused with respect to FDA [6], plant inspection for sanitation and the level that must be maintained, yet no such standards are required of foreign operators. It is hard to understand and I must say to me it hardly seems fair.

In a recently published book on mercury, authored by Goldwater, he made a statement that could very well apply to the total situation we are discussing today. He stated: "By no means all the activities dealing with mercury have been wasteful and non-productive. Along with opportunists, a number of established scientists turned their attention to the questions and many talented young people were attracted to the field of environmental studies." He went on to say: „As the midpoint of 1971 passed, it was clear that the amount of information on mercury in the environment that was a result from two years of effort will exceed a total production of all previous times." This, I think, is great, but I hope that we can soon lead the way out of the situation in which we find ourselves to a more orderly one and, above all, that federal, state, regional, area, county, district and city administrations will not only learn to work together, but with industry.

Furthermore, it is becoming apparent to me that there is a great need for an independent, prestigious and impeccable body that can serve as a forum in these areas – such as the Nutrition Foundation does for food safety and nutrition. I am glad to say that there is serious talk now about forming such an instrument.

---

6. Food & Drug Administration.

The Role of Clinical Research in Establishing Air Quality Criteria and Standards

John H. Knelson

Human Studies Laboratory
National Environmental Research Center
U.S. Environmental Protection Agency
Research Triangle Park, N.C. 27711, U.S.A.

Summary "Air quality criteria tell us what science has thus far been able to measure of the obvious as well as insidious effects of air pollution on man...". Standards, based on these criteria, are the legal means by which noxious emissions into the environment can be changed, lessened, or halted. Environmental criteria and standards have their foundation in human health effects research. The methods of classical toxicology and epidemiology have provided most of the information on which current criteria and standards are based. Controlled environmental laboratory research with human subjects is now providing additional and essential health intelligence for continued scrutiny of environmental criteria.

Introduction

Man has coped with natural envirnomental hazards from the beginning and with those of his own making for a very long time. When he began lighting fire in caves and storing food and drink in earthen pots, his early technology already had important health effects. Only recently, however, has man begun to assess the complicated interactions between himself and his ecosphere in a systematic, comprehensive way.

Three processes are responsible for the current environmental health crisis: 1) population growth, 2) population concentration, and 3) increased technology. All three of these are proceeding exponentially, so their combined effect is staggering. The first two processes are being addressed directly: 1) successful efforts are being made to slow population growth, 2) we are reducing the rate of urban concentration and, in some cases, actual urban outmigration is occurring. Most of us do not contemplate slowing the rate of technological progress, however. Qualitative, rather than quantitative change is necessary. We do not want to give up the benefits of our technological advances, but we do want to minimize or eliminate any adverse effect on our health or quality of life in general. We want to have our cake and eat it too. Can we? The answer lies in our development of environmental criteria and implementation of standards.

Environmental Criteria

Environmental criteria are the body of scientific information available which

* Sponsored by the International Academy of Environmental Safety.
Presented at the third International Clean Air Congress October, 1973, Düsseldorf, Federal Republic of Germany

describes the influence of environmental factors on human health and welfare. More specifically, "Air quality criteria tell us what science has thus far been able to measure of the obvious as well as insidious effects of air pollution on man...".[1] In the United States the Administrator of the Environmental Protection Ageny is required by law to produce air quality criteria documents summarizing the scientific basis for air quality standards.

Environmental Standards

Environmental criteria are useless unless they result in the development of standards with provisions for implementation. The standards are the legal means by which a concerned populace through the executive and judicial process can cause noxious emissions into the environment to be changed, lessened, or halted. A variety of skills must be brought to bear on the very complex problem of translating health effects information into judicious requirements for changes in technology. Biologists must express themselves in terms comprehensible to other specialists. Because biology is an imprecise science, not only experimental results, but an estimate of our confidence in those results, as well as reasonable interpretations of conflicting results, must be provided.

Health Effects Research

Environmental criteria and standards have their foundation in human health effects research. Our Clean Air Act, and its amendments specifically recognize certain points.
"... In carrying out the provisions of this section the Secretary shall, as may be necessary –

"(1) conduct epidemiologic studies of the effects of air pollution agents or combination of such agents on mortality or morbidity;

"(2) conduct clinical and laboratory studies on the immunologic, biochemical, physiological, and the toxicological effects including carcinogenic, teratogenic, and mutagenic effects of air pollution agents or combination of such agents;
..."

This excerpt of enlightened legislation not only reflects historic precedent, but succinctly describes the basis for our current investigation of human health effects of air pollution. Most environmental health effects research in the past has used the tools and strategies of epidemiology and toxicology. More recently researchers have begun to conduct carefully controlled laboratory exposure of humans to low concentrations of air pollutants. It is important to understand the advantages and disadvantages of these techniques as well as the relationships between them.

Epidemiology

The earliest observations of catastrophic results of air pollution were epidemiologic. Excess mortality associated with the historic Meuse Valley and Donora episodes was evident even to untrained observers. Since then, epidemiologic assessment of environmental health effects has become much more sophisticated and has provided much of the available data on this topic. Such information is most relevant because it relates health effects in humans to what is actually happening in the environment. There is no extrapolation from animal data; there is no simulation of environmental conditions.

There are three major problems in environmental epidemiology, however. Because one is studying humans moving about their natural habitat, it is difficult to measure the dose of a particular pollutant they may actually receive. Dose estimates can be calculated from aerometry data obtained in the general vicinity of the study population, but confidence intervals around these estimates are usually large. The second problem is measuring the health effect, and the third is disentangling these observations from other coexisting and uncontrollable environmental covariates such as occupational exposure or meteorologic conditions.

In dealing with the large numbers of people needed for good epidemiology, researchers usually do not have the means necessary for very sophisticated investigation of the health status of their subjects. Even when the means are available, there are serious logistic problems in processing large numbers of people from widely separated areas through specialized laboratory facilities. In the future, some of these difficulties may be overcome with the use of specially designed mobile physiologic laboratories. Because of the relative crudeness of dose estimates as well as inability to quantitate subtle changes in health status, it has not usually been possible to derive dose-response relationships from epidemiology data. In spite of these limitations, epidemiology remains a very important source of environmental health effects data and provides many insights for the design of clinical research.

Toxicology

The methods of classic toxicology are capable of giving the most accurate dose-response relationships for any environmental hazard. Because the animals or the *in vitro* systems used are expendable, the toxicologist can determine distribution of the pollutant throughout body tissues as well as resultant histopathology or subtle metabolic and biochemical changes. Environmental covariates and co-stressors can be carefully controlled. The greatest difficulty in using information provided by toxicology is the uncertainty that always accompanies the necessary extrapolation from animal data to human health effects. In some cases, especially in study of carcinogenesis, mutagenesis, or teratogenesis, the use of human subjects is impossible, and information from animal studies or epidemiologic observation are all we have. Although development of new techniques and concepts as well as modification of old ones is making possible more research involving human subjects, exhaustive toxicologic evaluation must always precede the clinical studies.

Clinical Environmental Research

The term "clinical" in this context refers to the use of humans as subjects of environmental health effects research in a laboratory setting such as one finds in a university teaching hospital. It does not necessarily imply, but neither does it exclude, use of hospital patients. The *sine qua non* of clinical research is protection of the rights and safety of the human subjects. It is incorrect to say that experiments with humans can be performed with no risk. All human activity involves risk. The wheels of commerce and industry cannot begin to turn without a certain measurable hazard for the human participants. What is essential is an accurate estimate of that risk and its reduction to a level acceptable to the individual and to society. Experiments must be designed so that any risk is comparable to that which the subject normally incurs in his day to day activities. This degree of risk must be accurately and fully explained to the scientist's disinterested but competent colleagues who, in a sense, pass judgment as representatives of society at large. This we call peer review. Finally, the subject himself, usually unsophisticated in matters of research, must have the experiment and the risks explained to him so carefully that he fully understands what is happening to him and accepts with no hesitation and under no duress whatsoever. This we call informed consent.

Inducement to participate in such research must be used with caution so as not to influence the subject's sound judgment. The most scientifically, morally, and socially acceptable inducement is the likelihood that the subject's health may actually be improved as a result of his taking part in the research. By this we usually mean that information will be gained that may improve management of a clinical condition, or a risk factor may be identified that can result in modifying the subject's life style to his eventual benefit. Monetary reward should be used only to the extent that it reimburses the subject for time and inconvenience, and is not a recompense for undue risk. One inducement that is often neglected or underestimated is simple altruism, or the satisfaction the subject experiences from participating in a worthwhile endeavor that may benefit humanity as well as himself.

There are three important factors in maintaining an acceptably low level of risk in clinical research. First, the environmental factors and co-stressors should be held to a level of intensity actually encountered in some areas. In other words, one should reproduce conditions under which many people are living anyway. This tends to minimize the risk as well as make the experiment relevant. Second, great care must be exercised in simulating the environmental conditions. The analytic chemist must be sure he is measuring what he thinks he is measuring in the air. The engineer must reproduce that environment, or components of it, as faithfully as technically possible. The engineer and chemist working together must design a foolproof (or "failsafe") control system that provides accurate monitoring of the controlled environment. When the fool-proof system malfunctions, as it surely will, then it must do so in a way that reduces the level of pollutant and alerts the investigator. Third, the human subject's response to this controlled environment must be monitored throughout the course of the experiment. It is not enough to know what has happened when the experiment is over. The investigator must be constantly apprised of the condition of his subject even while the experiment is in progress so he can alter conditions, or even stop the experiment if desired. Ideally, this "real-time" data acquisition and processing will not only assure the safety of the experiment, but improve the quality of information obtained.

Range of Susceptibility

Humans are not uniformly susceptible to various environmental influences on their health. When this self-evident principle is ignored, the result is confusing and contradictory data. Criteria for selection of research subjects must be prepared with great care so the normal range of susceptibility is controlled within each experiment. Our experiments must be designed to select as homogeneous a study population as possible, adjust the experimental conditions, and interpret the result appropriately. We know that patients with heart disease are more susceptible to the effects of small amounts of carbon monoxide than are healthy subjects. Thus, a level of exercise stress following carbon monoxide exposure in a normal man is entirely inappropriate in one with coronary artery disease. Likewise, the observation that such an experiment does not influence the electrocardiogram of the normal man does not mean such an effect does not exist, for it is striking in the abnormal subject.

Spectrum of Response

Whereas there is a range of susceptibility within a population, I would like to use "spectrum of response" to refer to the various ways an individual can manifest the effects of environmental stress. We have somewhat arbitrarily classified the spectrum into categories ranging from the mildest to the most severe. They are: 1) pollutant body burden, 2) changes of uncertain significance, 3) pathological changes, 4) morbidity, and 5) mortality. Because the proportion of any population falling into any category is greatest with 1) and the least with 5), it is evident that the concept of "range of susceptibility" is closely related to that of response spectrum. Consideration of the two concepts allows, conceptually, the construction of a three-dimensional dose-response relationship which can be used to calculate risk factors which reflect the degree of hazard as well as size of the population at risk. This kind of prediction is the final goal of environmental health effects research. We are trying to answer the question, "How many individuals in each category of our population are subjected to what levels of risk for a given range of pollutant concentration?"

In the United States Environmental Protection Agency, we are working toward that goal in many ways. One of them has been the development of a program for Clinical Laboratory Evaluation and Assessment of Noxious Substances, usually referred to by the acronym CLEANS. In that program we are following the principles and pursuing the goals I have outlined. We hope to be able to contribute some part of the answer to the question, "How should we modify or redirect our technological development to assure that environmental hazards will be kept at an acceptable level for the greatest number of people and at the least cost?"

References

[1] Air Quality Criteria for Carbon Monoxide. NAPCA Publication AP–62, p. 111, March 1970

[2] H. R. 17255, p. 35. In the Senate of the United States, 91st Congress, 2nd Session, September 22, 1970

Marine Biotoxicology[1]

Bruce W. Halstead

International Biotoxicological Center
World Life Research Institute
Colton, California, U.S.A.

Marine biotoxicology is the science of poisons produced by marine plants and animals, their cause, effects, nature, detection, and the treatment of intoxications produced by them. Marine biotoxicology can be conveniently divided into two major categories: 1) marine phytotoxicology, which deals with poisons produced by marine plants; and 2) marine zootoxicology, which deals with animal poisons.

Marine Phytotoxicology

Our knowledge of marine phytotoxicology, exclusive of toxic marine dinoflagellates,[2] is extremely meager. However, it is becoming increasingly evident from food web studies on poisonous fishes that toxic substances may occur in marine plants in greater abundance than was previously believed. Several species of marine plants have been incriminated as toxic, viz: *Lyngbya majuscula* Gomont (Habekost et al., 1955; Dawson et al., 1955; Dawson, 1959; Banner, 1959; Banner et al., 1960; Halstead, 1965), *Plectonema (Schizothrix calciola) terebrans* Bornet and Flahault (Cooper, 1964, 1966; Helfrich et al., 1968; Halstead, 1967), *Caulerpa racemosa* (Forskål) Agardh (Aguilar-Santos, 1966). There are further indications that large numbers of other species of marine algae are also involved.

A species of marine plant may be poisonous in one locality and nontoxic in another. Toxicity may also vary according to the season of the year, but whether this occurs with seasonal regularity is not known. Only a single marine phytotoxin has been studied to any extent and that is caulerpicin, derived from the marine alga *Caulerpa*. Caulerpicin is believed to be a secondary amide, but the structure has not been fully determined (Aguilar-Santos, 1966). If caulerpicin is ingested by humans, it results in numbness of the lips, tongue, and extremities, cold sensations, respiratory distress, and a loss of motor coordination. The toxicology and pharmacology of the poison are largely unknown. It is suggested that the poison is transmitted through a detritus food web rather than through the herbivore-carnivore sequence. However, this is conjecture because no one knows at present. Caulerpicin is believed to differ chemically from ciguatoxin, the poison found in ciguatera-producing tropical reef fish-

[1] This investigation was supported in part by a contract (No. N 00014–67–C–0379) from the Office of Naval Research, U. S. Navy, in a study on toxic marine animals.
[2] Some workers consider dinoflagellates as plants, but for the purpose of this discussion, they are considered as protozoans.

es. Caulerpicin may be passed on to humans through oysters, crabs, and various other marine organisms.

The biogenesis of these marine phytotoxins is presently unknown. Toxin production, at least in some instances, appears to be influenced by certain unknown chemical conditions in the substrate upon which the plant is growing. There is also evidence that the chemical constitution of the aqueous environment also influences toxigenesis. Undoubtedly, there are genetic factors which also influence toxin production in marine plants, but exactly what these factors are and the degree of interplay of these various factors are not known. The field of marine phytotoxicology is of importance in attempting to develop a thorough understanding of the economy of the sea. This is a highly promising area of chemoecological research for the future that is deserving of much greater attention than it has received to date.

Marine Zootoxicology

Marine zootoxic organisms are of three major types: 1) those that are *poisonous* to eat; 2) those that produce their poisons by means of specialized poison glands, but lack a traumagenic apparatus – the *crinotoxic* organisms; and 3) those that produce their poisons by means of specialized venom gland and posses a traumagenic organ – the *venomous* marine animals. Marine zootoxins are also sometimes grouped into two major categories, the oral poisons and the parenteral poisons – the venoms. Crinotoxins are thought to be largely parenteral poisons, but this has not been determined. Some of these crinotoxins may also be effective oral intoxicants. The term "poisonous" may be used in the generic sense, referring to both oral and parenteral poi-

sons; but it is more commonly used in the specific sense to designate oral poisons. Thus, all venoms are poisons, but not all poisons are venoms. Oral marine zootoxins are generally thought to be small molecular substances, whereas most venoms are believed to be large molecular substances, a protein, or in close association with one. Generally speaking, our knowledge of the chemistry of crinotoxins is too meager to permit a very intelligent classification at this time.

Our present system of classification of marine zootoxins attempts to take into consideration the phylogenetic relationships of the etiological organisms, the clinical characteristics of the biotoxication, and the chemical nature of the poisons involved. This classification can at this time be considered as only tentative pending further elucidation of the chemical and pharmacological properties of these poisons. The present system of classification is not ideal, but it has proved useful.

The realtionships of toxic marine animals and their position in the total framework of the Animal Kingdom can best be appreciated by a brief presentation of the major phylogenetic categories in which they occur.

Classification of Toxic Marine Animals

Toxic Invertebrates
Phylum Protozoa – One-celled animals.*
  Class Mastigophora: Flagellates.
    Order Dinoflagellata: Poisonous dinoflagellates.
Phylum Porifera – Sponges.
  Class Demospongiae: Toxic sponges.
Phylum Coelenterata – Hydroids, jellyfishes, sea anemones, corals.
  Class Hydrozoa: Venomous hydroids.

---

* Some authors include the dinoflagellates in the Kingdom Plantae whereas others place them in the Kingdom Protista.

Class Scyphozoa: Venomous jellyfishes.
Class Anthozoa: Venomous corals and sea anemones.
Phylum Echinodermata – Starfishes, sea urchins, sea cucumbers.
Class Asteroidea: Venomous starfishes.
Class Echinoidea: Venomous sea urchins.
Class Holothurioidea: Poisonous sea cucumbers.
Phylum Mollusca – Snails, bivalves, octopuses, etc.
Class Gastropoda: Poisonous and venomous snails, slugs, etc.
Class Pelecypoda: Poisonous bivalves.
Class Cephalopoda: Poisonous and venomous cephalopods.
Phylum Platyhelminthes – Flatworms.
Class Turbellaria: Crinotoxic flatworms.
Phylum Rhynchocoela – Ribbon worms.
Class Enopla: Venomous nemertean worms.
Phylum Annelida – Segmented worms.
Class Polychaeta: Poisonous and venomous marine annelids.

Toxic Vertebrates

Phylum Chordata – Chordates.
Class Agnatha: Poisonous lampreys and hagfishes.
Class Chondrichthyes: Poisonous and venomous sharks, rays, skates, and chimaeras.
Class Osteichthyes: Ichthyotoxic bony fishes.[3] A more detailed classification of toxic fishes appears below.
Class Amphibia: There are no marine amphibians reported to be toxic.
Class Reptilia: Poisonous turtles and venomous sea snakes.
Class Aves: There are no marine birds reported to be toxic.

[3] The term "ichthyotoxic fishes" includes poisonous, crinotoxic, and venomous forms.

Class Mammalia: Poisonous whales, dolphins, porpoises, seals, walruses, and polar bears.

Classification of Toxic Fishes

Fishes probably comprise the largest single group of toxic marine organisms. Toxic fishes are found scattered throughout a broad spectrum of phylogenetically unrelated species. Although most of these fishes are marine forms, some of them are restricted to fresh waters. Toxic fishes may be classified as follows:

Poisonous Fishes
This classification comprises those fishes which when ingested cause a biotoxication in humans due to a toxic substance present in the fish. It does not include fishes accidentally contaminated by bacterial food pathogens.
Ichthyosarcotoxic fishes – These fishes contain a poison within the flesh, i. e., in the broadest sense, musculature, viscera or skin, or slime, which when ingested by humans will produce a biotoxication. The toxins are oral poisons believed to be small molecular structures and are generally not destroyed by heat or gastric juices. The following groups of fishes are represented within this category:
Class Agnatha: Lampreys and hagfishes – causing cyclostome poisoning.
Class Chondrichthyes: Sharks, rays, skates, chimaeras – causing elasmobranch and chimaera poisonings.
Class Osteichthyes: This class contains serveral categories of ichthyosarcotoxic fishes, namely:
Ciguatoxic fishes causing ciguatera poisoning.
Clupeotoxic fishes – causing clupeoid fish poisoning.
Gempylotoxic fishes – causing gempylid fish poisoning.

Scombrotoxic fishes – causing scombroid fish poisoning.

Hallucinogenic fishes – causing hallucinatory fish poisoning.

Tetrodotoxic fishes – causing puffer poisoning.

Ichthyootoxic fishes – These fishes produce a poison which is generally restricted to the gonads of the fish. The musculature and other parts of the fish are usually edible. There is a definite relationship between gonadal activity and toxin production. Most of the fishes in this group are freshwater, but a few are marine. It should be noted that there is also a gonadal relationship with toxigenesis in tetrodotoxic fishes but in this latter instance the poison is more widely distributed within the body of puffers. In the case of a true ichthyootoxic fish the poison is restricted to the gonads. Ichthyootoxins are not destroyed by ordinary cooking procedures or by gastric juice.

Ichthyohemotoxic fishes – These fishes have poisonous blood. The poison is usually not destroyed by heat or gastric juices.

Ichthyocrinotoxic fishes – These are the fishes that produce a poison by means of spezialized glandular structures, but lack a traumagenic organ. The chemical nature of most of these poisons is unknown.

Marine Animal Biotoxications

Toxic Invertebrates

Protozoans — One-celled animals

Poisonous dinoflagellates are best known as causative agents of paralytic shellfish poisoning (Sommer et al., 1937; Needler, 1949). The species of dinoflagellates incriminated include *Gonyaulax catenella* Whedon and Kofoid, *G. tamarensis* Lebour, and *Pyrodinium phoneus* Wolos-zynska and Conrad. Paralytic shellfish poisoning occurs along the Pacific coast of North America, northeastern coast of North America, Europe, South Africa, and rarely elsewhere. The toxic dinoflagellates are ingested by a variety of mussels, clams, scallops, etc. The poison accumulates in the digestive glands of mussels and clams (Medcof et al., 1947). In some of the clams the gills may be quite toxic, whereas in *Saxidomus,* the butter clam, the poison is in the siphons (Chambers and Magnusson, 1950). The distribution of the poison in the body of the animal appears to vary somewhat with the species of shellfish and with the season of the year. Man is poisoned by eating shellfish that have been feeding on toxic dinoflagellates.

Paralytic shellfish poisoning may be diagnosed readily by the presence of pathognomonic symptoms which usually manifest themselves within 30 minutes. Initially, there is a tingling or burning sensation of the lips, gums, tongue, and face, with gradual progression to the neck, arms, fingertips, legs, und toes. The paresthesia later changes to numbness, so that voluntary movements are made with difficulty. In severe cases, ataxia and general motor incoordination are accompanied in most instances by a peculiar feeling of lightness, "as though one were floating in air." Constrictive sensations of the throat, incoherence of speech, and aphonia are prominent symptoms in severe cases. Weakness, dizziness, malaise, prostration, headache, salivation, rapid pulse, intense thirst, dysphagia, perspiration, anuria, and myalgia may be present. Gastrointestinal symptoms of nausea, vomiting, diarrhea, and abdominal pain are less common. As a rule, the reflexes are not affected. Pupillary changes are variable, and there may be an impairment of vision or even temporary blindness. Mental symptoms vary, but most victims are calm and conscious of their condition throughout their illness. Occasionally, patients complain that their teeth feel "loose or set on edge." Muscular twitchings and convulsions are rare (Combe, 1828; Stevenson, 1874; Thesen, 1901; Meyer et al., 1928).

The toxic principle is termed "saxitoxin" or "paralytic shellfish poison" and has the molecular formula of $C_{10}H_{17}H_7O_4$ (Scheuer, 1964). The principal action of the toxin is on the central nervous system (respiratory and vasomotor centers) and the peripheral nervous system (neuromuscular junction, cutaneous tactile endings, and muscle spindels). Absorption occurs through the gastrointestinal tract, and rapid excretion of the active toxin occurs through the kidneys. Treatment is largely symptomatic.

Dinoflagellates have also been incriminated as the causative agent of venerupin shellfish poisoning. The species involved is *Exuviaella mariae-lebouriae* Parke and Ballantine (Silva, 1956). Man is poisoned by eating shellfish that have been feeding on toxic dinoflagellates.

The symptoms of venerupin or asari shellfish poisoning usually develop 24 to 48 hours after ingestion of the toxic mollusks, but an incubation period is believed to extend up to 7 days (Togashi, 1943; Akiba and Hattori, 1949). The initial symptoms are: anorexis, gastric pain, nausea, vomiting, constipation, headache, and malaise. Body temperature usually remains normal. Within 2 to 3 days nervousness, hematemesis, and bleeding from the mucous membranes of the nose, mouth, and gums develops. Halitosis is a dominant part of the clinical picture. Jaundice, petechial hemorrhages, and ecchymoses of the skin are generally present, particularly about the chest, neck, and upper portion of the arms and legs. Leucocytosis, anemia, retardation of blood clotting time, and evidence of dis-

turbances in liver function have been noted. The liver is generally enlarged, but painless. In fatal cases the victim usually becomes extremely excitable, delirious, and comatose. There is no evidence of paralysis or other neurotoxic effects usually observed in paralytic shellfish poisoning. In the outbreaks that have been reported, there was found to be an average case fatality rate of 33.5 percent. In severe cases, death occurs within one week; in mild cases, recovery is slow, with the victum showing extreme weakness. The development of ascites is a frequent complication.

Treatment is symptomatic – bed rest, injections of intravenous glucose, and the administration of vitamins B, C and D and Insulin.

There is no information available concerning the chemistry and pharmacology of these poisons.

Dinoflagellates are also capable of producing respiratory irritants. Inhalation of toxic products contained in windblown spray from red tide areas of *Gymnodinium brevis* Davis outbreaks in Florida irritated mucous membranes of the nose and throat, and caused spasmodic coughing, sneezing, and respiratory distress (Woodcock, 1948).

A number of other species of marine dinoflagellates are believed to produce toxic substances, but there are no experimental data available.

For additional reading on this subject see Scheuer (1964), Schuett and Rapoport (1962), and Mosher (1966).

Porifera – Sponges

There is very little information available concerning toxic sponges although it is known that some species do produce poisonous substances. Sponges of the genera *Fibulia, Hemectyon, Tedania, Microciona,* and others are capable of inflicting a dermatitis which in some instances is believed to be due to a chemical irritant (Duchassaing and Michelotti, 1864; Verrill, 1907; De Laubenfels, 1936, 1953). Alcoholic extracts from the marine sponge *Suberites domunculus* Olivi produce vomiting, diarrhea, prostration, intestinal hemorrhages and respiratory distress when injected intravenously into laboratory animals (Richet, 1906 a, b). The chemistry and pharmacology of the poisons involved are unknown.

Coelenterata – Hydroids, jellyfishes, sea anemones, corals

Coelenterates inflict their injurious effects upon man by the use of their nematocyst apparatus. The venom is conveyed from the capsule of the nematocyst through the tubule into the tissues of the victim. Theoretically, any coelenterate equipped with a nematocyst apparatus is a potential stinger. The injurious effects may range from a mild dermatitis to almost instant death. The severity of the stinging is modified by the species of coelenterate, the type of nematocyst that it possesses, the penetrating power of the nematocyst, the area of exposed skin of the vitim, and the sensitivity of the person to the venom.

Some of the sea anemones have been found to be poisonous to eat – particularly when raw. It is not known whether oral actinian intoxications are caused by their nematocyst poisons, or are the result of other noxious chemical substances contained in the tissues of their tentacles.

Stinging hydroids include certain species of the genera *Sarsia, Liriope, Halecium, Millepora, Gonionemus, Olindias, Olindioides, Pennaria, Physalia, Aglaophenia, Lytocarpus,* and *Rhizophysa.* (Wood-Jones, 1912; Strong, 1944; Chu and Cutress, 1953, 1955; Aznaurian, 1958; Southcott, 1963). The stings produced by these organisms vary from a mild stinging sensation to an extremely painful one from Olindias and Physalia. There may be present redness of the skin, urticarial rash, hemorrhagic zosteriform or a generalized morbilliform rash, vesicle and pustule formation and desquamation of the skin, abdominal pain, chills, fever, malaise, and diarrhea. These signs and symptoms may be accompanied by headache, malaise, primary shock, collapse, faintness, pallor, weakness, cyanosis, nervousness, hysteria, chills, fever, muscular cramps, and abdominal rigidity. Death may result in rare instances.

Stinging jellyfishes include members of the genera *Aurelia, Carybdea, Cassiopea, Catostylus, Chironex, Chirodropus, Chiropsalmus, Chrysaora, Cyanea, Lobonema, Linuche, Lychnorhiza, Nausithoe, Pelagia, Rhizostoma, Sanderia,* and *Tamoya.* The stings from most of these jellyfishes are usually relatively mild. *Cassiopea, Catostylus, Chrysaora, Cyanea, Rhizostoma,* and *Sanderia* may be moderate to severe, but *Chironex* and *Chiropsalmus* can be fatal. The effects in severe cases may consist of extremely painful localized areas of whealing, edema, and vesiculation, which later result in necrosis involving the full thickness of the skin. The initial lesions, caused by the structural pattern of the tentacles, are multiple linear wheals with transverse barring. The purple or brown tentacle marks form a whip-like skin lesion. Painful muscular spasms, respiratory distress, a rapid weak pulse, prostration, pulmonary edema, vasomotor and respiratory failure, or death may result. The pain is said to be excruciating, with the victim frequently screaming and becoming irrational. Death may take place within 30 seconds to 3 hours, but the usual time is less than 15 minutes. The cough and mucoid expectoration that are present in some of the other forms of jellyfish attacks are generally absent in *Chironex* and *Chiropsalmus* stings (Nielly, 1881; Light, 1914 a, b; Russell, 1938; Machado, 1943; Phillips and Brady, 1953; Southcott, 1956, 1963; Barnes, 1969).

Sea anemone stings tend to be more localized in their effects. There may be itching and a burning sensation at the sting site, accompanied by swelling and erythema, ultimately followed by local necrosis and ulceration. Severe sloughing of the tissues may occur, with a prolonged period of purulent discharge. Multiple abscesses have been reported. Localized symptoms may be accompanied by such generalized effects as fever, chills, malaise, abdominal pain, nausea, vomiting, headaches, a feeling of extreme thirst, and prostration. Sea anemone ulcers tend to be resistant to treatment and are slow to heal. As in the case of other types of coelenterate stings, they can be quite mild with little or no ill effects to the victim.

Coral cuts and stings are ill-defined problems. Although such cuts and ulcers are well known to most individuals working in tropical waters, the actual stinging ability of scleractinian or stony hexacorals is not well defined. The scleractinian corals are generally considered to be of minor significance, among venomous coelenterates. However, there are a few genre which have members reputedly capable of stinging human beings: *Acropora, Astreopora, Goniopora*, and *Plesiastrea*. The effects have been described as a distinct stinging sensation, followed by weeping of the lesion, wheal formation, and itching. If coral cuts or stings are left untreated, a superficial scratch may within a few days become an ulcer with a septic sloughing base surrounded by a painful zone of erythema. Cellulitis, lymphagitis, enlargement of the local lymph glands, fever,

and malaise are commonly present. The ulcer may be quite disabling and usually the pain is out of proportion to the physical signs. If the ulcer occurs in the lower extremity, the patient may be unable to walk for weeks or months after the injury. Relapses, which occur without warning, are not uncommon.

The severity of coral lesions is probably due to a combination of factors – laceration of tissues by the razor-sharp exoskeleton of the coral, effects of the nematocyst venom, introduction of foreign materials into the wounds, secondary bacterial infection, and adverse climatic and living conditions. Coral ulcers are slow to heal.

Jellyfish tentacles that are adhering to the skin of the victim should be immediately removed with the use of sand, clothing, bathing towel, seaweed, gunny sacks, or other available materials. This is one of the most important steps, because as long as the tentacles are on the victim's skin, they continue to discharge their venom. Alcohol, sun lotion, oil, or other materials that are readily available should be applied promptly to the wheals or skin lesions to inhibit the further activity of adherent microscopic nematocysts. Numerous local remedies have been advocated in various parts of the world: sugar, soap, vinegar, lemon juice, papaya latex, ammonia solution, sodium bicarbonate, plant juices, boric acid solution, etc. These have been used with varying degrees of success (Bullard, 1911; Scott, 1921; Crutchfield, 1925; Hadley, 1941; Tweedie, 1941; Southcott, 1963). Topical or oral cortisone preparations are sometimes useful. Oral antihistamines and topical antihistaminic creams alleviate urticarial lesions and symptoms (Waite, 1951). Opiates may be required to alleviate pain. Severe sting may require epinephrine (7 minims) subcutaneously repeated as necessary. Intravenous hypertonic glucose solutions may also be useful. Muscular spasms can be relieved with the use of intravenous injections of 10 ml of 10 percent calcium gluconate or sodium amytal intravenously. Artificial respiration and oxygen may be required. A number of fatalities have occurred as a result of stings on the lower extremities; the immediate use of a tight tourniquet might save the life. Cardiac and respiratory stimulants and other supportive measures may be required (Southcott, 1963). There are no known specific antidotes for coelenterate venoms.

Coral cuts should receive the following prompt treatment: cleansing the wound, removing of foreign particles, debriding if necessary, and applying antiseptic agents. Considerable difficulty can be prevented by promptly painting coral abrasions with an antiseptic solution such as 2 percent tincture of iodine. In severe cases, it may be necessary to give the patient bed rest with elevation of the limbs, kaolin poultices, magnesium sulfate in glycerin solution dressings, and antibiotics (Keegan, 1960).

The chemistry and pharmacology of coelenterate toxins are largely unknown. It has now been determined that the rapid death in *Chironex* stings is not due to anaphylactic shock, but rather is due to the direct action of the venom on the heart muscle (Endean, 1967).

Echinodermata — Starfishes, sea urchins, sea cucumbers

Toxic substances have been reported as present in certain species of the asteroid genera *Aphelasterias, Asterias, Asterina, Astropecten, Echinaster, Marthasterias,* and *Solaster* (Cuénot, 1887; Pawlowsky, 1927; Sawano and Mitsugi, 1932; Fish and Cobb, 1954; Hashimoto ans Yasumoto, 1960; Chaet, 1962). Poisonous starfishes are believed to be toxic to eat.

Contact with the slime of some species of asteroids may result in a contact dermatitis. In both cases the poison is thought to be produced by the glandular cells which are present in abundance in the epidermis of starfish. The chemical and pharmacological properties of these asterotoxins have not been fully determined, but at least one of these poisons resembles holothurin which is found in certain species of toxic sea cucumbers. The treatment of biotoxications from starfishes is symptomatic.

Acanthaster planci is the only known venomous asteroid. The spines of this starfish are elongate, pungent, and covered by a venom-producing integument. The nature of the poison is unknown. Contact with the spines of *A. planci* may produce an extremely painful wound, redness, swelling, protracted vomiting, numbness, and paralysis.

Intoxications from sea urchins may result from ingestion of their poisonous gonads, such as is the case in *Paracentrotus lividus, Tripneustes ventricosus,* and *Centrechinus antillarum.* However, in most instances sea urchin poisonings are due to stings from either their spines or pedicellariae.

The hollow, elongate, fluid-filled spines of echinothurid and diadematid sea urchins are particularly dangerous to handle. Their sharp, needle-like points are able to penetrate the flesh with ease, producing an immediate and intense burning sensation. As the spines penetrate, they release a violet-colored fluid which causes discoloration of the wound. Intense pain is soon followed by redness, swelling, and aching sensations. Partial motor paralysis of the legs, slight anesthesia, edema of the face, and irregularities of the pulse have been reported (Pugh, 1913). Secondary infection is a frequent complication with some species (Earle, 1941). The pain usually subsides after several hours, but the discoloration may continue for 3 to 4 days.

There is a divergence of opinion as to whether the spines actually contain a venom. However, the clinical effects indicate that a poison of some type is present, since the pain far exceeds that produced by mere mechanical injury. According to Mortensen (1935), there is no doubt of the presence of venom in the spines of Araeosoma and Asthenosoma. Although numerous writers refer to the dangers of pedicellariae of Toxopneustes pileolus result in immediate and intense radiating pain, faintness, numbness, generalized paralysis, aphonia, respiratory distress, and death. The pain may diminish after about 15 minutes and completely disappear within one hour, but paralysis may continue for 6 hours or longer. The nature of sea urchin venoms is unknown.

Insofar as the venom is concerned, sea urchin stings should be handled in a manner similar to any other venomous sting. However, attention is directed to the need for prompt removal of the pedicellariae from the wound. When pedicellariae are detached from the parent animal, they frequently continue to be active for several hours. During this time they will introduce venom into the wound.

The extreme brittleness and retrorse barbs of some sea urchin spines present an added mechanical problem. Nielly (1881) recommended that grease be applied, stating that this would allow the spines to be scraped off quite easily. Cleland (1912), Earle (1940), and others are of the opinion that some sea urchin spines need not be removed, as they are readily absorbed. Absorption of the spines is said to be complete within 24 to 48 hours. However, the spines of some sea urchins are not readily absorbed, and months later roentgenological examina-

tion may reveal them in the wound. It is recommended that the spines of Diadema be removed surgically.

Intoxications can result from ingestion of toxic sea cucumbers. The poison of sea cucumbers is termed "holothurin." Holothurin is concentrated in the Organs of Cuvier. Holothurin is believed to be a steroidal glycoside having an empirical formula of $C_{50}H_{82}O_{26}S$ (Chanley et al., 1955). It appears to have a direct contractural effect on muscle. It also has a nerve blocking effect similar to that of cocaine, procaine, and physostigmine in laboratory animals, but its effects on humans have not been fully determined.

Little information is available regarding the clinical effects of holothurin in humans. Reported symptoms of dermal contact with sea cucumber poison are burning pain, redness, and a violent inflammatory reaction. If the fluid contacts the eyes of the victim, blindness may result. Ingestion of sea cucumber poison may be fatal (Cleland, 1913; Castellani and Chalmers, 1919; Fränkel and Jellinek, 1927; Moru, 1934; Nigrelli, 1952). Treatment is symptomatic, but pharmacological studies suggest that anticholinesterase agents may be effective in the event of ingestion of holothurin (Friess, 1963; Scheuer, 1964).

Mollusca — Snaila, bivalves, and cephalopods

Whelk poisoning is caused by the ingestion of toxic univalves of the genus Neptunea and some of their close relatives (Fänge, 1957; Asano and Ito, 1959, 1960). The poison is restricted to the salivary glands of the shellfish (Fänge, 1960). The poison is believed to be tetramine, which is an autonomic ganglionic blocking agent. The symptoms consist of nausea, vomiting, anorexia, weakness, fatigue, faintness, dizziness, photophobia, impaired vision, and dryness of the mouth (Asano, 1952). Treatment is symptomatic.

Cone shell envenomations are caused by univalves of the genus *Conus* (Cleland, 1912; Miner, 1923; Allan, 1935 a, b; Phillips and Brady, 1953; Kohn, 1958; Keegan, 1960). They inflict their stings by means of venomous radular teeth, originating in the radular sheath where they reside until used. When needed, a single tooth passes from the sheath through the pharynx, where it is charged with venom produced by a venom duct, and purveyed to the hollow supervoluted radular tooth under pressure by the muscular venom bulb. The tooth then passes from the pharynx into the anterior opening of the proboscis where it is held ready to be plunged into the flesh of the victim. Most cone stings result from the careless handling of the mollusk by curious shell collectors. The chemistry and pharmacology of cone shell venom has not been fully determined, but there is evidence that cone shell venoms may vary from one species to the next.

Stings produced by *Conus* are of the puncture wound variety. Localized ischemia, cyanosis and numbness in the area about the wound, or a sharp stinging or burning sensation are usually the initial symptoms. The presence and intensity of the pain varies considerably from one individual to the next. Some persons state that the pain is similar to a wasp sting whereas others find it excruciating. Swelling of the affected part usually occurs. Numbness and paresthesia begin at the wound site and may spread rapidly involving the entire body, particularly about the lips and mouth. In severe cases paralysis of the voluntary muscles is initiated early, first by motor incoordination and followed by a complete generalized muscular paralysis. Knee jerks are generally absent. Aphonia and dysphagia may become very marked and distressing to the victim. Some patients complain of a generalized pruritus. Blurring of vision and diplopia are commonly present. Nausea may be present, but gastrointestinal and genitourinary symptoms are usually absent. The recovery period in less serious cases varies from a few hours to several weeks. Until fully recovered, victims complain of extreme weakness and tiring easily with the least amount of physical exertion. Coma may ensue, and death is said to be the result of cardiac failure. Treatment is symptomatic.

Mollusks of the genus *Murex* contain a poison in their purple gland which has been termed "murexine" (Dubois, 1903; Maas, 1937; Emerson and Taft, 1945; Erspamer and Dordoni, 1947). Little is known about murexine poisoning in man. Treatment is symptomatic. Murexine chemically has the structure of β-[imidazolyl-(4)]-acrylcholine, otherwise known as urocanylcholine (Erspamer and Benati, 1953). Pharmacologically, murexine provokes a paralysis of skeletal muscle and possesses marked neuromuscular blocking and nicotinic actions, but is almost devoid of muscarinic effects.

Paralytic shellfish poisoning: See under Protozoa.

Venerupin shellfish poisoning: See under Protozoa.

Intoxications have been caused by the ingestion of poisonous cephalopods of the genera *Ommastrephes* and *Octopus* in certain areas of Japan (Kawabata et al., 1957). The nature of the poisons involved are unknown, but there is no evidence that bacterial contaminants are involved. The predominant symptoms consist of nausea, vomiting, abdominal pain, diarrhea, fever, headache, chills, weakness, and severe dehydration. Paralysis and convulsions are sometimes present, but death is rare. Most victims recover within a period of 48 hours. Treatment is symptomatic.

Cephalopods inflict their envenomations with the use of a well-developed apparatus, the beak and salivary glands. The sharp parrotlike beak produces the initial wound into which is introduced the toxic saliva or venom – cephalotoxin.

Cephalopod lesions usually consist of two small puncture wounds produced by the sharp, parrot-like, chitinous jaws of the mollusk. Usually the pain is immediate and consists of a sharp burning or stinging sensation. It is sometimes described as similar to a bee sting, which at first is localized, but may later radiate to include the entire appendage. Within a few minutes a tingling or pulsating sensation develops in the area about the wound. There is some indication that coagulation time is retarded since bleeding is profuse and prolonged in most cephalopod bites. Swelling, redness, and heat usually develop about the affected area. Motor and severe sensory disturbances are generally absent. In severe cases there may be numbness of the mouth and tongue, blurring of vision, difficulty in speech and swallowing, loss of tactile sensation, floating sensation of the hands, etc. (McMichael, 1957, 1963). Muscular paralysis, loss of equilibrium, and deaths have been reported. Treatment is symptomatic.

The chemical composition of cephalotoxin is unknown. The poisons may vary from one species to the next. Erspamer (1949) has described a pharmacologically active substance from octopus saliva which he has termed "moschatin" or "eledoisin." It is a powerful vasodilator, has a hypotensive action, and stimulates extravascular smooth muscle. This particular substance was found to have a polypeptide configuration (Erspamer and Anastasi, 1962). The sequence of amino acids has been determined as pyroglut-amyl-proline-serine-lysene-hydroxyaspartic acid-alanine-phenylalanine-isoleucine-glycine-leucene-methylamine.

Toxic Vertebrates — Phylum CHORDATA

Agnatha — Lampreys and hagfishes

The slime and flesh of certain lampreys and hagfishes are reported to produce gastrointestinal upset, nausea, vomiting, and dysenteric diarrhea. The slime and skin is said to contain a poison which is not destroyed by either gastric juices or heat. Nothing else appears to be known regarding the nature of cyclostome poisons (Coutière, 1899; Pawlowsky, 1927; Halstead, 1964).

Condrichthyes — Poisonous and venomous sharks, rays, skates, and chimaeras

The musculature of some sharks, such as the Greenland shark *Somniosus microcephalus* (Bloch and Schneider), may be poisonous to eat (Jensen, 1914, 1948). The livers of several species of tropical sharks can cause severe intoxication (Coutaud, 1879; Coutière, 1899; Phisalix, 1922; Fish and Cobb, 1954; Halstead, 1959; Helfrich, 1961). The musculature may cause symptoms of a mild gastroenteritis. Ingestion of toxic shark livers may be very severe, with the onset of symptoms within a period of less than 30 minutes. Nausea, vomiting, diarrhea, abdominal pain, headache, weak pulse, malaise, cold sweats, oral paresthesia, and a burning sensation of the tongue, throat, and esophagus may be present. The neurological symptoms develop at a later time, consisting of extreme weakness, trismus, muscular cramps, sensation of heaviness of the limbs, loss of superficial reflexes, ataxia, delirium, incontinence, respiratory distress, visual disturbances, convulsions, and death. The recovery period, if the victim recovers, varies from several days to several weeks. The mortality rate is not known. The severity of the symptoms varies with the amount of shark liver eaten, the species of shark, physical condition of the victim, and other factors which are not clearly understood. The nature of the poison is unknown. The poison is not destroyed by heat or gastric juices.

Horn sharks inflict their envenomations by means of two dorsal stings which are located adjacent to the anterior margins of each of the two dorsal fins (Evans, 1920, 1923, 1943; Taft, 1945; Prosvirov, 1963). The nature of the venom is unknown. Symptoms consist of immediate intense stabbing pain which may continue for several hours. Swelling and redness of the affected parts are usually present. Lesions are of the puncture wound variety. Deaths have been reported (Coutière, 1899).

Stingrays constitute the most important single group of venomous fishes since they cause the largest number of serious venomous fish stings (Coutière, 1899; Gimlette, 1923; Tweedie, 1941; Smith, 1950; Phillips and Brady, 1953; Fish and Cobb, 1954). Most marine stingrays inhabit shallow coastal waters, bays, brakish water, lagoons, and river mouths. Venom is secreted and introduced into the body of the victim by the sting or venom apparatus located on the tail of the ray. The chemical nature of stingray venom has not been fully determined. The venom appears to be a toxic protein. The poison affects the cardiovascular, respiratory, and central nervous systems of mammals. Death is the result of cardiac standstill. The venom also produces respiratory depression (Russell, 1965).

The musculature and viscera of some of the chimaeras or ratfishes have been found to be toxic (Evans, 1923, 1943; Phillips and Brady, 1953). However, aside from some vague references to the toxicity of these fishes in humans, nothing is known regarding the nature of the poisons or the symptoms which they produce. The reproductive organs have been reported to be poisonous. Chimaeras are also capable of inflicting stings with their venomous dorsal spines, but nothing is known about the nature of the venom.

Osteichthyes — Ichthyotoxic bony fishes

Ciguatoxic Fishes: Ciguatera poisoning is one of the most treacherous and common forms of fish poisoning in tropical waters because it is usually caused by fishes which appear to be edible and in most parts of the world are considered to be valuable food fishes. About 300 species of marine fishes have been incriminated in this form of ichthyosarcotoxism. The most common causative species consist of sea bass, grouper, barracuda, snapper, parrotfish, wrasse, surgeon fish, and various other types of shore fishes.

The symptoms consist of tingling about the lips, tongue, and throat. Numbness may develop immediately or at any time within a period of 30 hours after the ingestion of the toxin. The usual time interval for the development of symptoms is from one to six hours. The initial symptoms in some instances consist of nausea, vomiting, metallic taste, dryness of the mouth, abdominal cramps, tenesmus, and diarrhea, followed by perioral tingling and numbness. The muscles of the mouth, cheeks, and jaws may become drawn and spastic with a feeling of numbness. Generalized symptoms of headache, anxiety, malaise, prostration, dizziness, pallor, cyanosis, insomnia, chilly sensations, fever, profuse sweating, rapid weak pulse, weight loss, myalgia, and joint aches are frequently present. Victims usually complain of a feeling of profound exhaustion and weakness. The feeling of weakness may become progressively worse until the patient is unable to walk. Muscle pains are generally described as as dull, heavy ache or cramping sensation, but on occasion may be sharp, shooting, and affect particularly the arms and legs. Victims complain of their teeth feeling loose and painful in their sockets.

Visual disturbances consisting of blurring, temporary blindness, photophobia, and scotoma are common. Pupils are usually dilated and the reflexes diminished. Frequently reported are skin disorders which are generally initiated by an intense generalized pruritus, followed by erythema, maculopapular eruptions, blisters, extensive areas of desquamation – particularly of the hands and feet – and occasionally ulceration. There may also be a loss of hair and nails.

In severe intoxications, the neurotoxic components are especially pronounced. Paresthesia involves the extremities, and paradoxical sensory disturbances may be present in which the victim interprets cold as a "tingling, burning, dry-ice or electric-shock sensation." or hot objects may give a feeling of cold. Ataxia and generalized motor incoordination become progressively worse. The reflexes are diminished and muscular paralyses develop. There may be clonic and tonic convulsions, muscular twitchings, tremors, dysphonia, dysphagia, coma, and death by respiratory paralysis. The limmited morbidity statistics show a case fatality rate of about 12 percent (Halstead, 1967). Death may occur within 10 minutes, but generally requires several days.

In those instances in which the victim survives, recovery is slow and convalescence may be very prolonged, with extreme weakness, sensory disturbances, and excessive weight loss being the last symptoms to disappear. When patients survive severe intoxication, complete recovery requires a period of several years. Meyer-Ahrens (1855), Steinbach (1895), and Gudger (1918, 1930) have reported cases in which the symptoms persisted for as long as 25 years. Individuals who have been severely intoxicated have stated that during periods of stress, fatigue, exposure, or poor nutrition, there is a recurrence of the myalgia and joint aches similar to those suffered during the original acute period of the disease (Gudger, 1930; Helfrich et al., 1968).

Ciguatoxin is a complex poison which appears to have several fractions. There is a fat soluble fraction which is a light yellow, viscous lipid having an empirical formula of $C_{35}H_{65}NO_8C$. It is said to be a quarternary ammonium compound, and a positive ninhydrin test can be obtained on hydrolysis (Mosher, 1966), Scheuer, et al., 1967). There is also a water-soluble fraction which has been obtained from some species of ciguatoxic fishes, but it is not known which fraction or fractions is or are responsible for the ciguatera syndrome in humans. One or more fractions of ciguatoxin may occur within a single species of fish. Unfortunately the pharmacology of ciguatoxin is not fully understood. There is evidence that at least one of the fractions of ciguatoxin is an irreversible anticholinesterase. However, other fractions showed no evidence of anticholinesterase. The chain of events leading to death by ciguatera fish poisoning are: a) inhibition of cholinesterase, b) acetylcholine accumulation, c) disruption of nerve function – centrally, peripherally, or both, d) respiratory failure, and e) death by asphyxia (Li, 1965). According to Rayner (1972) the pharmacological actions of ciguatoxin appear to be related to its direct effects on excitable membranes rather than to its previously reported anticholinesterase properties in vitro (see

Rayner, et al., 1968; Li, 1965, 1970 in Halstead, 1970). Ciguatoxin was found to increase the permeability of frog skin to Na^+ moving down a concentration gradient and to produce a tetrodotoxin-sensitive depolarization of frog muscle membranes. Kinetic studies indicated that ciguatoxin may be regarded as a competative inhibitor of the membrane polarizing action of Ca^{++} ions. For recommended treatment of fish poisoning, see the end of this section.

Clupeotoxic Fishes: Clupeoid fish poisoning is caused by the ingestion of certain types of herring-like fishes. The disease is scattered and sporadic in its appearance. The poison is heat stable and not destroyed by gastric juices. The symptoms consist of nausea, vomiting, abdominal pain, tenesmus, tachycardia, cold sweats, dyspnea, cyanosis, dilated pupils, coma, convulsions, and paralysis. Death may occur within a period of 30 minutes (Helfrich, 1961; Halstead, 1967). The nature of the poison is unknown. Treatment is symptomatic.

Gempylotoxic Fishes: Some of the gempylids or escolars contain an oil within their flesh and bone marrow which has a pronounced purgative effect when ingested. Gempylid poisoning (Gudger, 1925) develops rapidly, generally without cramping or pain. Since there are no other untoward effects, ingestion of the oil can hardly be considered as an intoxication in the usual sense of the word. The oil contains a saponifiable fraction and an unsaponifiable fraction. The saponifiable fraction contained a saturated compound, ethyl oleate, and an unsaturated compound, ethyl hydroxyl oleate. The unsaponifiable fraction contained a saturated compound, cetyl acetate, and an unsaturated compound, oleyl acetate. The most active fraction pharmacologically was cetyl acetate.

Scombrotoxic Fishes: Some of the scom-

broids (tuna, skipjack, and bonito) may on rare occasions cause ciguatera, but usually they produce an entirely different form of intoxication termed "scombroid poisoning." This is the only type of fish poisoning in which bacteria appear to play an etiological role in the formation of the toxin. If scombroids are inadequately preserved, a toxic "histamine-like" substance is formed, possibly from the decarboxylation of histidine, a normal constituent of fish flesh. Kawabata and associates have termed this substance "saurine" (Kawabata et al., 1955). Victims complain of fish having a "sharp or peppery" taste. The symptoms most often present are nausea, vomiting, flushing of the face, intense headache, epigastric pain, burning of the throat, difficulty in swallowing, thirst, pruritus, and swelling of the lips and urticaria, which are typical of a histamine reaction. Symptoms generally subside within 12 hours. For some unknown reason, scombroid fish appear to be more prone to producing intoxications of this type than other fish. The mortality rate is unknown. The chemistry of scombrotoxin has been studied by Geiger (1944 a, b, 1948, 1955). It is an established fact that when scombroid and certain other types of fishes are left to stand at room temperature (about 15° C) for several hours, the histidine present in the musculature of the fish, due to the action of bacteria, undergoes decarboxylation and rapidly converts to histamine. (See also Geiger, Courtney, and Schnakenberg, 1944, and Kawabata et al., 1955.) The presence of histamine is used routinely in determining fish spoilage. For many years it was assumed that the toxic effects of scombroid poisoning were due primarily to histamine poisoning. However, experimental evidence has shown that the effects are due to some other substance (Geiger, 1955) since histamine is generally ineffective when taken by mouth. Scombrotoxin is apparently produced by certain little-known strains of marine bacteria, possibly acting on the musculature of the fish. The biogenesis of the poison saurine and its chemical structure are presently unknown. It is insoluble in ether, acetone, benzene or chloroform, and possibly alcohol. Saurine is extracted with 80 percent methanol at room temperature. It is stable to boiling for one hour in 60 percent methanol at room temperature. It is stable to boiling for one hour in 60 percent methanol with one percent concentrated HCl. Saurine may be a basic substance with a relatively low molecular weight in regard to its dialyzability, electrodialytic character, and precipitability with phosphotungstic acid. Studies on the chemistry of this substance are being continued by the National Institute of Health in Japan.

Hallucinogenic Fishes: This form of poisoning is caused by the ingestion of certain types of fishes inhabiting the tropical Pacific. Most of the fishes incriminated have been members of the genera *Mugil, Neomyxus, Mulloidichthys, Upeneus, Acanthurus,* or *Kyphosus* (Helfrich and Banner, 1960; Bouder et al., 1962). The poison is heat stable and not destroyed by gastric juices. The symptoms may develop within minutes to two hours after ingestion, persisting for up to 24 hours. Symptoms consist of dizziness, loss of equilibrium, lack of motor coordination, hallucinations, and mental depression. A common complaint is that "someone is sitting on my chest." The conviction that they are going to die, or other terrible nightmares is a consistent part of the clinical picture. Other complaints consist of itching, burning of the throat, muscular weakness, and rarely abdominal distress. According to the reports received to date the intoxication is generally mild and non-fatal (Helfrich,

1961). The nature of the poison is unknown. Treatment is symptomatic.

Tetrodotoxic Fishes: Tetrodon poisoning is one of the most violent forms of fish poisoning. It is produced by tetraodontoid or puffer-like fishes. The disease is characterized by rapidly developing violent symptoms. The onset and symptoms in puffer poisoning vary according to the person and the amount of poison ingested. However, malaise, pallor, dizziness, paresthesia of the lips and tongue, and ataxia most frequently develop within 10 to 45 minutes after ingestion of the fish; but cases have been reported in which the symptoms did not develop for three hours or more. The paresthesia, which the victim usually describes as a "tingling or prickling sensation," may subsequently involve the fingers and toes, then spread to other portions of the extremities and gradually develop into severe numbness. In some cases the numbness may involve the entire body, in which instance the patients have stated that it felt as though their bodies were "floating". Hypersalivation, profuse sweating, extreme weakness, precordial pain, headache, subnormal temperatures, decreased blood pressure, and a rapid, weak pulse usually appear early in the succession of symptoms.

Gastrointestinal symptoms of nausea, vomiting, diarrhea, and epigastric pain are sometimes present early in the disease, whereas in other cases they are totally lacking. Contradictory statements appear in the literature relative to pupillary changes, but these differences can probably be resolved on the basis of the time at which the examination is made. Apparently the pupils are constricted during the initial stage and later become dilated. As the disease progresses the eyes become fixed, and the pupillary and corneal reflexes are lost.

Shortly after the development of parethesia, respiratory symptoms become a prominent part of the clinical picture. Respiratory distress, increased rate of respiration, movements of the nostrils, and diminution in depth of respiration are generally observed. Respiratory distress later becomes very pronounced, and the lips, extremities, and body become intensely cyanotic. Petechial hemorrhages involving extensive areas of the body, blistering, and subsequent desquamation have been reported. Severe hematemesis has also been known to occur. Muscular twitching, tremor, and incoordination become progressively worse and finally terminate in an extensive muscular paralysis. The first areas to become paralyzed are usually the throat and larynx, resulting in aphonia, dysphagia, and later complete aphagia. The muscles of the extremities become paralyzed, and the patient is unable to move.

As the end approaches, the eyes of the patient become fixed and glassy, and convulsions may occur. The victims may become comatose, but in most instances they retain consciousness, and their mental faculties remain acute until shortly before death. Death results from a progressive ascending paralysis involving the respiratory muscles. On the basis of Japanese statistics, the case fatality rate is 59.4 percent (Halstead, 1967). If death occurs, it generally takes place within the first six hours, or within 24 hours at the latest. The prognosis is therefore good if the patient survives for 24 hours.

Puffer poison has been given greater attention by pharmacologists than any other fish poison. Studies by Iwakawa and Kimura (1922), Yano (1938), and Murtha (1960) have shown that the primary action of puffer poison or tetrodotoxin, is on the nervous system, producing both central and peripheral effects. Comparatively low doses of the poison will readily inhibit neuromuscular function.

Major effects include respiratory failure and hypotension. It is believed that puffer poison has a direct action on respiratory centers. There are little or no effects on gut activity. The retching and vomiting that is observed in tetradon poisoning are believed to be elicited by action of the compound on the chemoreceptive trigger zone of the area postrema. Puffer poison has no major direct cardiotoxic effects, but the poison still causes significant decreases in cardiac contractile force associated with hypotension. The Japanese workers have reported that tetrodotoxin depresses the vasomotor centers (Takahashi and Inoko, 1892; Iwakawa and Kimura, 1922; Yano, 1937; Murtha, 1960). The finding that blockage of peripheral sympathetic fibers may contribute to the hypotension suggests that the negative effect observed in the intact animal is caused largely by indirect actions of puffer poison (see also Nagayosi, 1941). It is believed that the neuromuscular paralysis may be due to inhibition of conductivity (Katagi, 1927). Murtha (1960) gives the intraperitoneal LD_{50} for mice as 0.02 g/gm, killing the mice within 3.4 to 3.7 minutes after injection.

The chemistry of tetrodotoxin has been under study by Japanese chemists for several decades (Tahara, 1897; Nagai and Ito, 1939; Yokoo, 1952; Nagai, 1954; and others). Chemists have isolated and identified a decomposition product of the toxin which is believed to be of significance in establishing the formula of the poison. The product obtained was by alkaline hydrolysis of puffer poison and was shown to have the structure of 2-amino-6-hydroxymethyl-8-quinazolinol, with oxalic acid formed as a by-product. The poison reacts with water under mild conditions to yield a substance with the empirical formula $C_{11}H_{19}O_9N_3$ (Tsuda et al., 1963). This derivative has acid properties and has been termed "tetrodonic acid". This acid yields a hydrobromide salt on treatment with hydrobromic acid, a molecule of water being concomitantly released. This hydrobromide salt serves satisfactorily as a form for X-ray ana-lysis. From such studies, it has been established that the molecular weight is 400 and that the probably structural arrangement is one of the structures shown below.

(From Tsuda et al., 1963)

Ichthyootoxic Fishes: Most ichthyotoxic fishes are freshwater species and do not come within the scope of this presentation. One of the few marine fish offenders is the cabezone *Scorpaenichthys marmoratus* which is found along the California coast (Hubbs and Wick, 1951). Symptoms develop soon after ingestion of the roe, and consist of abdominal pain, nausea, vomiting, diarrhea, bitter taste, dryness of the mouth, intense thirst, cold sweats, rapid irregular weak pulse, pupillary dilatation, syncope, chest pain, pallor, dysphagia, and tinnitus. In severe cases there may be muscular cramps, convulsions, and coma. The victim usually recovers within a period of five days. No deaths have been reported from eating marine ichthyootoxic fishes, but deaths have been caused by some of the freshwater species (Asano and Itoh, 1962; Halstead, 1964; Russell, 1965). The nature of most ichthyootoxins is unknown.

Ichthyohemotoxic Fishes: Very little is known about fish blood poisoning in humans. The poison is considered to be a parenteral poison and is largely destroyed by heat and gastric juices. There have been a few instances in which persons have ingested large quantitites or fresh blood from certain species of European freshwater eels *Anguilla* and the marine eel *Muraena helena.* There are two types of ichthyohemotoxism, systemic and local. The symptoms in the systemic type are of a general nature consisting of diarrhea, dysenteric stools, nausea, vomiting, frothing at the mouth, skin eruptions, cyanosis, apathy, irregular pulse, weakness, paresthesia, paralysis, respiratory distress, and possibly death. The systemic form is exceedingly rare and results from ingestion of the blood of certain species of fishes. The local type is the result of eel blood coming in contact with the mucous membranes, i.e., eye, tongue, etc., and results in a local inflammatory response. Oral symptoms consist of burning, redness of the mucosa, and hypersalivation. Ocular symptoms consist of severe burning and redness of the conjunctivae which develop within 5 to 20 minutes after contamination. Lacrimation and swelling of the eyelids are usually present. A sensation as though a foreign body was present in the eye may persist for several days. Repeated inoculations of eel serum in the eye gradually result in an immunity with progressing decrease in the severity of symptoms with each subsequent inoculation.

Ichthyohemotoxins obtained from the blood fishes are believed to be protein in nature. Serum collected from the eel *Anguilla vulgaris* have been fractionated by Ghiretti (1964) using a Dease cellulose column. Several fractions were obtained by linear gradient elution from 0.02 M pH 7.5 to 0.2M pH 6.5 with tris-phosphate buffer. The fraction obtained between pH 7.3 and 7.0 were found to contain 30 to 40 percent of the total proteins and the entire toxic activity. Similar results have been obtained for the moray eel *Muraena helena*. For other work on the chemistry of ichthyohemotoxins, see Mosso (1889) and Ghiretti and Rocca (1963). The exact chemical nature of these poisons is unknown.

Ichthyocrinotoxic Fishes: The subject of ichthyocrinotoxic fishes is one of the least known areas of marine zootoxicology. Ichthyocrinotoxins are produced by specialized glandular structure, but there are no traumagenic organs present for injecting the poisons. Ichthyocrinotoxins are generally excreted by skin glands and thereby released into the environment. The victim is intoxicated by ingesting the fish, coming in contact with the slime of the fish, or by ingestion of water containing the poisons. Fishes that have been incriminated as ichthyocrinotoxic include such groups as lampreys, hagfishes, moray eels, seabass, triggerfishes, puffers, trunkfishes (Engelsen, 1922; Pawlowsky, 1927; Maass, 1937; Tani, 1945; Eger, 1963; Thomson, 1963). It should be kept in mind that ichthyocrinotoxic fishes may also contain one or several other different types of ichthyotoxins.

The means by which persons become intoxicated by ichthyocrinotoxic fishes apparently varies from on species to the next. Very little has been reported regarding the actual mechanism by which these poisons are encountered by man. The slime of some species of cyclostomes is toxic to ingest and may produce an inflammatory reaction if brought in contact with the mucous membranes of humans. The skin of certain species of moray eels and puffers in poisonous to eat. Dermal contact with the slime of *Rypticus saponaceus* and probably other species of ichthyocrinotoxic fishes, may produce a dermatitis.

Whether the poisons that are produced in the skin of these fishes are chemically identical with those found in the flesh of these same fishes is not known. The skin secretions of only two ichthyocrinotoxic fishes have been chemically identified thus far. One of these is ostracitoxin (pahutoxin) from *Ostracion lentiginosus*. The poison has been identified as choline chloride ester of 3-acetoxyhexadecanoic acid. The biological activity of ostracitoxin resembles that of the steroidal saponins isolated from echinoderms (Thomson, 1964; Boylan and Scheuer, 1967). A second ichthyocrinotoxin that has been studied to some extent is derived from the toxic skin secretions of the soapfish *Rypticus saponaceus*. The skin of this fish releases a foamy toxic secretion when it is disturbed. The poison is believed to be a protein or polypeptide (Maretski and Castillo, 1967).

Tetrodotoxin has been studied at length, but it is not known whether tetrodotoxin obtained from the viscera is chemically identical with the poison produced by the skin of these fishes.

Venomous or Ichthyoacanthotoxic Fishes: Venomous or acanthotoxic fishes are widespread throughout the piscine phylogenetic series. They vary greatly in size, coloration, habits, and general biology. One of their common denominators is the presence of a venom apparatus which usually consists of venom glands and a traumagenic device of some kind. The more important groups of venomous fishes include the sharks, stingrays, chimaeras, catfishes, weeverfishes, scorpionfishes, toadfishes, stargazers, and rabbitfishes. Venomous fish stings vary according to the type of venom apparatus involved, nature and quantity of the venom introduced into the wound, mechanical trauma produced, the area of the body involved, and the physical condition of the patient. Stingrays and catfishes frequently produce severe lacerations because of their retroserrate fin spines. Lacerations of this type may result in the surrounding tissues becoming severely traumatized, swollen, and infected in addition to the damages produced directly by the venom. Wounds from most other types of venomous fishes are of the puncture-wound type. The character and intensity of the pain are variable. The pain may amount to only a prick or stinging sensation, or it may be intense, causing the victim to cry out in extreme anguish and lose consciousness. Stingray, oriental catfish, scorpionfish, zebrafish, and stonefish stings are especially severe. Deaths from stingrays, scorpionfishes, weevers, etc., have been reported (Meinard, 1905; Taschenberg, 1909; Whitley, 1940; Evans, 1943; Gudger, 1943; Smith, 1951). Stonefish wounds can be very dangerous, resulting in numbness about the area of the wound, paralysis of the limb, sloughing of the tissues about the wound site, delirium, convulsions, cardiac failure, and death. The most common findings in fish stings are swelling, redness, and cyanosis in the area about the wound. Shock and secondary infections, together with a variety of more generalized symptoms are not uncommon. None of the fish venoms have been chemically characterized. Stingray venom is believed to be a protein of average molecular weight. It is extremely labile, nondialyzable, and rapidly inactivated by heat (Russell et al., 1958). Weever venom is believed to be similar to stingray venom (Russell and Emery, 1960). Scorpionfish venoms contain a considerable quantity of protein, and the active principle is nondialyzable, which suggests that the poison is a protein or mixture of proteins (Saunders, 1959, 1960; Saunders and Taylor, 1959).

Treatment of Oral Fish Poisoning

The treatment of oral fish poisonings is largely symptomatic (Khlentzos, 1950). There are no specific antidotes, and an attack does not impart immunity. Gastric lavage and catharsis should be instituted at the earliest possible time. In many instances 10 percent calcium gluconate given intravenously has given prompt relief, whereas in others it has been ineffective. Paraldehyde and ether inhalations have been reported to be useful in controlling the convulsions.

Nikethamide or one of the other respiratory stimulants is advisable in cases of respiratory depression. In cases where excessive mucus production is a factor, aspiration and constant turning are essential. Atropine has been found to make the mucus more viscid and difficult to aspirate, and is not recommended. Oxygen by inhalation and intravenous administration of fluids supplemented with vitamins given parenterally are usually beneficial. If laryngeal spasm is present, intubation and tracheotomy may be necessary.

In case of severe pain, opiates such as morphine, given in small divided doses will probably be required. Cool showers have been found to be effective in relieving severe itching. Patients suffering from paradoxical sensory disturbance should be given fluids slightly warm or at room temperature, as well as vitamin B complex supplements. Antihistaminic drugs will be found to be useful in the treatment of scombroid poisoning. Banner et al. (1965) have recommended the use of 2-PAM (2-pyridine aldoxime methochloride) for the treatment of ciguatoxications, but caution is advisable in employing any anticholinesterase drug in the routine therapy of ciguatera fish poisoning since ciguatoxin appears to be a complex of poisons having multiple actions.

Treatment of Venomous Fish Stings

Efforts in treating venomous fish stings should be directed toward achieving three objectives: 1) alleviating pain, 2) combatting effects of the venom, and 3) preventing secondary infection. The pain results from the effects of the trauma produced by the fish spine, venom, and the introduction of slime and other irritating foreign substances into the wound. In the case of stingray and catfish stings, the retrorse barbs of the spine may produce severe lacerations with considerable trauma to the soft tissues. Wounds of this type should be promptly irrigated with cold salt water or sterile saline if such is available. Fish stings of the puncture-wound variety are usually small in size, and removal of the poison is more difficult. It may be necessary to make a small incision across the wound and then apply immediate suction and possibly irrigation. At any rate, the wound should be sucked promptly in order to remove as much of the venom as possible. However, it should be kept in mind that fishes do not inject their venom in the manner employed by venomous snakes, so at best, results from suction will not be too satisfactory (Russell, 1953, 1965).

There is a division of opinion as to the advisability and efficacy of using a ligature in the treatment of fish stings. If used, the ligature should be placed at once between the site of the sting and the body, but as near the wound as possible. The ligature should be released every few minutes in order to maintain adequate circulation. Most doctors recommend soaking the injured member in hot water for 30 minutes to one hour. The water should be maintained at as high a temperature as the patient can tolerate without injury, and the treatment should be instituted as soon as possible. If the wound is on the face or body, hot moist compresses should be used. The heat may have an attenuating effect on the venom since boiling readily destroys stingray venom *in vitro*. The addition of magnesium sulfate or epsom salts to the water is believed to be useful. Infiltration of the wound area with 0.5–2 percent procaine has been used with good results. If local measures fail to prove satisfactory, intramuscular or intravenous demerol will generally be efficacious. Following the soaking procedure, debridement and further cleansing of the wound may be desirable. Lacerated wounds should be closed with dermal sutures. If the wound is large, a small drain should be left in it for a day or two. The injured area should be covered with an antiseptic and sterile dressing.

Prompt institution of the recommended treatment usually eliminates the necessity of antibiotic therapy. If delay has resulted to any extent, the administration of antibiotics may be desirable. A course of tetanus antitoxin is advisable as a precautionary measure.

The primary shock which follows immediately after the stinging generally responds to simple supportive measures. However, secondary shock resulting from the action of stingray venom on the cardiovascular system requires immediate and vigorous therapy. Treatment should be directed toward maintaining cardiovascular tone and the prevention of any further complications. Respiratory stimulants may also be required. The Commonwealth Serum Laboratories, Melbourne, New South Wales, Australia, have recently developed an antivenin for the treatment of stonefish *Synanceja* stings (Wiener, 1959).

Toxic Reptiles: There are five species of marine turtles which have been incriminated in human intoxications. They are members of the genera *Caretta, Chelonia, Eretmochelys, Dermochelys,* and *Pelochelys* (Anson, 1745; Tennent, 1861; Bierdrager, 1936; Read, 1937; Pillai et al., 1962). The symptoms of chelonitoxication vary with the amount of flesh ingested and the person. Symptoms generally develop within a few hours to several days after eating the turtle. In one large outbreak involving 100 persons, most of the victims developed symptoms about 12 hours after eating the turtle. The initial signs and symptoms usually consist of nausea, vomiting, diarrhea, facial tachycardia, pallor, severe epigastric pain, sweating, coldness of the extremities, and vertigo. There is frequently reported an acute stomatitis, consisting of a dry burning sensation of the lips, tongue, lining of the mouth, and throat. Some victims complained of a sensation of tightness of the chest. The victim frequently becomes lethargic and unresponsive, swallowing becomes very difficult, and hypersalivation is pronounced. The oral symptoms may be slow to develop but become increasingly severe after several days. The tongue develops a white coating, the breath becomes foul, and later the tongue may become covered with multiple pinhead-sized reddened papules. The pustules may persist for several months, whereas in some

instances they break down into ulcers. Desquamation of the skin over most of the body has been reported (Cooper, 1964). Some victims develop a severe hepatomegaly with right upper quadrant tenderness. The conjunctivae become icteric. Headaches and a feeling of "heaviness of the head" are frequently reported. Deep reflexes may be diminished. Somnolence is one of the more pronounced symptoms present in severe intoxications and is usually indicative of an unfavorable prognosis. At first the victim is difficult to awaken and then gradually becomes comatose, which is followed rapidly by death. The symptoms presented are typical of a hepatorenal death. The overall case fatality rate on reported outbreaks is about 28 percent. Treatment is symptomatic. The nature of chelonitoxins is unknown.

There are more than 50 species of venomous sea snakes, but only 14 species have been incriminated in human envenomations. The species most frequently causing human envenomations are *Enhydrina schistosa* (Daudin), *Hydrophis cyanocinctus* (Daudin), *H. spiralis* (Shaw), *Kerilia jerdoni* (Gray), and *Pelamis platurus* (Linnaeus) (Kermorgant, 1902; Fish and Cobb, 1954; Reid and Lim, 1957; Klemer, 1965). Sea snakes inflict their wounds with the use of fangs which are reduced in size but are of the Elapid or cobra type. There is no clinical evidence of direct cardiovascular involvement. Failing vision is considered to be a terminal sign. The generalized pains resulting from muscle movements and the myoglobinuria are said to be the outstanding clinical signs of sea snake envenomation. In fatal cases, respiratory paralysis with terminal hypertension and cyanosis usher in death. In some cases little or no peripheral paralysis may be evident, and the victim dies from bulbar paralysis. Death may take place within several hours or several days after the bite.

Sea snake poisoning is a medical emergency requiring immediate attention and the exercise of considerable judgement. Tragic consequences may result from delayed or inadequate treatment. Before any first aid or therapeutic measures are instituted, it is always important to determine if envenomation has occurred (Reid, 1961, 1963; Reid and Lim, 1957; Russell, 1963; Russell et al., 1966). Needless treatment can cause discomfort and deleterious results. A sea snake may bite without injecting venom. The fangs and teeth of a sea snake are generally small and may not have penetrated the skin sufficiently to have resulted in envenomation. Absorption of sea snake venom is rapid. In most instances the venom is absorbed before first aid can be administered. Suction is of value only if it can be applied within the first few minutes following the bite. Incision and suction are said to be of little value in sea snake envenomations. It is generally advisable to leave the bite alone. The affected limb should be immediately immobilized and *all exertion must be avoided*. The patient should lie down and keep the immobilized part below the level of the heart. A tourniquet should be applied tight enough to occlude the superficial venous and lymphatic return. Apply the tourniquet to the thigh in leg bites or arm above the elbow in upper limb bites. It should be released for 90 seconds every ten minutes. A tourniquet is of little value if applied later than 30 minutes following the bite, and it should not be used for more than 4 hours. The tourniquet should be removed as soon as antivenin therapy has been started. Some workers believe that the tourniquet is of little or no value in sea snake bites. If sea snake antivenin or polyvalent antivenin containing a krait (Elapidae) frac-

tion is available, it should be administered intramuscularly either in the buttocks or at some other site distant from the bite. The antivenin should be given only after the appropriate skin or conjunctival test has been made. Usually one unit (vial or ampule) is sufficient until the patient can be transported to a physician. Keep the patient warm. He should not be given alcoholic beverages of any kind. Transport the patient to a physician.

Poisonous Marine Mammals: Marine mammals incriminated in human intoxications involve the following: polar bears, walruses, porpoises, sea whale, and bearded and ringed seals (Sahashi, 1933; Read, 1939; Cleland, 1942; Stéfansson, 1944; Rodahl, 1949; Mizuta et al., 1957; Fay, 1960). In most instances it is the liver of the animal that, when eaten, causes the poisoning. In the case of the arctic mammals it is believed that intoxication is largely due to hypervitaminosis A (Rodahl and Moore, 1943; Rodahl, 1949; Jeghers and Marraro, 1958). However, there are several instances in which there appears to be a neurotoxic substance present. The nature of these poisons is unknown. The symptoms vary considerably, but are predominantly gastrointestinal in nature. Neurological disturbances may be present. Treatment is symptomatic.

References for further reading and information on marine biotoxicology are Russell, 1965, Halstead, 1956, 1959, 1965, 1967, 1970, and Bagnis et al., 1970.

References

Aguilar-Santos, G.: A toxic constituent of *Caulerpa* caulerpicin. Proc. 11th Pacific Sci. Congr. (Unpublished data) 1966
Akiba, T., and Y. Hattori: Food poisoning caused by eating asari (*Venerupis semidecussata*) and oyster (*Ostrea gigas*) and studies on the toxic

substance venerupin. Japan. J. exp. Med. 20: 271–284, 1949

Allan, J. K.: Shellfish poisoning. Aust. Mus. Mag. 5 (11): 393–394, 1935a

Allan, J. K.: Poisonous shellfish. Med. J. Aust. 2 (16): 554–555, 1935b

Anson, G.: A voyage round the world, in the years 1740, 1, 2, 3, 4. J. and P. Knapton, London 1745, p. 219–221

Asano, M.: Studies on the toxic substances contained in marine animals, 1. Locality of the poison of Neptunea (Barbitonia) arthritica Bernardi. Bull. Japan. Soc. Sci. Fish. 17 (8–9): 73–77, 1952

Asano, M,. and M. Ito: Occurrence of tetramine and choline compounds in the salivary gland of a marine gastropod, Neptunea arthritica Bernardi. Tohoku J. Agr. Res. 10 (2): 209–227, 1959

Asano, M., and M. Ito: Salivary poison of a marine gastropod, Neptunea arthritica Bernardi, and the seasonal variation of its toxicity. Ann. N. Y. Acad. Sci. 90 (3): 674–688, 1960

Asano, M., and M. Ito: Toxicity of a lipoprotein and lipids from the roe of a blenny Dinogunellus grigorjewi Herzenstein. Tohoku J. Agr. Res. 13 (2): 151–167, 1962

Aznaurian, M. C.: Clinical effects of the venomous medusae of the Far East. Klin. Med. (Moscow) 36 (6): 105–108, 1958 [In Russian]

Bagnis, R., F. Berglund, P. S. Elias, G. J. van Esch, B. W. Halstead, and K. Kojima: Problems of toxicants in marine food products. 1. Marine biotoxins. Bull. Wld Hlth Org. 42: 69–88, 1970

Banner, A. H.: A dermatitis-producing alga in Hawaii. Hawaii Med. J. 19: 35–36, 1959

Banner, A. H., M. M. Okihiro, J. P. Keenan, A. C. Ivy, and K. M. Li: Ciguatera fish poisoning: a symposium. Hawaii Med. J. 24: 353–361, 1965

Banner, A. H., P. J. Scheuer, S. Sasaki, P. Helfrich, and C. B. Alender: Observations on ciguatera-type toxin in fish. Ann. N. Y. Acad. Sci. 90 (3): 770–787, 1960

Barnes, J. H.: Chironex fleckeri. Image 31: 24–29, 1969

Bierdrager, J.: Een geval van massale schildpadvergiftiging in Nw. Guinee. Ned. Tijdschr. Geneesk. 76 (18): 1933–1944, 1936

Bouder, H., A. Cavallo, and M. J. Bouder: Poissons vénéneux et ichtyosarcotoxisme. Bull. Inst. Océanogr. 59 (1240), 1962

Boylan, D. B., and P. J. Scheuer: Pahutoxin: a fish poison. Science 155 (3758): 52–56, 1967

Bullard, W. E.: Alcohol in the treatment of poi-

soning by the Portuguese man-of-war. J. Amer. med. Ass. 56 (18): 1346, 1911

Castellani, A., and A. J. Chalmers: Venomous animals: protozoa to arthropoda, p. 203–241. In A. Castellani and A. J. Chalmers, Manual of tropical medicine. 3d ed. W. Wood Co., New York, 1919

Chaet, A. B.: A toxin in the coelomic fluid of scalded starfish (Asterias forbesi). Proc. Soc. exp. Biol. (N. Y.). 109 (4): 791–794, 1962

Chambers, J. S., and H. W. Magnusson: Seasonal variations in toxicity of butter clams from selected Alaska beaches. U. S. Fish Wildlife Serv., Spec. Sci. Rept., Fish. No. 53, 1950

Chanley, J. D., S. K. Kohn, R. F. Nigrelli, and H. Sobotka: Further chemical analysis of holothurin, the saponin-like steroid from the sea-cucumber, 2. Zoologica 40: 99, 1955

Chu, G. W., and C. E. Cutress: Human dermatitis caused by marine organisms in Hawaii. Proc. Hawaiian Acad. Sci. 1953: 9 (Abst.), 1953

Chu, G. W., and C. E. Cutress: Dermatitis due to contact with the hydroid. Syncoryne mirabilis (Agassiz, 1862). Hawaii Med. J. 14 (5): 403–404, 1955

Clark, A. H.: Echinoderms from the Cocos-Keeling Islands. Bull. Raffles Mus., Singapore (22): 53–67, 1950

Cleland, J. B.: Injuries and diseases of man in Australia attributable to animals (except insects). Australasian Med. Gaz. 32 (11): 269–274; 32 (12): 297–299, 1912

Cleland, J., B.: Injuries and diseases of man in Australia attributable to animals (except insects). J. trop. Med. Hyg. 16: 25–31, 1913

Cleland, J. B.: Injuries and diseases in Australia attributable to animals. Med. J. Aust. 2 (14): 313–320, 1942

Combe, J. S.: On the poisonous effects of the mussel (Mytilus edulis). Edinb. med. J. 29 (94): 86–96, 1828

Cooper, M. J.: Ciguatera and other marine poisonings in the Gilbert Islands. Pacific Sci. 18 (4): 411–440, 1964

Cooper, J. T.: Destruction of marine flora and fauna in Fiji caused by the hurricane of February 1965. Pacific Sci. 20 (1): 137–141, 1966

Coutaud, H.: Observations sur sept cas d'empoisonnement par le foi de requin à l'Ile des Pins (Nouvelle Caledonia) en 1873. Thesis, Montpellier, p. 9–47, 1879

Coutière, H.: Poissons venimeux et poissons vénéneux. Thèse Agrég. Carré et Naud, Paris, 1899

Crutchfield, E. D.: Dermatitis produced by the Portuguese man-of-war. Arch. Derm. 12 (1): 72–75, 1925

Cuénot, L.: Contribution à l'étude anatomique des astérides. Arch. Zool. Exp. Gen., 2, 5 (2): 134–135, 1887

Dawson, E. Y.: Changes in Palmyra Atoll and its vegetation through the activities of man, 1913–1958. Pacific Nat. 1 (2), 1959

Dawson, E. Y., A. A. Aleem, and B. W. Halstead: Marine algae from Palmyra Island with special reference to the feeding habits and toxicology of reef fishes. Allan Hancock Found. Pubis., Occ. Pap. 17, 1955

DeLaubenfels, M. W.: A discussion of the Dry Tortugas in particular and the West Indies in general, with material for a revision of the families and orders of the Porifera. Paps. Tortugas Lab., vol. 30, Publ. No. 467, 1936

DeLaubenfels, M. W.: A guide to the sponges of eastern North America. Marine Lab., Univ. Miami Publ., 1953

Dubois, R.: Sur le venin de la glande à pourpre des murex. C. R. Soc. Biol. Paris, 55: 81, 1903

Duchassaing, P., and G. Michelotti: Spongiaires de la mer caráibe. Natuurk. Verhandel. Hollandsche. Maatsch. Wetenschap, 2, 21 (2): 1–124, 1864

Earle, K. V.: Pathological effects of two West Indian echinoderms. Trans. roy. Soc. trop. Med. Hyg. 33 (4): 447–452, 1940

Earle, K. V.: Echinoderm injuries in Nauru. Med. J. Aust. 2 (10): 265–266, 1941

Eger, W. H.: An exotoxin produced by the puffer, Arothron hispidus, with notes on the toxicity of other plectognath fishes. M. Sc. Thesis, Univ. Hawaii, 1963

Emerson, G. A., and C. H. Taft: Pharmacologically active agents from the sea. Tex. Rep. Biol. Med. 3 (3): 302–338, 1945

Endean, R.: The venomous sea-urchin Toxopneustes pileolus. Med. J. Aust 1 (9): 320, 1961

Endean, R.: Regarding rapid death in Chironex stings. (Personal communication, 1967)

Engelsen, H.: Om giftfisk og giftige fisk. Nord hyg. T. 3: 316–325, 1922

Erspamer, V.: Ricerche preliminari sulla moschatina. Experientia (Basel) 5: 79–81, 1949

Erspamer, V., and A. Anastasi: Structure and pharmacological actions of eledoisin, the active endecapeptide of the posterior salivary glands of Eledone. Experientia Basel 18: 58, 1962

Erspamer, V., and O. Benati: Identification of murexine as β-[imidazolyl-(4)]-acrylcholine. Science 117 (3033): 161–162, 1953

Erspamer, V., and F. Dordoni: Ricerche chimiche e farmacologiche sugli estratti di ghiandola ipobranchiale di Murex trunculus. Murex brandaris e Tritonalia erinacea. 3. Presenze negii estratti di un nuovo derivato della colina

or di una colina omologa: la murexina. Arch. int. Pharmacodyn. 74 (3–4): 263–285, 1947

Evans, H. M.: The poison of the spiny dog-fish. Brit. med. J. 1 (3087): 287–288, 1920

Evans, H. M.: The defensive spines of fishes, living and fossil, and the glandular structure in connection therewith, with observations on the nature of fish venoms. Phil. Trans. B, 212: 1–33, 1923

Evans, H. M.: Sting-fish and seafarer. Faber and Faber, Ltd., London. 1943

Fänge, R.: An acetylcholine-like salivary poison in the marine gastropod Neptunea antiqua. Nature 180: 196–197, 1957

Fänge, R.: The salivary gland of Neptunea antiqua. Ann. N. Y. Acad. Sci. 90 (3): 689–694, 1960

Fay, F. H.: Carnivorous walrus, some arctic zoonoses. Arctic 13 (2): 111–122, 1960

Fish, C. J., and M. C. Cobb: Noxious marine animals of the central and western Pacific Ocean. U. S. Fish Wildlife Serv., Res. Rept. No. 36, p. 14–23, 1954

Fränkel, S., and C. Jellinek: Über essbare Holothurien. Biochem. Z. 185: 389–391, 1927

Friess, S. L.: Some pharmacological activities of the sea cucumber neurotoxin. A. I. B. S. Bull. 13 (2): 41, 1963

Geiger, E.: Histamine content of unprocessed and canned fish. A tentative method of quantitative determination of spoilage. Food Res. 9: 293–297, 1944a

Geiger, E.: On the specificity of bacterium-decarboxylase. Proc. Soc. exp. Biol. (N. Y.) 55: 11–13, 1944b

Geiger, E.: On the mechanism of histamine formation. Arch. Biochem. 17: 391–395, 1948

Geiger, E.: Role of histamine in poisoning with spoiled fish. Science 121 (3155): 865–866, 1955

Geiger, E., G. Courtney, and G. Schnakenberg: The content and formation of histamine in fish muscle. Arch. Biochem. 3: 311–319, 1944

Ghiretti, F.: A toxic protein from eel serum. (Personal communication, 9. January 1964)

Ghiretti, F., and E. Rocca: Some experiments on ichthyotoxin, p. 211–216. In H. L. Keegan and W. V. MacFarlane [eds.]. Venomous and poisonous animals and noxious plants of the Pacific region. Pergamon Press, New York, 1963

Gimlette, J. D.: Malay poisons and charm cures. 2d ed. J. and A. Churchill, London, 1923

Gudger, E. W.: Sphyraena barracuda; its morphology, habits, and history. Carnegie Inst. Wash. Publ. 252, p. 53–108, 1918

Gudger, E. W.: A new purgative, the oil of the

"castor oil fish." Boston med. surg. J. 192: 107–111, 1925

Gudger, E. W.: Poisonous fishes and fish poisoning, with special reference to ciguatera in the West Indies. Am. J. trop. Med. 10: 43–55, 1930

Gudger, E. W.: Poisonous fishes and fish poisonings, with special reference to ciguatere in the West Indies. Am. J. trop. Med. 10 (1): 43–55, 1930

Gudger, E. W.: Is the sting ray's sting poisonous? A historical resume showing the development of our knowledge that it is poisonous. Bull. Hist. Med. 14: 467–504, 1943

Habekost, R. C., I. M. Fraser, and B. W. Halstead: Observations on toxic marine algae. J. Wash. Acad. Sci. 45 (4): 101–103, 1955

Hadley, H. G.: The sea nettle. Med. Ann. D. C. 10 (5): 178–180, 1941

Halstead, B. W.: Animal phyla known to contain poisonous marine animals, p. 9–27. In E. E. Buckley and N. Porges [ed.]. Venoms. Am. Assoc. Adv. Sci., Washington, D. C., 1956

Halstead, B. W.: Poisonous fishes. Public Health Repts. 73 (4): 302–312, 1958

Halstead, B. W.: Dangerous marine animals. Cornell Maritime Press, Cambridge, 1959

Halstead, B. W.: Fish poisonings – their diagnosis, pharmacology, and treatment. Clin. Pharmacol. Ther. 5 (5): 615–627, 1964

Halstead, B. W.: Poisonous and venomous marine animals of the world, vol. 1. Vertebrates. U. S. Government Printing Office, Washington, D. C., 1965

Halstead, B. W.: Poisonous and venomous marine animals of the world, vol. 2. Vertebrates. U. S. Government Printing Office, Washington, D. C., 1967

Halstead, B. W.: Poisonous and venomous marine animals of the world, vol. 3. Vertebrates, continued. U. S. Government Printing Office, Washington, D. C., 1970

Hashimoto, Y., and T. Yasumoto: Confirmation of saponin as a toxic principle of starfish. Bull. Japan. Soc. Sci. Fish. 26 (11): 1132–1138, 1968

Helfrich, P.: Fish poisoning in the tropical Pacific. Hawaii Mar. Lab., Univ. Hawaii, Contribution No. 155, 1961

Helfrich, P., and A. H. Banner: Hallucinatory mullet poisoning. J. trop. Med. Hyg. 1960: 1–4, 1960

Helfrich, P., T. Piyakarnchana, P. S. Miles, and A. H. Banner: Ciguatera fish poisoning. Occ. Pap. Bernice P. Bishop Mus. 23 (14): 305–382, 1968

Hubbs, C. L., and A. N. Wick: Toxicity of the roe of the cabezon, Scorpaenichthys marmoratus. Calif. Fish and Game 37 (2): 195–196, 1951

Iwakawa, K., and S. Kimura: Experimentelle Untersuchungen über die Wirkung des tetrodonotoxins Fugugift. Arch. Exp. Pathol. Pharmacol. 93: 305–331, 1922

Jeghers, H., and H. Marraro: Hypervitaminosis A: its broadening spectrum. Am. J. clin. Nutr. 6 (4): 335–339, 1958

Jensen, A. S.: The selachians of Greenland. Mindeskrift J. Steenstrup 30: 12–16, 1914

Jensen, A. S.: Contributions to the ichthyofauna of Greenland. Skrift. Univ. Zool. Mus. Copenhagen 9: 20–25, 1948

Katagi, R.: Influence of some stimulating drugs on the action of tetrodotoxin on skeletal muscle. Okayama Igakkai Zasshi 39: 1869–1880, 1927 [In Japanese]

Kawabata, T., B. W. Halstead, and T. F. Judefind: A report of a series of recent outbreaks of unusual cephalopod and fish intoxications in Japan. Am. J. trop. Med. Hyg. 6 (5): 935–939, 1957

Kawabata, T., K. Ishizaka, and T. Miura: Studies on the allergy-like food poisoning associated with putrefaction of marine products, 1. Episodes of allergy-like food poisoning caused by "samma sakuraboshi" (dried seasoned saury) and other kinds of marine products. Japan. J. med. Sci. Biol. 8 (6): 487–501, 1955

Keegan, H. L.: Some venomous and noxious animals of the Far East. Med. Gen. Lab. (406), U. S. Army Med. Command, Japan, 1960

Kermorgant, A.: Les serpents de mer et leur venin. Ann. Hyg. Méd. colon, 5: 431–435, 1902

Khlentzos, C. T.: Seventeen cases of poisoning due to ingestion of an eel, Gymnothorax flavimarginatus. Am. J. trop. Med. 30 (5): 785–793, 1950

Klemmer, K.: Liste der rezenten Giftschlangen: Elapidae, Hydropheidae, Viperidae und Crotalidae, p. 255–464. In Behringwerk-Mitteilungen ed., Die giftschlangen der erde. N. G. Elwert Universitäts- und Verlags-Buchhandlung, Marburg, 1963

Kohn, A. J.: Recent cases of human injury due to venomous marine snails of the genus Conus. Hawaii med. J. 17: 528–532, 1958

Li, K. M.: Ciguatera fish poison: A potent cholinesterase inhibitor. Science 147 (3665): 1580–1581, 1965

Light, S. F.: Another dangerous jellyfish in Philippine waters. Philipp. J. Sci. 9: 291–295, 1914a

Light, S. F.: Some Philippine Scyphomedusae, including two new genera, five new species, and one new variety. Philipp. J. Sci. 9 (3): 195–231, 1914b

Maass, T. A.: Gifttiere. In W. Junk [ed.], Tabulae biologicae, vol. 13. N. V. Van de Garde and Co. Drukkerji, Zaltbommel, Holland, 1937

Machado, O.: Catálogo sistemático dos animais urticantes e peconhentos do Brasil. Bol. Inst. Vital Brazil (25): 41–65, 1943

McMichael, D. F.: Poisonous bites by octopus. Proc. Zool. Soc. London 1957: 110–111, 1957 (not seen by author)

McMichael, D. F.: Dangerous marine molluscs, p. 74–80. In J. W. Evans chmn., Proc. first international convention of life saving techniques, 3. Scientific section. Suppl. Bull. Post Grad. Comm. Med., Univ. Sydney, 1963

Maretzki, A., and J. del Castillo: A toxin secreted by the soapfish Rypticus saponaceus. Toxin 4: 245–250, 1967

Medcof, J. C., A. H. Leim, A. B. Needler, A. W. Needler, J. Gibbard, and J. Naubert: Paralytic shellfish poisoning on the Canadian Atlantic coast. Bull. Fish. Res. Board Can. 75, 1947

Meinard: Piqûres de poisson venimeux. Bull. Med. Algérie 16: 357–360, 1905

Meyer, K. F., H. Sommer, and P. Schoenholz: Mussel poisoning, J. Prev. Med. 2 (5): 365–394, 1928

Meyer-Ahrens, K. M.: Von den giftigen fische. Schweiz. Z. Med. Chir. Geburtsh. (3): 188–230 (4–5): 269–332, 1855

Miner, R. W.: The glory of the sea. Nat. Hist. 23 (4): 325–328, 1923

Mizuta, M., T. Ito, T. Murakami, and M. Mizobe: Mass poisoning from the liver of Sawara and Iwashikujira. Nihon Iji Shimpo (1710): 27–34, 1957 [In Japanese]

Mold, J. D.: The isolation and identification of the toxic principle of the sea mussel, Mytilus californianus Conrad. Ph. D. Thesis, Northwestern Univ., Evanston, Ill., 1947

Mortensen, T.: A monograph of the Echinoidea: Bothriocidaroida, Melonechinoida, Lepidocentroida, and Stirodonta, vol. 2. Carlsberg-Fund, C. A. Reitzel, Copenhagen, 1935

Moru, J.: Contribution à l'étude de la toxicité des animaux marins. Thèse, Fac. Méd. Paris, 1934

Mosher, H. S.: Non-protein neurotoxins. Science 51 (3712): 860–861, 1966

Mosso, U.: Ricerche sulla natura del veleno che si trova nel sangue dell'anguilla. Rend. Reale Accad. Lincei 5 (1): 804–810, 1889

Murtha, E. F.: Pharmacological study of poisons from shellfish and puffer fish. Ann. N. Y. Acad. Sci. 90 (3): 820–836, 1960

Nagai, J.: Chemistry of fugu (Tetraodontidae) – poison and biochemistry of its intoxication. Fukuoka Acta med. 45: 1–12, 1954 [In Japanese]

Nagai, J., and T. Ito: On the chemical study of fugu (Spheroides) poison. J. Biochem. (Tokyo) 30 (2): 235–238, 1939

Nagayosi, S.: Fukuoka Acta Med. 34: 312, 1941 [Not seen by the author]

Needler, A. B.: Paralytic shellfish poisoning and Gonyaulax tamarensis. J. Fish. Res. Bd. Can. 7 (8): 490–504, 1949

Nielly, M.: Animaux et vegetaux nuisibles, p. 709–710. In M. Nielly, Eléments de pathologie exotique. Delahaye and Lecrosnier, Paris, 1881

Nigrelli, R. F.: The effects of holothurin on fish and mice with sarcoma 180. Zoologica 37: 89–90, 1952

Pawlowsky, E. N.: Gifttiere und ihre Giftigkeit, G. Fischer, Jena. 1927

Phillips, C., and W. H. Brady: Sea pests – poisonous or harmful sea life of Florida and the West Indies. Univ. Miami Press, Miami, 1953

Phisalix, M.: Animaux venimeux et venins. Masson et Cie., Paris, 1922

Pillai, V. K., M. B. Nair, K. J. Ravindranathan, and C. S. Pitchumoni: Food poisoning due to turtle flesh (a study of 130 cases). J. Ass. Phycns India 10 (4): 181–187, 1962

Prosvirov, E.: Poisonous fishes. Kaliningrad Publ. Ofc., Moscow. 1963 [In Russian]

Pugh, W. S.: Report of case of poisoning by sea urchin. U. S. nav. med. Bull. 7 (2): 254–255, 1913

Rayner, M. D.: Mode of action of ciguatoxin. Fed. Proc. 31 (3): 1139–1145, 1972

Rayner, M. D., T. I. Kosaki, and E. L. Fellmeth: Ciguatoxin: More than an anticholinesterase. Science 160 (3823): 70–71, 1968

Read, B. E.: Chinese materia medica; turtle and shellfish drugs. Peking Natural History Bulletin, Peking, 1937

Read, B. E.: Chinese materia medica; fish drugs. Peking Natural History Bulletin, Peking, 1939

Reid, H. A.: Diagnosis, prognosis, and treatment of sea-snake bite. Lancet 2: 399–402, 1961

Reid, H. A.: Snakebite in Malaya, p. 355–362. In H. L. Keegan and W. V. MacFarlane [eds.], Venomous and poisonous animals and noxious plants of the Pacific region. MacMillan Co., New York, 1963

Reid, H. A., and K. J. Lim: Sea-snake bite, a survey of fishing villages in northwest Malaya. Brit. med. J. 1957: 1266–1272, 1957

Richet, C.: De l'action toxique de la auberitine (extrait aqueux de *Suberites domuncula*). C. R. Soc. Biol. (Paris) 61: 598–600, 1906a

Richet, C.: De la variabilité de la dose toxique de suberitine. C. R. Soc. Biol. (Paris) 61: 686–688, 1906b

Rodahl, K.: Toxicity of polar bear liver. Nature (Paris) 164 (4169): 530–531, 1949

Rodahl, K., and T. Moore: The vitamin A content and toxicity of bear and seal liver. Biochem. J. 37: 166–168, 1943

Russel, F. S.: Toxicity of jellyfish, *Chrysaora hysoscella*. School Sci. Rev. 78: 275, 1938

Russell, F. E.: Stingray injuries: a review and discussion of their treatment. Am. J. med. Sci. 226: 611–622, 1953

Russell, F. E., and J. A. Emery: Venom of the weevers *Trachinus draco* and *Trachinus vipera*. Ann. N. Y. Acad. Sci. 90 (3): 805–819, 1960

Russell, F. E., T. C. Panos, L. W. Kang, A. M. Warner, and T. C. Colket: Studios on the mechanism of death from stingray venom – a report of two fatal cases. Am. J. med. Sci. 235 (5): 566–584, 1958

Russell, F. E., J. J. Quilligan, Jr., S. J. Rao, and F. A. Shannon: Snakebite. J. Am. med. Ass. 195 (7): 596–597, 1966

Russell, F. E.: Research review: snake venom and antivenins. Med. News, (N. Y.) p. 1–4, 1963

Russell, F. E.: Marine toxins and venomous and poisonous marine animals, p. 255–384. *In* F. S. Russell [ed.], Advances in marine biology, vol. 3. Academic Press, New York, 1965

Sahashi, Y.: Nutritive value of sperm whale oil and finback whale oil. Sci. Paps., Inst. Phys. Chem. Res. (Tokyo) 20 (416): 245–253, 1933

Saunders, P. R.: Venoms of scorpionfishes. Proc. West. Pharm. Soc. 2: 47–54, 1959

Saunders, P. R.: Pharmacological and chemical studies of the venom of the stonefish (genus *Synauceja*) and other scorpionfishes. Ann. N. Y. Acad. Sci. 90 (3): 784–804, 1960

Saunders, P. R., and P. B. Taylor: Venom of the lionfish *Pterois volitans*. Am. J. Physiol. 197 (2): 437–440, 1959

Sawano, E., and K. Mitsugi: Toxic action of the stomach extracts of the starfishes on the heart of the oyster. Sci. Rept. Tohoku Univ., 4, 7 (1): 79–88, 1932

Scheuer, P. J.: The chemistry of toxins isolated from some marine organisms. Fortsch. Chem. Organ. Naturst. 22: 265–278, 1964

Scheuer, P. J., W. Takahashi, J. Tsutsumi, and T. Yoshida: Ciguatoxin: Isolation and chemical nature. Science 155 (3767): 1267–1268, 1967

Schuett, W., and H. Rapoport: Saxitoxin, the paralytic shellfish poison. Degradation to a pyrrolopyrimidine, J. Amer. chem. Soc. 84: 2266, 1962

Scott, H. H.: Vegetal and fish poisoning in the tropics, p. 790–798. *In* W. Byam and R. G. Archibald [eds.]. The practice of medicine in the tropics, vol. 1. H. Frowde and Hodder and Stoughton, London, 1921

Silva, E. S.: "Red water" por *Exuviaella baltica* Lohm. com simultânea mortandade de peixe nas águas litorais de Angola. Trabalhos Missao Biol. Maritime (Lisboa), 1956 [Not seen by author]

Smith, J. L.: The sea fishes of southern Africa. Central News Agency, Cape Town, S. Africa, 1950

Smith, J. L.: A case of poisoning by the stonefish, *Synanceja verrucosa*. Copeia (3): 207–210, 1951

Sommer, H. W., W. F. Whedon, C. A. Kofoid, and R. Stohler: Relation of paralytic shellfish poison to certain plankton organisms of the genus *Gonyaulax*. Arch. Path. 24: 537–598, 1937

Southcott, R. V.: Studies on Australian cubomedusae, including a new genus and speces apparently harmful to man. Austr. J. Marine Freshwater Res. 7 (2): 254–280, 1956

Southcott, R. V.: Coelenterates of medical importance, p. 46–65. *In* H. L. Keegan and W. V. MacFarlane [eds.]. Venomous and poisonous animals and noxious plants of the Pacific region. Pergamon Press, Oxford. 1963

Stéfansson, V.: Arctic manual. Macmillan Co., New York, 1944

Steinbach, E.: Bericht über die Gesundheitsverhältnisse der Eingeborenen der Marshall-Inseln im Jahre 1893/94 und Bemerkung über Fischgift. Mitt. Forschungslab. Gelehrt. Dtsch. Schutzgeb. 8 (2): 157–171, 1895

Stevenson, T.: Poisoning by mussels. Guy's Hosp. Rept., London, 3, 19: 420–421, 1874

Strong, R. P.: Poisonous arthropods, fish and coelenterates, p. 1544–1551. *In* R. P. Strong, Stitt's diagnosis, prevention, and treatment of tropical diseases, vol. 2. Blakiston Co., Philadelphia, 1944

Taft, C. H.: Poisonous marine animals. Tex. Rep. Biol. Med. 3 (3): 339–352, 1945

Tahara, Y.: Report on puffer poison. Yakugaku Zasshi (328): 587–625, 1897 [In Japanese]

Takahashi, D., and Y. Inoko: Localization of poison in the body of tetrodon. Sei-i-Kai med. J. 11 (5): 46–50; (6): 81–82, 1892

Tani, I.: Toxicological studies on Japanese puffers. Teikoku Tosho Kabushiki Kaisha 2 (3), 1945 [In Japanese]

Taschenberg, E. O.: Die giftigen Tiere. F. Enke, Stuttgart, Germany, 1909

Tennent, J. E.: Sketches of the natural history of Ceylon. Longman, Green, Longman, and Roberts, London, 1861

Thesen, J.: Studier over den paralytiske form af forgiftning med blaaskjael (*Mytilus edulis* L.). T. norske Laegeforen. (20): 1153–1184; (21): 1228–1252 (22): 1285–1300, 1901

Thomson, D. A.: A histological study and bioassay of the toxic stress secretion of the boxfish, *Ostracion lentiginosus*. Ph. D. Thesis, Univ. Hawaii, 1963

Thomson, D. A.: Ostracitoxin: an ichthyotoxic stress secretion of the boxfish, *Ostracion lentiginosus*. Science 146 (3641): 244–245, 1964

Togashi, M.: Clinical study of the poisoning by *Venerupia semidecussata*. Japan Iji Shimpo (May) 1943 [In Japanese] [Not seen by author]

Tsuda, K., C. Tamura, R. Tachikawa, K. Saksi, O. Amakasu, M. Kawamura, and S. Ikuma: Die Konstitution und Konfiguration der Tetrodonsäure. Chem. pharm. Bull. 11 (11): 1473–1475, 1963

Tweedie, M. W.: Poisonous animals of Malaya. Malaya Publishing House, Singapore, 1941

Verrill, A. E.: The Bermuda Islands, 5. Characteristic life of the Bermuda coral reefs. Trans. Connecticut Acad. Arts Sci. 12: 204–323, 1907

Waite, C. L.: Medical problems of an underwater demolition team. U. S. armed Forces med. J. 2 (7): 1325–1326, 1951

Wiener, S.: Observations on the venom of the stonefish (*Synanceja trachynis*). Med. J. Aust. 1959: 620–627, 1959

Whitley, G. P.: The fishes of Australia, 1. The sharks, rays, devil-fish, and other primitive fishes of Australia and New Zealand. Royal Zoological Society of New South Wales, Sydney, 1940

Woodcock, A. H.: Note concerning human respiratory irritation associated with high concentrations of plankton and mass mortality of marine organisms. J. Marine Res. Sears Found. Marine Res. 7 (1): 56–62, 1948

Wood-Jones, F.: Coral and atolls. Lovell Reene and Co., London, 1912

Yano, I.: The pharmacological study of tetrodotoxin. Fukuoka Med. Coll. J. 30 (9): 1969–1704, 1937 [In Japanese]

Yano, I.: An experimental study on the globefish (fugu) intoxication. Japan. Soc. Int. Med., 33d Ann. Mtg. 5: 99–101, 1938

Yokoo, A.: Studies on toxin of a globefish, 4. Proc. Japan. Acad. 28 (4): 200–202, 1952

Subject Index

Information for Authors

Language of Publication

English.

Contents

Original scientific articles, reviews, presentations by governmental agencies, surveys and other communications with global environmental aspects of chemistry, toxicology, engineering, physics, etc.

The editors are particularly interested in receiving original scientific papers or reviews dealing with the evaluation of safety of chemicals, drugs, natural products and physical agents on plants, animals, and man. Particular emphasis will be given to manuscripts that help define the chemical hazards involving the ecology of the food supply. Negative or confirmatory data will be published when of sufficient interest. The editors desire papers from investigators in different scientific disciplines and from industrial and govermental groups who are interested in the protection and safety of the biosphere from harmful chemicals.

The contributions should not have been published before and the author must possess the publication rights.

Articles should be concise. Submit two complete copies including the original in a typewritten form, double-spaced, with one-inch margins on all sides. The title should be limited to 15 words or 80 characters. The abbreviated running title should contain no more than 40 characters. Use generic names of chemicals wherever possible. Proprietary names and trade marks should appear only to identify the source of the chemical and subsequently only the generic name should be used. All abbreviations should be unpunctuated. The name and mailing address of the author(s) must be clearly indicated.

The manuscripts have to be submitted ready for press. The authors receive only page proofs for information and no corrections deviating from the manuscript are permitted. Return of such information proofs to the competent editors must be made within two weeks. Corrections are the responsibility of the editors of Environmental Quality and Safety.

Standards and References

All abbrevations and journal names should follow the style of Chemical Abstracts; Vol. 55, 1961. Chemical names should be according to the IUPAC Nomenclature of Organic Chemistry, Butterworths, London. References should be listed by number in the text. Entries in the reference list should include authors' names, name of the title, the journal, the volume, and the actual pages the article occupies in the journal, and date.

DuBois, K. P., F. K. Kinoshita, J. P. Frawley: Quantitative measurement of inhibition of alieste: ases, acylamidase, and cholinesterase by EPN and Delnav. Exp. Molec. Path. 12: 173—284, 1968

Abstracts

As a rule a brief summary is to precede original articles and of reviews. It may be omitted, however, if the structure of the contribution makes it unnecessary.

Keywords

In the running text of the manuscript up to five keywords per page should be underlined. They will be printed in italic letters and serve as the basis for the subject index.

Tables and Figures

Tables and figures should be completely understandable even without reading the text. Every table should have a title directly above it. Every figure should have a legend. Figures and tables should be identified consecutively with Arabic numerals. All charts and graphs must be done with black ink on coordinate paper.

Photographs

Photographs are desirable wherever necessary to substantiate and illuminate the text. Black and white photographs and photomicrographs may be submitted as glossy prints. Do not clip or mark the photograph in any way. All drawings should be done on heavy, white drawing board with black India ink. Authors should write their names on the back of each glossy print.

If the number of black-and-white half tones is above average a surcharge for printing costs shall paid upon the editors' request. Color illustrations will be accepted only against surcharge.

The editors reserve the right to accept contributions and to make formal corrections or shortening, where necessary, after contact with the authors.

Manuscripts

Manuscripts from Europe, Great Britain, Ireland, Africa and the Far East should be submitted to Dr. W. Klein
Institut für ökologische Chemie
D 5205 St. Augustin 1
Postfach 1260
Manuscripts from the Americas and Australia should be submitted to
Dr. I. Rosenblum
Dept. of Pharmacology
Albany Medical College of Union University
ALBANY, N. Y. 12208
U. S. A.

Environmental Quality and Safety

Chemistry, Toxicology and Technology

Global Aspects of Chemistry, Toxicology and Technology as Applied to the Environment

Edited by Prof. Dr. E. COULSTON, Albany/N. Y., Prof. Dr. F. KORTE, Schloß Birlinghoven/St. Augustin

Assistant Editors: W. Klein, Schloß Birlinghoven/Bonn and I. Rosenblum, Albany/N. Y.

With contributions by specialists

Volume I: 1972. X. 267 pages, 160 figures, 66 tables, 17x24 cm, «Thieme Edition» cloth DM 58,–

ISBN 3 13 486001 5

Volume II: 1973. XVIII, 333 pages, 64 illustrations 92 tables, 17x24 cm, «Thieme Edition» cloth DM 58,–

ISBN 3 13 498001 0

Georg Thieme Publishers Stuttgart
Academic Press New York/London

SYNTHESIS

International Journal of Methods in Synthetic Organic Chemistry

Editors:
G. SCHILL, Freiburg/Br.
G. SOSNOVSKY, Milwaukee/Wis.
H. J. ZIEGLER, Basel

Advisory Board:
F. Asinger, Aachen
D. H. R. Barton, London
E. D. Bergmann, Jerusalem
H. C. Brown, Lafayette/Ind.
H. Hellmann, Marl
O. Isler, Basel
M. I. Kabachnik, Moscow
K. Ley, Leverkusen
J. Mathieu, Romainville
Eu. Müller, Tübingen
W. P. Neumann, Dortmund
R. Oda, Kyoto
G. A. Olah, Cleveland/O.
E. G. Rozantsev, Moscow
H. E. Simmons, Wilmington/Del.
F. Sondheimer, London
F. Sorm, Prague
H. A. Staab, Heidelberg
A. Steinhofer, Ludwigshafen/Rh.
E. E. van Tamelen, Stanford/Calif.
K. Weissermel, Frankfurt/M.
R. West, Madison/Wis.
G. Wilke, Mülheim/Ruhr

Editorial Office:
R. E. Dunmur and W. Lürken,
Stuttgart

Reviews and Communications
are published in English
or German;
Abstracts appear only in English

Published monthly.
Annual subscription price
(1974) DM 180,—
plus forwarding charges

As a matter of necessity, there is a contribution deadline for each voluminous scientific work. But, you as an organic chemist want to stay abreast of methods which are published after the deadline. The journal SYNTHESIS will keep you up to date. By requesting a sample copy you can form your own ideas on the germane selection of topics presented in SYNTHESIS, the practical reactions published in survey articles, original papers and reports on current topics. If your work lies in the field of organic preparation, the material presented in SYNTHESIS is of prime importance to you.

Georg Thieme Publishers Stuttgart
Academic Press New York · London